CHOICE
TREES, SHRUBS
WALL PLANTS
AND CLIMBERS

Lucie Tyrell
1946.
from Mr Pool

W. J. MARCHANT
KEEPER'S HILL NURSERY, STAPEHILL
WIMBORNE, DORSET

First printed in 1937

THE AUTHORITIES REFERRED TO IN THE COMPILATION OF THIS BOOK ARE AS FOLLOW:

KEW HAND LIST OF TREES AND SHRUBS		(1934)
W. J. BEAN	"Trees and Shrubs Hardy in the British Isles" Vols I-III	(1919-1933)
A. REHDER	"Manual of Cultivated Trees and Shrubs"	(1927)
G. NICHOLSON	"Dictionary of Gardening"	(—1900)
T. F. CHEESEMAN	"Manual of the New Zealand Flora"	(1925)
P. RUSSELL	"The Oriental Flowering Cherries"	(1934)
B. L. BURTT & SIR A. W. HILL	"The Genera Gaultheria and Pernettya in New Zealand, Tasmania and Australia"	(1935)
YEAR BOOK OF THE RHODODENDRON ASSOCIATION		(1936)

CHOICE
TREES, SHRUBS, WALL PLANTS
AND CLIMBERS

IN ALPHABETICAL ORDER.

All plants marked "E" are Evergreens, and "C" Climbers.

E **Abelia floribunda.**—Mexico. A splendid semi-scandent shrub for a south or west wall ; flowers large, pendulous, funnel-shaped, rosy-red, in June and July 2/6 3/6

„ **Graebneriana.** This rare species from C. China grows 4—8 ft. high and its leaves resemble those of A. triflora. The pink flowers with yellow throats are borne during May and June. It is the hardiest of the Abelias. ... 3/6 5/-

E „ **grandiflora (rupestris).**—Hybrid. (chinensis × uniflora). A delightful shrub, 3—5 ft. high, perfectly hardy around the south and west coast ; requires wall protection inland ; freely produces its white, tinged pink flowers from July to autumn frosts 2/6 3/6

E „ **Schumannii (longituba).**—China. In many gardens within reach of the salt air it grows 4 ft. high and as much wide. Its semi-pendulous branches are a fine sight from early May to mid-July when bearing the numerous 1 in. funnel-shaped rose suffused lilac flowers ... 2/6 3/6

„ **serrata.**—Japan. A compact twiggy shrub slowly growing to 3 ft., suitable for a choice position. Its pretty, tubular, flesh-coloured flowers with orange markings are borne in pairs during June 3/6 5/-

„ **triflora.**—Himalayas. Usually a shrub, attains small tree size in mild, sheltered gardens ; flowers white, suffused rose, sweetly scented, in June 3/6

„ **Zanderi.**—C. & N.W. China. An upright shrub, new to cultivation, with ovate-lanceolate leaves 1½—3 in. long and half as much wide, each leaf having three pairs of wide teeth. These and the current growths are covered with hairs. The ½ in. tubular flowers, with spreading lobes, are borne during May and June ... ... — —

Abeliophyllum distichum.—C. Korea. A dainty twiggy shrub, 2—4 ft. high, with leaves similar to those of Forsythia ovata, and one destined to become a favourite on account of its early flowering season. From mid-January to early April, according to position and climate, the ends of the shoots bear many racemes of narrow, tubular, scented, pure white flowers 7/6

E **Abutilon megapotamicum (vexillarium).**—Brazil. A unique   each. shrub, 3—10 ft. high, quite hardy within 10—15 miles of the south and west coast, on a south or west wall ; slender wiry growths ; produces for at least 8 months, numerous drooping bright red and yellow flowers   ...   2/6   3/6

E   „   **Milleri.**—A hybrid between A. megapotamicum and A. pictum. Graceful slender growths ; attains 6—9 ft. ; best on a south wall ; flowers bell-shaped, clear orange-yellow, with bronze anthers 3/6

   „   **vitifolium.**—A rampant Chilian shrub, quickly attaining 20 ft. ; flowers single, hollyhock-like, variable shades of blue, during the summer ; dislikes cutting winds ; short-lived on some soils 2/6   3/6

   „   „   **album.**—White flowering form 3/6

Acacia   (See **Robinia**).

Acanthopanax Henryi (Eleutherococcus).—China. Attains a height of about 6 ft. ; wood dark brown ; its pale yellow spines are decurved 5/-   7/6

   „   **ricinifolius.**—Japan. Leaves palmate, deeply five or seven lobed ; height 18—20 ft. ; wood dark brown, armed with stout yellowish prickles ; a striking shrub or small tree 3/6   5/6   7/6

   „   **Simonii.**—China. Leaves consist of five leaflets, maple like, with bristly hairs above ; branches armed with decurved spines 5/-   7/6

Acer ambiguum. A very rare small tree of rounded form from Japan. It has brown-red stems and deep red growths throughout the growing season. The dense, 5-lobed reticulate leaves, deep green above, pale beneath, are 2 x 3 ins., undulated and unevenly toothed 3/6   5/6

   „   **argutum.**—A native of the Japanese mountains ; of elegant appearance. Its pale green leaves are five-lobed and deeply toothed, colouring well in autumn ; a strong grower 3/6   5/6

   „   **barbinerve.**—S.E. Manchuria. This distinct species soon grows into a small tree. Its pretty deep green ovate leaves are 5-lobed, each lobe being deeply incised and unevenly toothed, with the two lower ones partly covering the leaf stalk 5/-   7/6

   „   **Buergerianum (trifidum).**—Japan and E. China. A choice small tree for a sheltered spot ; leaves deeply 3-lobed, each lobe irregularly toothed, glaucous beneath ; unfolding leaves bright red ; beautifully coloured in autumn. 7/6

   „   **capillipes.**—Japan. A rare tree with striated wood ; current growths red. The unfolding lobed leaves are brightly coloured, age to green, and become beautifully tinted again in autumn 5/-   7/6

   „   **cappadocicum (laetum).**—Caucasus to W. Himalaya. A splendid species that soon attains tree size. Its bright green lobed leaves turn rich buttercup-yellow in autumn. 3/6   5/6   7/6

   „   **carpinifolium.**—The Hornbeam-foliaged Maple of Japan is one of the very best for the autumn garden. The leaves fade through many shades of yellow and it is one of the last to colour at Westonbirt 5/-   7/6   10/6

	each.	

Acer circinatum.—The Vine-leaved Maple of N. America attains 10—20 ft. and should be in every collection. For many weeks in autumn the foliage assumes rich colourings varying from orange to deep red and scarlet 3/6 5/6 **7/6 10/6**

„ **cissifolium.**—Japan. Usually a large shrub of compact round form with distinct foliage consisting of three leaflets ; autumn tints orange yellow and red **3/6 5/6**

„ **crataegifolium.**—This rarity is one of the most attractive of all the Japanese Maples. It has a beautiful green stem with white lines. The acuminate 3—5 shallow-lobed leaves are irregular and deeply toothed and are gloriously coloured during autumn **10/6**

„ **creticum.** (See **orientale**).

„ **dasycarpum (saccharinum).** Better known as the Silver Maple of N. America. A tall and graceful tree with deeply 5-lobed leaves, silvery beneath, which are very effective when swaying in the slightest wind. A well furnished and lofty specimen in a well-known Scottish garden is a magnificent sight every autumn with its glorious coloured foliage. This and A. rubrum colour quite as well in Wigtownshire and Perthshire as they do in Gloucestershire or Dorset. 2/6 **3/6 5/6**

„ „ **laciniatum (Wieri).**—It is quick-growing and of graceful appearance and, like the type, suitable for planting in cold districts. The large leaves are finely dissected and silvery-white beneath and they colour well every autumn **3/6 5/6**

„ „ **rubrum (fulgens).**—A distinct form with growing leaves bright red, maturing to dark green, and changing in autumn to bright crimson **3/6 5/6**

„ **Davidii.**—China. A beautiful species of spreading habit with dark red wood ; conspicuous throughout the winter with its white striped bark covered with blue bloom. Its undivided leaves fade to many hues during autumn 5/- **7/6 10/6**

„ **Dieckii(Lobelii × platanoides)**—Garden Origin. A splendid tree probably reaching 30 ft. or more. Its handsome leaves, 8 in. or more across, are often 7-lobed and become brilliantly coloured in autumn even in the mild and humid climate of Killarney. Large plants ... **10/6**

„ **distylum.**—Japan. An uncommon species of bushy habit, with wiry growths, possibly reaching 20 ft. It bears ovate unevenly serrated leaves, sharply acuminated and heart-shaped at the base, turning in autumn dark brown. **3/6 5/6**

„ **Ginnala.**—China, Japan, Manchuria. Seldom more than a large shrub ; thin slender growths ; its three-lobed leaves become gloriously crimson tinted in early autumn 2/6 **3/6 5/6**

„ **griseum.**—Perhaps the most beautiful of all China's gifts to western gardens. It forms a bushy-headed tree 15 ft. or more in height. During autumn the mahogany-coloured bark peeling reveals an orange coloured newer bark beneath. The green trifoliate leaves, with dove-coloured reverse, are gorgeously tinted during October, and remain so for many weeks after they have fallen ... 10/6 **5/6 7/6** **15/6 21/-**

„ **Henryi.**—China. A choice ornamental, not a fast grower, with divided foliage, dull purple turning to vivid red in autumn 5/- **7/6 10/6**

Acer Hersii.—China. A conspicuous striped bark Maple with   each.
dogwood-red growths and broadly ovate trilobed leaves.
A good grower, quickly attaining small tree size. 3/6 5/6 7/6 10/6

   " **Hookeri.**—Himalaya and China. This species when grown
as at Killarney or Cork, attains small tree size and is
probably the handsomest member of the genus. The
large coriaceous 3-lobed leaves are cordate-lanceolate
in outline and have brilliantly coloured veins 10/6

   " **insigne.**—Caucasus & N. Persia. A distinct strong-growing
tree of the Sycamore section, with wide-lobed, green
leaves, changing in autumn to bright yellow   ... 2/6 3/6 5/6

   " **japonicum.**—Japan. A plant in the trade much confused
with forms of A. palmatum. It grows to a large bush of
rounded form. The deep green leaves, round in outline, are seven to eleven-lobed and deeply serrated.
During autumn they become brilliantly coloured   5/- 7/6 10/6

   "   " **laciniatum (filicifolium) (Hauchiwa).**—Japan.
An open stiff-branched shrub, 10 ft. or more high. The
beautiful,deeply cut nine to thirteen-lobed leaves are dark
green, and for many weeks during autumn they are
magnificently coloured 5/- 7/6 10/6

   "   " **vitifolium.**—Garden origin. A much stronger
grower with vine-like leaves as its name implies. These
like those of the type are richly coloured and can be seen
from afar 7/6 10/6

   " **laxiflorum (Forrestii).**—One of the most handsome of the
striped bark Maples from Western China ; current
growths dark red ; the leaves are heart-shaped, three to
five-lobed, undulated and unevenly toothed. They are
metallic green in colour with stalks and veins brick-red   10/6

   " **Lobelii.**—S. Italy. A free-growing tree of fastigiate habit.
The current growths are distinctively striped and covered
with blue-grey bloom. The dark green leaves have 5
acuminate lobes and they ripen through various tints of
yellow during October. A beautiful illustration of this
handsome tree is given in the R.H.S. Journal (Vol. LXI,
part III, page 108) for March, 1936   ...   ... 2/6 3/6 5/6

   " **macrophyllum.**—The "Oregon Maple" thrives in most
soils and grows into a large tree of rounded form. Its
bright green leaves, often 10 ins. wide, are usually 5-
lobed whilst the upper three are sometimes trilobed, and
they change to orange red in October 2/6 3/6 5/6

   " **mandschuricum.**—N. Korea, Manchuria. Possibly not
more than a large shrub with us ; requires shelter from
cutting winds ; related to A. nikoense. The trifoliate
leaves become splendidly coloured in autumn ... 10/6 15/6 21/-

   " **Maximowiczii.**—This small free-growing tree from C.
China is beautiful at any time of the year. Its upright
crimson-red stems carry pretty 3-lobed acuminate
bronze-tinted green leaves, each with a brilliant red
petiole. Each lobe is deeply notched 5/6 7/6 10/6

   " **micranthum.**—Japan. An elegant small tree or shrub with
deep red stems, striped with white and covered with
blue bloom. Its five-lobed leaves are distinctly ovate
whilst the midrib and veins are beetroot-red. The
foliage in autumn assumes orange-red and crimson
tints 2/6 3/6 5/6

			each.

Acer Miyabei.—Japan. An ornamental tree of rather open habit, with dark brown stems and branches, becoming corky with age. The ivy-like leaves are deep green, with three lobes, the lower two often divided. Autumn foliage bright yellow **3/6**   5/6   7/6

„ **nikoense.**—Japan, C. China. A splendid ornamental 10—20 ft. high, especially if given woodland conditions or where it does not get the scorching sun it so dislikes. Its handsome three parted leaves, covered beneath with bristly hairs, become as gorgeously coloured as those of A. griseum or Aronia arbutifolia erecta **3/6   5/6   7/6 10/6**

„ **Oliverianum.**—C. China. A very scarce Maple belonging to the palmatum series and one which may attain small tree size in these Islands. Its pretty green leaves are 4—6 ins. wide, bronze tinted on the underside and have 5 pointed lobes, each neatly notched and serrated ...   **10/6**

E „ **orientale.**—Asia Minor. The Cretan Maple is very hardy and is represented here as a small shrub, only a foot or so high, carrying tiny evergreen leaves which may be either oblong, ovate or trilobed. It is ideal as a point plant on the rockery. Previously distributed as A. creticum **3/6**   5/6   7/6

E „ „ **obtusifolium.**—This distinct sub-species may attain small tree size under cultivation. The ovate evergreen leaves, 2 ins. long and almost as wide, have three lobes and are unevenly serrated. Both this and the type are choice plants for collectors of the uncommon.   **7/6 10/6**

„ **palmatum.**—Better known as the Japanese Maple, it is a small tree reaching 15 ft. Its palmate bright green leaves fade through many tints to scarlet. The members of this group are invaluable for planting in woodlands **2/6   3/6   5/6   7/6**

„ „ **atropurpureum.**—The best form of the many coloured Japanese Maples ; upright habit ; spring and summer foliage dark red, becoming bright red towards autumn. **3/6   5/6   7/6 10/6**

„ „ **dissectum (multifidum).**—Being a bushy slow-growing weeping shrub, only a few feet high, it is suitable for the front of borders or for a point plant on the rockery. The dark green leaves are 7—11 lobed and deeply serrated. This and the two following plants are known as the Japanese Umbrella Maples ... **5/–   7/6 10/6**

„ „ „ **atropurpureum.**—The dense, thread-like weeping growths of this beautiful form are decorated with deep red leaves from spring to autumn 5/–   **7/6 10/6**

„ „ „ **ornatum.**—This form differs in having green suffused bronze red leaves which become magnificently coloured every autmn **5/–   7/6 10/6**

„ „ **koreanum.**—Korea. This splendid striped bark form attains small tree size and is worthy of wide cultivation. Its pointed five-lobed leaves are larger than those of the type and they become as brilliantly coloured during autumn as those of A.p.s. Osakazuki ... **5/–   7/6 10/6**

„ „ **linearilobum.**—Of compact habit, growing to about 8 ft. It is a pretty plant from spring to autumn with its green, deeply five-lobed, linear leaves 5/–   **7/6 10/6**

                                                    each.

Acer palmatum septemlobum.—Deep green seven-lobed leaves, larger than palmatum, red when young, finally dazzling red during autumn 5/-   7/6 10/6

  ,,   ,,   ,, **elegans (ampelopsifolium).**—An elegant form with deeply lobed green leaves; as beautiful in autumn as Ampelopsis Veitchii ... 5/-   7/6 10/6

  ,,   ,,   ,, **purpureum.**—Foliage similar to the former, but dark crimson ... 5/-   7/6 10/6

  ,,   ,,   ,, **Osakazuki.**—Japan. A choice shrub not more than 10—15 ft. high. The green deeply lobed leaves change in autumn through many shades to vivid scarlet. One of the first to plant. 5/-   7/6 10/6

E ,, **Paxii.**—Himalaya. An uncommon small tree, of upright habit, suitable for the South and West, Ireland and West of Scotland. The variable, leathery, trilobed, acuminate leaves are olive-green above and conspicuously blue-grey beneath 10/6

  ,, **pennsylvanicum (Snake-bark Maple).**—Possibly the most conspicuous of all the N. American Maples. It is free-growing and its white striped stems, covered with blue bloom, are attractive at any time of the year. The large handsome three-lobed leaves fade to golden-yellow in autumn. It should be in every collection ... 5/-   7/6 10/6

  ,, **pictum.**—An uncommon species from Manchuria and Japan, with spreading branches, ultimately growing into a small tree. It is clothed with large leaves with five to seven ovate-triangular lobes, fading to various tints of yellow during autumn 3/6   5/6 7/6

  ,,   ,, **parviflorum.**—Korea, N. China. This rarity has brown branches and grows into a small tree. The deeply 7—9 lobed leaves, borne on 4 in. stalks, are broadly cordate and they become beautifully tinted during September and October 5/6   7/6

  ,, **platanoides (Norway Maple).**—A good grower, soon forming a large tree and some splendid specimens may be seen growing in the chalk soil around Salisbury. Its beautiful autumn tints are very effective in thin woodlands or against evergreen backgrounds 2/6 3/6   5/6   7/6

  ,,   ,, **Schwedleri.**—The Purple Maple is suitable for many positions and quickly makes a fine head. Its leaves are brilliantly coloured when young, ageing to purple-red and remaining so until they fall. A.p. Reitenbachii is not so good 3/6   5/6   7/6

  ,, **pseudoplatanus.**—The common Sycamore is one of the most useful trees for windy and exposed positions ... 2/6   3/6

  ,, **purpurascens (diabolicum purpurascens).**—It is one of the most distinct of the Japanese Maples but is exceedingly rare in cultivation. The brown branches are decorated with red flowers before the handsome 5-lobed dentated, red leaves, which later turn to green, unfold. It is very hardy and should grow in most soils. ... 3/6   5/6   7/6

  ,, **rubripes.**—An exceedingly rare and hardy species received from E. Manchuria. Its 3—4 in. puckered, green, bronze-tinted leaves, held on thin crimson stalks, are cordate in outline and have 5 deeply notched lobes. It is one of the best of the genus for its autumn tints and ultimately develops into a small tree 3/6   5/6

Acer rubrum.—(Also known as the Canadian Red Leaf Maple   each.
and the Red Maple of N. America). It is of compact
habit and in some soils soon attains tree size. Its large
3—5 lobed leaves are deep green above, blue-grey
beneath, and in autumn become gorgeously coloured,
varying in shade day by day, from orange-red to scarlet
and crimson 2/6   **3/6**   **5/6**

   „   **tomentosum.**—An attractive small tree, resembling a distinct species rather than a form, with ascending
thin stiff branches. Its grey-green leaves are 4—7 ins.
long and half as much in width, covered with a dense
tomentum. Each leaf is five-lobed, divided almost to the
midrib, and deeply toothed. The foliage for weeks
during autumn is changed to dark red, ageing through
many tints to royal scarlet **7/6**   **10/6**

   „   **rufinerve.**—China & Japan. A noble ornamental, with
upright branches, quickly growing to 10—25 ft. in
height. It is attractive with its blue-grey stems which
become striped with white. Few trees can compare
with it for about six weeks in autumn when it is so
gorgeously coloured. 2/6   3/6   **5/6**   **7/6**

   „   **saccharinum.**—(See **dasycarpum**).

   „   **Sieboldianum.**—Japan. This is a pretty and little known
free-growing shrub worthy of wide cultivation. It is
of rounded form and 8—12 ft. high. The leaves, composed of 7—11 acuminate lobes, incised and red-tipped,
become vividly coloured in autumn and remain so for
weeks. 5/6   **7/6**   **10/6**

   „   **spicatum (Mountain Maple).**—U.S.A. A most desirable
small tree, especially during the winter, with its deep red
growths ageing to light brown in the second year. Here
its attractive three to five-lobed leaves are richly coloured
every autumn 2/6   **3/6**   **5/6**

   „   **tartaricum (cordifolium) (Tartarian Maple).**—An interesting slow-growing species from E. Europe, of shrubby
habit ; autumn foliage dark yellow and red ... 3/6   **5/6**   **7/6**

   „   **Trautvetteri.**—Caucasus. A true Sycamore ; large
lustrous green leaves, fading to dark yellow and red ;
conspicuous in autumn with its bright red seed wings,
which at a distance might easily be taken for flowers 2/6   **3/6**   **5/6**

   „   **triflorum.**—A rarity, from Korea and Manchuria, closely
related to A. nikoense and A. griseum. Its three-parted
ovate or oblong-lanceolate leaves, dove coloured beneath
are intermediate in size between those two species. 10/6   **15/6**   **21/-**

   „   **truncatum.**—N. China. An easy species to establish and
one which ultimately grows into a round-headed tree
15—25 ft. in height according to locality. The long,
deeply toothed, pointed, five or seven-lobed leaves are
bronze-red, ageing to deep green and becoming vividly
coloured in autumn 3/6   **5/6**   **7/6**

   „   **Tschonoskii.**—Hondo, Japan. It is related to the beautiful
A. Maximowiczii and is a graceful large shrub or small
tree 15 ft. or more high. Its pretty green leaves are
orbicular-ovate in outline and are 2—4 ins. long, each
having five lobes edged with both deep and shallow,
pointed teeth ; they change to orange-red and buttercup-
yellow before fading. The branches with their carmine-
red bark are conspicuous during the winter months ...   **10/6**

E **Acradenia Frankliniae.**—Tasmania. An attractive shrub,   each.
4—7 ft. high, for mild parts ; compact pyramidal habit ;
densely clothed with aromatic trifoliate dark green
leaves ; flowers white, five-petalled, small, profuse,
from March to May 3/6   5/6

C **Actinidia arguta.**—Japan, Korea & Manchuria. This sturdy
climber is suitable for pergolas, covering old trees, etc.
Its hermaphrodite, globe-shaped, white-green, fragrant
flowers have purple anthers and are almost 1 in. across.
They are freely borne during June and July 2/6   3/6

C   „   **Kolomikta.**—Amurland, China & Japan. It is suitable
for east and west walls and grows to about 10 ft. high by
as much wide. The heart-shaped, acuminate leaves,
6 ins. long by 4 ins. wide, are metallic green in the spring,
while towards summer the terminal half of each becomes
blotched with pink and white in some soils. 3/6

C   „   **polygama.**—A climber, known as the Silver Vine, from
the mountains of Japan. The 3—5 in. ovate-oblong,
pointed leaves and the petioles have dense bristly hairs.
The ¾ in. fragrant white flowers open during June   ...   2/6   3/6

Aegle sepiaria (Citrus trifoliata).—The hardy orange is better
known under the prettier name of Limonia trifoliata.
It grows into a round bush, 3—6 ft. high, and during
May and June it seldom fails to produce its numerous
showy, pure white, fragrant, flake-like flowers ...   2/6   3/6   5/6

Aesculus austrina.—S.E. United States. An uncommon shrub,
seldom more than 6 ft. high, having five-parted leaves
which are edged with saw-like teeth and covered with
down on the underside. It is attractive during May
with many 6 in. panicles of orange-red flowers, paler
within, each bloom being about 1 in. long 10/6

   „   **carnea (rubicunda).**—The Red Horse Chestnut is a
beautiful tree where enough space can be given for it to
develop its large round head. It is attractive during
May when laden with its 6—8 in. panicles of red
flowers 5/6   7/6   10/6

   „   „   **Briotii.**—Garden origin. The flowers of this
form are a brighter red than those of the type ...   5/6   7/6   10/6

   „   **indica.**—W. Himalayas. This grows into a stately tree,
25 ft. or more high. It is probably the most beautiful
of the ornamental hardwoods, in June and July, with its
profuse 12—16 in. panicles of pure white flowers, each
with a yellow blotch. In some soils its foliage colours
well every autumn 3/6   5/6   7/6

   „   **mutabilis Harbisonii.**—An exceedingly rare large shrub
from N. America. Its twigs are crowned with 8 in.
panicles of bright red flowers, with paler throats, during
May and June. The five-parted, 3—6 in. obovate-
acuminate, bright green leaves are covered beneath with
minute hairs 10/6

   „   **parviflora (macrostachya).**—S.E. United States. A
free-growing shrub, 6 ft. or more high and of spreading
habit, for planting in semi-shade. It is invaluable during
August for its many 8—12 in. erect panicles of white
flowers with red anthers 2/6   3/6   5/6

   „   **plantierensis.**—This desirable tree is a hybrid between
Hippocastanum and carnea. The beautiful 8—12 in.
panicles of rose-coloured flowers are borne during May   7/6   10/6

Aesculus turbinata (Japanese Horse Chestnut).—It makes a well shaped tree and is clothed with distinct foliage which turns a rich golden yellow in autumn. The many 8 in. panicles of creamy-white, yellow tinted flowers are borne during May and June ... ...   each. 10/6

Ailanthus Giraldii.—China. A sub-tropical-looking small tree with dark brown stems and leaves 2 ft. or more in length, composed of thirty to forty metallic-tinted leaflets ageing to bright green 5/-   7/6

„ **Vilmoriniana.**—W. China. This has pinnate leaves even larger than the preceding species. When first introduced its young growths were covered with spines, but under cultivation these have almost disappeared. To obtain extra large leaves, both species should be cut back during March 5/-   7/6

C **Akebia lobata (trifoliata).**—Japan. C. China. A climber with trifoliate leaves, that soon reaches 15—25 ft. Numerous small purple flowers in April ; its conspicuous fruits are seldom seen 2/6   3/6

C „ **quinata.**—C. China to Japan & Korea. Distinct from A. lobata in having leaves composed of five leaflets ; flowers pale purple in short racemes, fragrant. Both species do well on shady walls 2/6   3/6

Alexandrian Laurel. (See **Danaë racemosa**).

Allspice. (See **Calycanthus**).

Almonds. (See **Prunus Amygdalus**).

Alnus incana aurea.—The Golden Alder forms a large bush or small tree if given a moist but not stagnant position. It is very pretty during the winter months with its golden-red stems 3/6   5/6   7/6

Aloysia citriodora. (See **Lippia citriodora**).

Amelanchier alnifolia.—N.W. America. Erect habit ; leaves ovate ; 2 in. erect racemes of pure white flowers during May ; fruits dark purple, somewhat like black currants ; a beautiful shrub 2/6   3/6   5/6

„ **asiatica.**—Japan. This is a worthy ornamental 10 ft. or more high, decorated with racemes of white, pink-tinted, almond scented flowers in May and again in September. In autumn its leaves become as richly coloured as those of Photinia villosa 3/6   5/6   7/6

„ **canadensis.**—N. America. The true plant is rare in British gardens. It has ovate leaves and these, as well as the current growths, are completely covered with thick whitish tomentum. The many 3—4 in. erect racemes of ligulate white flowers are borne in May and often again in September 3/6   5/6

„ **florida (oxyodon).**—W. & C. N. America. A dense erect habited shrub with 2 in erect racemes of white flowers ; autumn foliage bright yellow 2/6   3/6   5/6

„ **grandiflora (canadensis × levis).**—This splendid natural hybrid from E. N. America grows into a large shrub or small tree, its numerous, obtuse-petalled, white flowers being borne in April and May. The oval-elliptical, purple-tinted leaves are downy beneath and become as richly coloured in autumn as those of Enkianthus perulatus 5/-   7/6

Amelanchier grandiflora rubescens.—One of the best shrubs   each.
given us by N. America and in habit it resembles A. levis.
It freely produces drooping racemes of deep pink-lined
flowers which age to flesh colour. The leaves assume
gorgeous autumn tints 5/-   7/6

„ **levis.**—E. N. America. Often seen in gardens incorrectly
named A. canadensis. It is a beautiful small tree in
spring with its wealth of drooping white flowers nestling
amongst the young pink foliage and again in autumn with
its bright red tinted leaves which are held for several
weeks 2/6   3/6   5/6   7/6

„ **oblongifolia.**—East N. America. A charming shrub in
spring when bearing erect racemes of linear-oblanceolate-
petalled white flowers and also during the autumn when
its obovate-oblong leaves, serrulate almost to the base,
assume blood red and scarlet tints 2/6   3/6   5/6

„ **rotundifolia (vulgaris).**—Europe. The common Amelanchier or snowy Mespilus ; flowers pure white, in May,
the largest of the genus 2/6   3/6

„ **sera.**—A new graceful shrub from Virginia and Maryland
with oblong-ovate leaves, wedge-shaped at the base and
edged with forward-pointing saw-like teeth. They
colour well every autumn. The many racemes of narrow-
petalled white flowers are borne during April and May   5/-   7/6

„ **stolonifera.**—Newfoundland. An uncommon shrub,
seldom more than 4 ft. high, with elliptical leaves which
are dark green above and grey-green beneath. Its large
deep red fruits are covered with bloom. Last June, a
fruiting plant at Wisley looked very attractive ... 2/6   3/6   5/6

„ **utahensis.**—N. America. A compact growing shrub not
more than 4 ft. high here ; masses of white flowers in
May ; autumn foliage dark yellow 2/6   3/6

Amorpha canescens.—U.S.A. The Lead Plant is a sub-shrub
and grows to about 4 ft. in ordinary soil. The many purple-
blue, small, pea-like flowers are borne at the ends of the
erect growths from July to September 1/6   2/6

Ampelopsis Veitchii. (See **Vitis inconstans**).

E **Andromeda glaucophylla (polifolia angustifolia).**—East N.
America. Similar to A. polifolia but with narrower foliage   2/6   3/6

E „ **polifolia.**—Northern and Arctic Regions. A native
known as the Bog Rosemary. Compact habit, usually
under 2 ft. high ; very pretty in May with its clusters of
pure pink bell-shaped flowers 1/6   2/6

E „ „ **minima.**—Native of the extreme north of Japan.
This little gem forms a compact tuft 3 ins. high. Its
thread-like stems carry $\frac{1}{2}$–$\frac{3}{4}$ in. oblong-pointed, deep
green leaves and they are glaucous blue beneath. During
May and June it produces groups of pretty pale pink
flowers 3/6   5/6

E „ „ **nana (compacta).**—A dainty dwarf alpine shrub
from the mountains of Japan and suitable for the Ericaceae
border. It is densely clothed with pea-green leaves
which are conspicuously blue-grey beneath. Its bell-
shaped, flesh pink flowers are quite as pretty as those of
our native Andromeda, which is found in Yorkshire,
etc. 2/6   3/6   5/6

See also **Cassandra, Cassiope, Enkianthus, Leucothoe, Lyonia, Oxydendrum, Phyllodoce, Pieris**
and **Zenobia.**

E **Anopterus glandulosa.**—Tasmania. A very desirable tender each. shrub. Its dark green foliage and erect spikes of white cup-shaped blossoms are singularly beautiful. It makes a shapely plant, flowering in its youth, during April and May. There is a good illustration in W. J. Bean's 3rd volume of Trees and Shrubs 7/6 10/6

E **Arbutus Menziesii (procera).**— The Madrono of California. A tree 20—40 ft. high ; 9 in. panicles of pitcher-shaped flowers in May. Its peeling bark in spring reveals a striking cinnamon-coloured inner bark ... ...   —   —

E   „   **Unedo.**—S. Europe, Ireland. One of the very best small trees with its mass of orange-red fruits in late autumn, and flowers in winter. Inland its fruits are not so freely produced as when growing near the sea 2/6   3/6   5/6

E **Arcterica nana.**—An extremely rare Japanese shade-loving minia-ture shrub with tiny leaves and sprays of lily of the valley-like flowers during May. There is a beautiful plate of it in the New Flora & Silva Vol. III, No. 1, page 55 (Oct. 1935) 3/6   5/6

E **Arctostaphylos Manzanita.**—A noble evergreen shrub from California, but a most difficult plant to establish. It loves a cool lime-free soil. The bell-shaped pink flowers are borne in March and April 10/6

E   „   **nummularia.**—"Jepson's Manual of the Flowering Plants of California." Mendocino, Coastal Plain, California. This rarity grows into a bush 6—12 in. high with stems ascending or diffuse. The pilose-pubescent branches are thickly clothed with small elliptic to ovate or oblong, ciliate and glossy leaves. It produces small white flowers during the spring. At first sight it may easily be mistaken for a Pernettya 5/-   7/6

EC **Aristolochia altissima.**—Sicily & Algeria. An evergreen climber with smilax-like leaves ; flowers yellowish, in June and July ; not generally hardy 3/6   5/6

C   „   **Sipho.**—U.S.A. A rampant wall climber with beautiful foliage ; flowers Dutch pipe-like, yellow and brown, in June and July 2/6   3/6   5/6

E **Aristotelia Macqui.**—Pretty variegated leaves ; only hardy around the south and west coast and similar gardens ; grows 15—20 ft. high, as a small tree 2/6   3/6

E   „   **racemosa.**—New Zealand. Only suitable for the mildest gardens ; handsome serrated reddish foliage ; profusion of small pink flowers in late spring 2/6   3/6

Aronia arbutifolia (Red Chokeberry.)—U.S.A. It develops into a bush 5 ft. or more high and its slender brown-red and green growths are furnished with pointed, obovate-oval, glossy green leaves, the undersides of which are pale green and coated with down. The corymbs of white pink tinted flowers borne in May are succeeded by numerous brilliant red fruits which hang long after the magnificently coloured leaves have dropped. Previously distributed as Pyrus aronia arbutifolia 2/6   3/6

  „   „   **Brilliant.**—This has proved to be A. melanocarpa   —   —

Aronia arbutifolia erecta.—As erect growing as the Lombardy each. Poplar and Prunus Amanogawa, 5—8 ft. high, and with slender branches. The 2½—4 in. dark green, oblong obovate leaves become vividly coloured every autumn. This plant has become a great favourite and is ideal where space is limited 1/6 2/6 3/6 5/6

„ **floribunda.**—Nova Scotia & Florida. This shrub is 5 ft. or more in height with dense, upright, twiggy, red-brown branches bearing obovate-oval, pointed, glossy green leaves rather smaller than those of A. arbutifolia and covered with downy wool on the underside. Its many corymbs of glistening, globe-shaped, ¼-in. dark red fruits age to purple-red and they are retained long after the attractively coloured leaves fall 2/6 3/6

„ **melanocarpa.**—It sends up many red-brown base shoots and these form a neat, dense shrub, 2—4 ft. in height, though 6 ft. in some gardens. It presents an unusual sight during the autumn with its heavy crop of jet-black fruits nestling among the richly coloured, pointed, obovate leaves 1/6 2/6 3/6

The Aronias are of easy cultivation in almost any soil and they are invaluable for their autumn display of gorgeously coloured leaves.

Asimina triloba.—South U.S.A. This shrub is not often seen in English gardens, though it is well worth growing for its striking foliage. It attains 6—15 ft., according to locality 2/6 3/6 5/6

E **Atherospermum moschatum.**—The rare Tasmanian Sassafras can be grown in many gardens if it is given a semi-shady position. The opposite, aromatic, sparsely-toothed, oval-acuminate leaves are deep green above and glaucous beneath. The pretty, ½ in., 5—8 petalled, cup-shaped, ivory-white flowers are borne in the axils of the leaves from February onwards. The base of each petal and the many stamens are rose-red 5/- 7/6 10/6

E **Aucuba japonica (male and female).**—One of the few evergreens to do well in the shade of trees ; large handsome foliage ; beautiful in autumn and winter with its mass of bright red berries 2/6 3/6

Azalea Albrechtii.—Japan. An invaluable shrub, about 5 ft. high, carrying showy, purple-rose, campanulate flowers in May. In its best form the obovate-oblanceolate wavy leaves are in groups of five, are bronze-red in colour, ageing to green, and change in autumn to orange-yellow and red ... ...7/6 to 21/-

„ **arborescens.**—A much neglected choice N. American species, about 5 ft. high, which produces its fragrant flesh coloured flowers in July and August. Its foliage becomes richly tinted every autumn 3/6 5/6 7/6

„ **calendulacea.**—N. America. This choice ornamental is uncommon in British gardens and few plants are more beautiful during June and July, when it is covered with showy buff-yellow flowers, ageing to orange-yellow 2/6 3/6 5/6 7/6

„ „ **aurantiaca.**—Georgia, U.S.A. In its native habitat it is known as the Flame Azalea. The flowers are glowing orange-scarlet ageing to crimson-red, and smaller 5/- 7/6

Azalea calendulacea crocea.—A good shrub 3—5 ft. high and as much wide. From late May to July it is almost covered with clusters of flowers, orange-yellow suffused orange-red in colour **5/– 7/6**

each.

„ **Daviesii (molle × viscosum).**—Garden Hybrid. A first rate shrub about 3 ft. high, but much wider, and it appears to love semi-shade. The dense deep green leaves form a splendid background for the mass of white, yellow-blotched flowers borne during May and June 3/6 **5/6 7/6**

„ **Diamio (Kaempferi forma).**—Japan. It is semi-evergreen in the south and west and it attains 3—5 ft. in height. Its leaves are almost hidden by large salmon-coloured flowers in June and July **3/6 5/6**

„ **mollis (molle).**—Home grown plants from seed of a good strain, are offered in many shades. 15/– to 60/– doz., 1/6 2/6 **3/6 5/6**

„ **nudiflora.**—E. United States. A splendid shrub, about 5 ft. high, for the early spring garden. In March and April, before the leaves appear, it bears clusters of 6—9 carnation-scented pale pink flowers 2/6 **3/6 5/6**

„ **obtusa (amoena) (indica) (EVERGREEN SECTION).** —Japan. Small foliage, mass of crimson-coloured flowers in spring 2/6 **3/6 5/6**

„ „ **balsaminaeflora (rosaeflora).**—Quite a dwarf ; pretty double salmon flowers 1/6 2/6 **3/6 5/6**

„ „ **Caldwellii.**—Covered during May with pale pink hose in hose flowers **3/6 5/6**

„ „ **Forsteriana.**—Flowers semi-double, bright crimson 2/6 **3/6 5/6**

„ „ **Hinodegiri.**—Bright green foliage ; flowers bright red 2/6 **3/6 5/6**

„ „ **Hinomayo.**—Dwarf habit ; bright pink flowers in May and June 2/6 **3/6 5/6**

„ „ **H. O. Carre.**—A pretty shrub during April and May, covered with semi-double bright pink flowers ... **3/6 5/6**

„ „ **Illuminata.**—Of spreading habit 2—3 ft. high and one of the most striking evergreens in June and early July with its 2½ in. Azalea mollis-shaped, brilliant rose-coloured flowers with dark red markings ... 3/6 **5/6 7/6**

„ „ **rosea.** — The hardiest of this section. The bright pink flowers are freely produced during May 2/6 **3/6 5/6**
   The above evergreen **Azaleas** love the shade of distant trees and are not generally hardy.

„ **occidentalis.**—Rocky Mountains, W. N. America. This attractive species has a beauty all its own, despite the many beauties raised from it. The terminal clusters of six to twelve sweetly scented white flowers, with a yellow blotch, are borne during June and July. Its leaves turn scarlet and yellow in autumn 3/6 **5/6 7/6**

„ „ **rosea.**—Rocky Mountains, W. N. America. This is as free-growing as the former and its foliage colours well every autumn. The lovely sweet-scented flowers are pink, with tubes of a deeper colour, and are produced in quantity from late May to early July **5/– 7/6**

				each.
Azalea occidentalis Delicatissima				
,, ,, **Exquisite**				
,, ,, **graciosa**		5/-	7/6	
,, ,, **Irene Koster**				
,, ,, **magnifica**				
,, ,, **suberba**				

These beautiful hybrids are of good constitution and soon grow into large bushes 5—8 ft. high and quite as wide. They bloom during June when the ordinary Azaleas have finished. The large trusses of tubular sweet-scented flowers are of various shades of pink and rose, with yellow, buff and apricot markings.

,, **pentaphylla (Rhododendron quinquefolium).—**Japan. This rare and choice shrub grows to 5 ft. or more high and has whorls of 1½—3 in. oval or oval-lanceolate hairy leaves, long drawn out at the base. It is particularly attractive with its 5-lobed bright rose or white unspotted flowers borne in April and May and again during the autumn. It loves semi-shade or woodland conditions and its foliage is tinted with fiery red from early September until the end of the year 3/6 5/6   7/6 10/6

,, **pontica (Rhododendron luteum).—**Caucasus. A useful shrub, growing 6—8 ft. high ; flowers bright yellow, very fragrant ; foliage in autumn richly coloured. 24/- to 60/- doz. 2/6   3/6 5/6

,, ,, **altaclerense.—**Garden origin. A magnificent form having large orange yellow flowers with deeper coloured markings and they are as beautiful as those of many of the named forms of A. mollis. It is also attractive in autumn with its glowing orange-red to deep red foliage 2/6   3/6 5/6

,, **reticulata (Rhododendron rhombicum) (R. dilatatum).—**This choice shrub seldom exceeds 5 ft. in height and it loves a semi-shady position. The ends of its thin growths carry whorls of two or three broadly ovate or diamond-shaped leaves, ¾—1½ in. long and net veined. Its delightful 1½—2 in. purple-red, azalea-like flowers are borne freely on leafless branches from late March to early May. It is also a fine ornament in the autumn with its highly coloured foliage 5/- 7/6

,, **rosea (Rhododendron).—**East N. America. An uncommon twiggy shrub about 5 ft. high. Its leaves are bluish green. It is singularly beautiful during May and June when covered with tubular, rose-coloured and carnation-scented blossoms on its naked wood ... 3/6   5/6 7/6

,, **Vaseyi.—**Caroline Mountains. Grows to a large shrub with pink flowers in May ; perhaps the most beautiful deciduous Azalea 2/6 3/6   5/6 7/6

,, **viscosa.—**E. N. America. The Swamp Honeysuckle is a delightful shrub with clusters of six or more very fragrant white or pale pink flowers in mid-summer ... 2/6   3/6 5/6

E **Azara Browneae.—**Chile. Larger foliage than A. integrifolia ; small bright yellow flowers from December to March ...   5/-

E ,, **dentata.—**Chile. A good evergreen growing to 8 ft. in chalk soil in N.W.Dorset, free from north and east winds ; numerous small bright yellow flowers in May ...   3/6 5/6

E **Azara Gilliesii (crassifolium).**—Chile. A beautiful evergreen each on a west wall ; a small tree in favoured spots ; handsome round leathery serrated foliage ; numerous small bright yellow flowers in April and May 3/6 5/6

E „ **integrifolia.**—Chile. Also best on a wall ; profusion of small bright yellow flowers from December to March ... 3/6 5/6

E „ **lanceolata.**—This new graceful erect shrub from Chile should be given a sheltered position or placed against a south or west wall, although in an open garden in the New Forest, a plant facing S.E. has attained 5 ft. x 3 ft. The showy clusters of small yellow mimosa-like flowers are borne in the axils of the widely-serrated lanceolate leaves 3/6 5/6

E „ **microphylla.**—Chile. An elegant shrub or small tree with frond-like branches clothed with glistening small box-like leaves ; the vanilla scent of its yellow flowers can be detected for yards around it, from March to May ; loves semi-shade, in the south and west 2/6 3/6

E **Banksia quercifolia.**—Australia. A noble evergreen to collectors of rare plants ; conspicuous ash-grey foliage, white beneath ; suitable for mild gardens ... ... 5/6 7/6 10/6.

Bay. (See **Laurus nobilis**).

Benthamia fragifera. (See **Cornus capitata**).

EC **Berberidopsis corallina.**—Chile. An ideal climber for sheltered shady walls and it will even ramble among Rhododendrons in the south and west. Its beautiful drooping racemes of coral-red or dark crimson Berberis-like flowers are a grand sight from early August to October. It is supposed to hate limey soils but plants put against N. Walls in such districts, and started in a mixture of loam, leaf mould and sand, have now penetrated into the natural soil and grow and flower freely 2/6 3/6 5/6

E **Berberis actinacantha.**—Chile. A semi-evergreen shrub with arching branches covered in spring with sweet-scented deep yellow flowers on short stalks 5/-

E „ **acuminata.** (See **Veitchii**).

„ **aemulans.**—W. China. A distinct erect growing species ; branches slightly covered with glaucous bloom ; autumn foliage a mass of scarlet 3/6 5/6

„ **aggregata (Geraldii of Veitch).**—W. China. This compact brown branched small shrub is conspicuous every autumn when laden with 2 in. racemes of densely packed terra cotta coloured fruits showing above the small obovate scarlet leaves 1/6 2/6 3/6

„ „ **Prattii.**—W. China. A splendid form with stronger whip-like growths which are weighed down throughout the autumn with longer racemes of larger brilliant red fruits 2/6 3/6

„ **amurensis (Regeliana).**—Manchuria. An upright shrub with angled branches clothed with elliptical or oblong-obovate leaves often 3 in. in length. It is attractive during the autumn with many pendulous racemes of brilliant red ellipsoid fruits 3/6 5/6

„ **angulosa.**—A Himalayan species with growths 3—5 ft long ; flowers large orange-yellow ; fruits oval, bright scarlet as if varnished ; foliage colours well in autumn. 2/6 3/6

Berberis aristata.—N.W. Himalaya. This attractive spreading shrub grows 6 ft. or more high and is semi-evergreen in southern gardens. It has tufts of 2—7, 1½—3 in. obovate oblong, spine-tipped leaves, a few of which are edged with spiny teeth. During June and July the extensions of the light brown angled growths bear 2—3 in. racemes of golden yellow flowers and these are succeeded by conspicuous, spindle-shaped, carmine-red fruits. This rare species and B. chitria have been confused for many years   ...   .   each. 3/6   5/6

„   „   **coriaria (Schneider) (aristata floribunda. Bean).**—Distributed by Messrs. Späth of Berlin about 1905. It is a strong grower 6 ft. or more high and bears 4—6 in. racemes of bright yellow flowers followed by oval-oblong, red-purple fruits covered with blue bloom. Its large obovate-oblong leaves assume scarlet and orange-red tints from October until the New Year. Previously distributed as B. macrophylla 3/6   5/6

„   **aristata × Hookeri.**—A handsome shrub, 6 ft. or more high, evergreen around the south coast but deciduous inland. The various sized green obovate leaves, grey beneath and 1—2 ins. long, are in tufts and margined with spiny teeth. Many 2—3 in. racemes of yellow flowers are borne during June and July and these give place to banana-shaped purple berries covered with glaucous bloom.   2/6   3/6

E   „   **asiatica.**—Himalayas. This rare pyramidal-growing species attains 6 ft. or more in height. In the south and west it is quite hardy and evergreen. The distinct obovate-orbicular, grey-green, spiny leaves are glaucous beneath. The branches are a beautiful sight in autumn when laden with glaucous blue egg-shaped berries.   2/6   3/6   5/6

E   „   **atrocarpa (levis).**—W. China. Semi-evergreen ; long narrow leaves ; clusters of yellow flowers ; fruits bright red, finally jet black ; some of the leaves become vividly coloured during winter 1/6   2/6   3/6

„   **Beaniana.**—W. China. A choice shrub 4 ft. or more high with arching branches furnished with tufts of oval-lanceolate leaves. Its red, crimson and scarlet coloured foliage does not fall before the new year 2/6   3/6

E   „   **Bergmanniae.**—W. China. Deep green, acuminated, serrated leaves ; grows to about 8 ft. 2/6   3/6

„   **brachypoda.**—C. & N. China. A choice Barberry having 3—5 in. racemes of yellow flowers succeeded by masses of oblong, scarlet-red berries nestling among the brilliantly coloured 1½—3in. oval-oblong leaves. It was one of the best fruiting shrubs in a well-known garden near Dorchester last autumn 2/6   3/6

„   **Bretschneideri.**—Japan, China. Stiff, bushy habit, 3—5 ft. high ; distinct brown-red branches ; broad obovate pale green leaves with winged stalks ; 2 in. racemes of small yellow flowers in May ; fruits bright red 3/6

„   **buxifolia (dulcis).**—Chile. A semi-evergreen species growing to a large bush. The drooping, sweetly scented resin-yellow flowers are borne during April, followed by purple fruits 1/6   2/6

E   „   „   **nana (minima).**—A little pygmy about 6 or 9 in. high ; a capital shrub for dwarf hedges or rockeries   ...   1/6

each.

E **Berberis calliantha. K.W. 6308.**—Tsangpo Gorge, China.
Although found in Tibet in 1924, this beautiful Barberry
was not named until 1935. It much resembles B. Hookeri
in appearance, but only grows to 2—3 ft. in height.
The leaves are waxen white beneath and the very large
flowers, produced 1—3 at each joint in May, are followed
by barrel-shaped purple-black berries. A.M. June 7th,
1932 (as B. Hookeri glauca) **2/6 3/6**

E „ **candidula (hypoleuca).**—C. China. A dwarf compact
evergreen shrub less than 2 ft. high ; leaves oblong, persistent, glaucous white beneath ; a good rock garden
shrub **1/6 2/6**

„ **chinensis (Guimpelii).**—Caucasus. A small, very rare
shrub, seldom over 2 ft. high ; leaves oblanceolate ;
pendent 3 in. racemes of pale yellow flowers ; foliage
in late autumn glowing scarlet **5/-**

„ **chitria.**—Himalayas. A strong-growing bushy shrub,
5—10 ft. high, and semi-evergreen in the south and
west. Its obovate-oval, 1—3 in. green leaves have 1—5
spiny teeth on each side. The red-brown stems carry
pendulous panicles of yellow flowers and these are followed by oval-oblong berries covered with purple bloom **2/6 3/6**

„ **colburyensis.**—This distinguished hybrid between B.
polyantha and B. Wilsonae was raised in 1915 by the
late Mr. Louch of Colbury, Totton. In the autumn
few ornamentals are better, as it is then laden with large
clusters of round, vivid carmine fruits nestling among
the scarlet leaves which are held till mid-winter. It
has a splendid habit and will grow to about 6—9 ft. ... **2/6 3/6**

„ **concinna (of Hooker).**—Sikkim-Himalayas. A compact
shrub, 3 ft. high ; leaves bright green, pure white
beneath, gorgeously coloured in autumn ; conspicuous
oblong carmine-red fruits **2/6 3/6**

„ „ **K.W. 6326.**—Collected by Captain Kingdon Ward
in the Tsangpo Gorge in 1924. It differs from the
former in having wiry drooping growths clothed with
smaller leaves, pure white beneath. The numerous egg-
shaped carmine-red fruits and coloured leaves make a
fine show every autumn **5/-**

E „ **congestiflora.**—Chile. This rarity grows into a shrub 4 ft.
or more high and as much wide. It was considered for
many years as synonymous with B. hakeoides. The
twiggy, angled growths carry tufts of wavy, grey-green,
cordate leaves ¼—1½ in. long, glaucous beneath. The
many clusters of 7—11 small yellow flowers, held on long
thread-like stalks are produced during April and May and
are succeeded by small, elliptical, purple fruits **5/- 7/6**

E „ **Darwinii.**—Chile. A well-known favourite ; one of the
most beautiful of all shrubs during April and May ; will
grow in semi-shade ; a selected form with orange-yellow
flowers ; propagated from cuttings **1/6 2/6 3/6**

E „ „ **Flame.**—One of the most striking shrubs in
spring, with its branches smothered with deep orange
flowers, suffused with crimson on the outside, and with
stalks and sepals of glowing red. It grows 4—6 ft. high
according to soil and site **3/6 5/-**

E **Berberis Darwinii Gold.**—An indispensable shrub for any garden   each.
for its wealth of rich golden-yellow flowers. In ordinary
good soil it will grow 6 ft. high and as much wide. This,
together with B. Darwinii Flame and B. stenophylla
corallina are three of the very best shrubs there are for
brightening up the garden from late February till the end
of May **3/6   5/-**

E   „   „   **macrophylla (Darwinii × buxifolia).**—A natural hybrid found in the Daisy Hill Nursery, Newry, in
1906. A worthy shrub of splendid compact habit, 3—4 ft.
high ; polished box-like foliage ; large orange-yellow
flowers on long thread-like stalks in threes and fives, during
May ; one of the few sweetly scented Berberises   1/6   **2/6   3/6**

E   „   „   **pendula.**—A natural hybrid with 2—3 ft. slender
pendulous branches, wreathed during May with orange
yellow flowers 1/6   **2/6   3/6**

E   „   „   **prostrata.**—Natural Hybrid. The semi-prostrate branches are smothered during May with racemes
of coral-red flowers ; useful for bold rock work, sloping
banks, etc. 1/6   **2/6   3/6**

E   „   **Delavayi.**—Yunnan, China. An uncommon species,
growing 4—6 ft. high, and furnished with 3—4 in. oval
polished green leaves edged with spiny teeth   ...   ...   **—   —**

„   **diaphana.**—W. China. One of the most distinct, though
little known, members of the genus. Its short, grooved,
stiff, brown growths carry tufts of $\frac{3}{4}$—$2\frac{1}{2}$ in. oblong-
obovate, netted leaves, pea-green above and distinctly
glaucous beneath. The flowers are followed by conspicuous red fruits. It will attain 4 ft. and is a worthy
shrub for the autumn garden **2/6   3/6**

„   **dictyophylla.**——Yunnan, China. An upright-growing
shrub, 4—7 ft. high with a spreading head quite as wide.
It is grey-blue in appearance and is attractive from spring
to autumn.   It has become a great favourite, even in the
coldest gardens, for its magnificent late tints of scarlet,
gold and crimson 1/6   **2/6   3/6**

„   „   **albicaulis.**—Another form, smaller in all its
parts, with pure white stems and greyish leaves **3/6**

„   „   **epruinosa.**—A Chinese form, with semi-weeping
habit, white stems and glaucous grey leaves **2/6   3/6**

„   „   **Tali-Range.**—China. The general character of
this shrub suggests a distinct species ; short stiff erect
branches ; compact habit ; its medium-sized leaves
turn in late autumn and winter a flame of orange red and
scarlet **2/6   3/6**

„   **Dielsiana.**—W. China. A choice species of dense habit,
4—6 ft. high, with a glaucous appearance ; tufts of 3—5
ovate to oblanceolate leaves, 2—4 ins. long, fade in
autumn from pale yellow to orange **3/6   5/6**

„   **Edgeworthiana (brachybotrys).**—Himalayas. Compact
habit ; autumn foliage bright orange yellow **3/6**

E   „   **empetrifolia.**—Chile. A dwarf shrub 2 ft. high ; slender
trailing branches ; tiny reflexed leaves ; flowers golden-
yellow, in May **2/6   3/6**

each.

E **Berberis Ferdinandii-Coburgii.**—China. A distinct member of a large genus. It is of compact habit and grows to a height of about 5 ft. The bronze or metallic-green acuminate leaves are reticulated and edged with long spiny teeth. Most of its leaves become richly coloured during winter **2/6 3/6**

„ **Francisci-Ferdinandii.**—W. China. A noble shrub, 4—6 ft. high, decorated in spring with mottled, ovate-lanceolate leaves margined with spiny teeth. The drooping racemes of pale yellow flowers are followed by ellipsoid scarlet fruits. At Westonbirt, it is one of the best autumn colouring shrubs **2/6 3/6 5/6**

E „ **Gagnepainii.**—China. Dense erect habit, attaining 4 ft. ; leaves linear-lanceolate, undulated ; clusters of bright yellow flowers ; berries jet black, covered with blue bloom **1/6 2/6 3/6**

E „ „ **forma.**—An elegant form growing to 7 ft. ; leaves much larger and more undulated **2/6 3/6**

„ **Gilgiana.**—C. China. A rare relative to B. brachypoda with narrower leaves, smaller deeper yellow flowers and orange-red autumn foliage **3/6**

„ **Giraldii.**—N. & C. China. This rare and splendid shrub attains 5 ft., is of open habit and has brown stems carrying long, three-parted prongs. Its pretty 1½—4 in. oblong-ovate serrated leaves are red when unfolding and age to green, becoming gorgeously coloured during autumn. Many 4 in., pendulous, spike-like racemes of yellow flowers are followed by fruits very similar to those of B. brachypoda. The plant previously distributed under this name is the upright form of B. rubrostilla ... **5/-**

E „ **hakeoides.**—Chile. This choice shrub of upright habit attains 5—8 ft. in semi-shade in the southern counties. Its tapering branches carry dense tufts of holly-like, pea-green leaves on ½—2½ in. stalks. The small clusters of sweetly scented bright yellow flowers are borne in the axils of the leaves during April and May **5/- 7/6**

E „ **Hookeri** — Himalayas. A compact small shrub, 3 ft. high with dark glossy green leaves. It will grow as well in shade as in the open **1/6 2/6**

E „ „ **latifolia (Knightii) (xanthoxylon of Schneider and Rehder).**—This splendid evergreen attains a height of 6 ft. and is used as a hedge plant in Ireland. It is densely furnished with handsome, glossy green leaves and it freely produces large golden yellow flowers on long stalks. It will grow as well in shade as in the open **1/6 2/6**

E „ **hypokerina.**—Upper Burma. This was sent home by Captain Kingdon Ward as B. Silver Holly. It makes an open bush 3—4 ft. high, the stiff branches furnished with conspicuous holly-like leaves, wedge-shaped at the base and silver-white beneath **5/6 7/6**

E „ **insignis.**—Sikkim, E. Nepal, Bhotan. It grows 6 ft. or more high and is much hardier than is generally supposed. It is handsome at any time of the year with its narrow, long, acuminate, green leaves, paler beneath **1/6 2/6**

Berberis Jamesiana.—Yunnan, China. A rare and beautiful each.
slender habited species, 5—8 ft. high with glaucous
stems. It is particularly attractive during the autumn
with its richly coloured obovate leaves and quantities of
red currant-like fruits **3/6   5/6**

E „ **Julianae.**—China. A handsome evergreen ultimately 6 ft.
high ; leaves dark green, acuminated, serrated, prominently veined ; many assume striking autumn tints 1/6 **2/6   3/6**

„ **Knightii. (See Hookeri latifolia).**

„ **koreana.**—Korea. This small shrub, about 4 ft. high, is
of easy culture and bears 3—4 in. racemes of round
brilliant red fruits. The erect branches are particularly
attractive when the large ovate-elliptic bronze mottled
leaves become richly coloured **1/6   2/6**

„ **leptoclada.**—China. Thin semi-weeping branches ;
leaves grey or light blue ; fruits globose, carmine red,
freely produced in autumn ; a graceful shrub, 3ft. high 1/6 **2/6 3/6**

„ **leucocarpa (F. 29085).**—Yunnan, China. An elegant
wiry stemmed shrub, 4—6 ft. high. The round leaves
are heart-shaped at the base and glaucous beneath and
they colour splendidly every autumn. The fruits are
coated with white bloom **3/6**

E „ **linearifolia.**—Chile. This rare and very hardy Barberry
is of open habit, 4—6 ft. high, and its branches are
clothed with tufts of various sized, attractive, leathery,
deep glossy green, linear leaves, glaucous beneath.
The clusters of large flowers, orange coloured inside and
deep apricot suffused scarlet outside, are borne in great
profusion during March and April and often again in
the autumn. The black fruits are covered with blue
bloom. In its best form it is undoubtedly the most
attractive Berberis yet known *5/6, 7/6.* **10/6**

E „ **lologensis (Darwinii × linearifolia).**—A natural hybrid
from Chile, and a strong grower. It has dense deep
green, glossy, linear and obovate leaves, paler beneath
and edged with 3—11 spiny teeth. During April it
bears flowers ½ in. or more wide, orange-yellow within
and deep apricot without **5/6   7/6 10/6**

„ **lycioides.**—A semi-deciduous species, from the north-
western Himalaya, related to B. asiatica and may even be
a hybrid from it. The oblanceolate, grey-green leaves
are usually spineless. The racemes of yellow flowers
are often compound, and they are followed by oval, blue
black fruits thickly covered with white bloom. A.M.
August 28th, 1934 ... ... **3/6   5/6**

E „ **lycium.**—Himalayas. An evergreen, tall species of elegant appearance ; leaves obovate, glaucous or bluish ;
3 in. racemes of numerous bright yellow flowers ; fruits
oblong, black, covered with blue bloom **2/6   3/6**

„ **mekongensis.**—Yunnan, China. One of the best of the
Barberries ; foliage in autumn, scarlet, gold and orange,
reverse side buff-yellow **3/6**

„ **morrisonensis.**—Mt. Morrison, Formosa. A rare species
of compact habit, 3 ft. high, and suitable for the higher
points of the rock garden or the front of a border. It is
particularly attractive from mid-August to December
when it has many globose-ovoid, carmine-red fruits
nestling among the obovate scarlet leaves **2/6   3/6**

Berberis orthobotrys.—Himalaya, Persia. A rare shrub growing up to 5 ft. high. Its brown-red stems are clothed with clusters of 5—8 obovate or oblanceolate leaves. The extensions of its branches are a brilliant sight when laden with large, oval, glistening crimson-red berries which are held till mid-November. Berberis Unique and this plant appear to be identical 2/6 3/6

„ **pallens.** — China. A beautiful Barberry, growing 5—6 ft. high; current growths are dogwood-red and semi-arching ; flowers bright yellow, followed by large red fruits ; foliage during autumn vividly coloured 2/6 3/6

„ **parvifolia.**—W. China. Erect habit, growing to 4 ft. ; the small foliage becomes bright red from the suffusion of the striking plum red on the reverse side 2/6 3/6

„ **Poiretii.**—Manchuria. A small shrub about 3 ft. high ; long racemes of many flowers producing bright red fruits 2/6 3/6

„ **polyantha.**—W. China. An elegant species attaining 7 ft.; the 4 in. erect, lilac-shaped panicles of thirty to fifty yellow flowers are followed by coral-red fruits, ripe in autumn. The true plant is offered 3/6 5/6

E „ **pruinosa.**—Yunnan, China. Strong growing ; leaves oval or obovate, bright green, glaucous beneath ; flowers lemon-yellow ; fruits black covered with whitish bloom 3/6

E „ **replicata.**—S. W. China. An attractive and graceful slender branched small shrub ; leaves long and narrow, reflexed, grey-white beneath ; covered throughout the autumn with blue-black fruits 1/6 2/6 3/6

„ **rubrostilla (of Wisley).**—This is considered to be a hybrid, B. Wilsonae being one of its parents, but is undoubtedly an unrecorded species from W. China. It makes a thicket of arching branches 3—5 ft. high and they carry, during the autumn months, numerous large, bright carmine-scarlet fruits, very similar to those of B. orthobotrys and B. concinna. It should be given a place in every garden for its fruits and scarlet autumn leaves 2/6 3/6

E „ **sanguinea.**—Mts. of Szechuan, China. A small, compact shrub, about 3 ft. high ; leaves linear-lanceolate ; numerous golden-yellow flowers with reddish sepals ... 2/6 3/6

E „ **Sargentiana.**—W. Hupeh, China. One of the most beautiful of evergreen Barberries ; dark green leaves, 3—5 ins. long ; does remarkably well on chalk soils 1/6 2/6 3/6

„ **Sieboldii.**—China and Japan. A beautiful species with marbled foliage in spring, attaining 3 ft. in semi-shade ; 2 in. racemes of pale yellow flowers followed by round orange-yellow berries ; in November its oval leaves are dazzling scarlet, which few shrubs can surpass ; distinct rare and little known 3/6 5/6

„ **Silva-Taroucana.**—W. China. An open-branched small shrub, 4 ft. high ; pretty bronze and pink foliage throughout the growing season 3/6 5/–

„ **Smithiana.**—Hybrid. Small grey-green leaves ; its 3 ft. spreading pendulous branches are wreathed from end to end, in autumn, with bright coral-red berries ; a splendid fruiting shrub 1/6 2/6 3/6

E **Berberis Soulieana.**—C. China. A rare species with angled branches ; leaves thick, lanceolate, deeply serrated ; pretty lemon-yellow flowers ... ...   each.   2/6 3/6

E   „ **species F. 1030.**—W. China. A choice erect, open-branched evergreen related to B. Hookeri ; leaves much larger, dark green with a persistent bluish bloom beneath ; some fade towards autumn to bronzy red, finally bright scarlet in the new year 2/6 3/6

  „ **Stapfiana.**—W. China. A semi-evergreen shrub about 5 ft. high, beautiful in autumn with its pendulous branches weighted with quantities of coral-red berries 1/6 2/6

E   „ **stenophylla (empetrifolia × Darwinii).**—One of the most beautiful shrubs when massed for effect. Its arching branches, wreathed from end to end with sweetly scented golden-yellow flowers in April and May are a beautiful sight 1/6 2/6

E   „   „ **autumnalis.**—One of autumn's charms ; slender graceful, overlapping branches smothered with drooping racemes of bright golden-yellow flowers during May and June and again in late autumn. Height 3 ft. 1/6 2/6

  „   „ **Brilliant.**—A unique break, aptly named ; its semi-deciduous foliage turns gorgeous tints in the new year. Height 3 ft. 1/6 2/6

E   „   „ **coccinea.**—One of the most beautiful of all April and May dwarf shrubs ; flowers scarlet, fading to orange red ; foliage glaucous blue 1/6 2/6 3/6

E   „   „ **compacta.**—A distinct and compact free-flowering form, about 3 ft. high, with very slender growths 1/6 2/6 3/6

E   „   „ **corallina.**—One of the most beautiful raised and sent out by the late Mr. T. Smith of Newry. It forms a dense bush, 4—6 ft. high, and its 2—4 ft. pendulous growths are lit up, from end to end, with rich coral-red flowers. It is one of the first twelve shrubs to plant for its magnificent spring effect 1/6 2/6 3/6

E   „   „   „ **nana.**—A true pygmy, of compact habit, which ultimately is only a foot or so high ; its flowers are even brighter than those of its parent. A pretty plant for the rockery 1/6 2/6 3/6

E   „   „ **Crawley Gem.**—Grey-green foliage ; wiry arching branches ; conspicuous loose pendent racemes of deep coral-red buds opening to bright orange-yellow during May ; height 2 ft. 2/6 3/6

E   „   „ **diversifolia.** — Compact habit ; dark green leaves, spined and spineless ; profusion of bright yellow flowers 1/6 2/6

E   „   „ **glauca.**—Grey-blue foliage ; quite prostrate habit ; orange-yellow flowers ; a unique shrub for the rock garden 2/6 3/6

E   „   „ **gracilis.**—A graceful slender branching shrub attaining 4 ft ; bright yellow flowers in spring and again in early autumn 1/6 2/6

E   „   „   „ **nana.**—A dense habited, free-flowering little pygmy ideal for rock gardens 1/6 2/6 3/6

E   „   „ **Irwinii.**—Dense habit, branches overlapping ; large orange-yellow flowers in April and May ; an ideal shrub for a dwarf hedge, 2 ft. high 1/6 2/6

E **Berberis stenophylla latifolia.**—A giant, will attain 10 ft. ;   each.
foliage very dark green ; flowers golden-yellow ; a
handsome shrub in or out of flower 1/6 2/6

E   „   „   **semperflorens.**—A small dense-habited shrub
with wiry branches ; young foliage bronze tinted ; the
coral-red flowers are freely produced from April to late
autumn 1/6 2/6
    The foregoing group of Berberises includes some of the
most beautiful and interesting hybrid shrubs ever
raised.

„   **subcaulialata (Coryi of Veitch).**—W. China. A pleasing
small shrub with grey or light blue foliage ; flowers pale
yellow, in July ; mass of round coral-pink berries,
retained till December 1/6 2/6

„   **Thunbergii.**—Japan. A popular shrub, either in spring
with its yellow, suffused red flowers, or in autumn with
its bright red berries and brilliant tints 1/6 2/6

„   „   **atropurpurea.**—A worthy shrub that has merited
its introduction and should be in every collection. The
colour of its deep red foliage is constant throughout the
growing season but during autumn it fades to vivid red,
finally scarlet. It associates well with Rhus Cotinus
foliis purpureis 1/6 2/6

„   „   **Maximowiczii.**—Attains 3 ft., yet stiffer in
appearance than B. Thunbergii ; foliage in autumn
orange-red and yellow 2/6 3/6

E   „   **triacanthophora.**—C. China. This graceful Berberis
grows 4—8 ft. high and though very hardy, is rare in
British gardens. The green, wavy, linear or lanceolate,
spiny leaves are in tufts and are blue-white beneath.
The many fascicles of pale yellow flowers, tinted red
outside, are succeeded by oval, blue-black fruits ... 3/6 5/6

„   **umbellata.**—Bhutan. This uncommon shrub, 5—7 ft.
high and as much wide, is evergreen in the south and
west but deciduous inland. The grooved growths carry
obovate-oblong, partly net-veined, green leaves, glaucous beneath. The singly borne, or sub-umbels of
yellow flowers on long stalks give place to ½ in. long
fruits, each containing one to three seeds... ... ... 3/6

E   „   **Veitchii (acuminata of Veitch).**—C. China. An erect
branched shrub with lance-shaped leaves, 4—6 ins. long ;
current season's growths bright red ; flowers large,
sulphur yellow ; many of the leaves turn scarlet towards
the winter 1/6 2/6

„   **Vernae.**—N. W. China. A graceful branched shrub,
5—10 ft. high ; dense racemes of yellow fragrant
flowers in May ; the obovate leaves, slightly glaucous
beneath, change in autumn to lemon and orange-yellow.
One of the best of a large genus 2/6 3/6

E   „   **verruculosa.**—W. China. A beautiful evergreen shrub,
4 ft. high, of elegant habit, with pendulous branches ;
leaves small dark green ; flowers golden-yellow ; fruits
black, covered with blue bloom 1/6 2/6

„   **virescens.**—Sikkim Himalayas. A charming autumn
garden shrub with conspicuous brown-red branches ;
brilliant autumn foliage and mass of bright red berries 2/6 3/6

„   „   **macrocarpa.**—As beautiful as the former,
differing only in its jet black berries 1/6 2/6

Berberis vulgaris.—It is unfortunate that this beautiful plant is a host to wheat rust.   See R.H.S. Journal, Vol. LX, Part II, page 512... ... ...   — —   *each.*

E   „   **Wallichiana (D. C. and Hooker).**—Nicholson's Dictionary of Gardening.   A stately compact shrub, 5—8 ft. high, with 3—5 in. ovate-oblanceolate leaves, richly coloured from September till March, and then reverting to deep green.   It bears many large yellow flowers which are succeeded by oblong, black fruits.   This beautiful evergreen is worthy of wide cultivation   ...   2/6   3/6

   „   **Wilsonae.**—W. China.   An invaluable elegant small shrub ; flowers pale yellow, in July ; masses of salmon-red berries, contrasting well with the vivid red autumn foliage 1/6   2/6

   „   **yunnanensis.**—W. China.   This is one of the very best of the Chinese Barberries.   The 3—5 ft. growths are a magnificent sight every autumn when the obovate grey-green leaves, grey-white beneath, turn to gold, red and scarlet.   The ½ in. oval fruits are brilliant red 2/6   3/6

       The **Berberises** are valuable to the Apiarist, especially those flowering in early spring.

MAHONIA SECTION.

E **Berberis Aquifolium.**—N. America.   Does well in shade ; mass of yellow flowers from March to May ; foliage colours well in winter 1/6   2/6

E   „   **Bealei.**—China.   Commonly and incorrectly grown as B. (Mahonia) japonica.   The leaflets are broad, spade-shaped, sometimes waxy-white beneath, flattened at the base and often pressed close against the stalk.   The terminal leaflet is much broader than the others, but this is not so in M. japonica.   The flowers are carried upright, or nearly so, on short stiff racemes, from January till April.   This beautiful ornamental and B. (Mahonia) japonica are clearly described in Rehder's Manual of Trees and Shrubs 1/6   2/6   3/6

E   „   **Fortunei.**—China.   A rare erect-growing shrub attaining 8 ft. ; leaves pinnate, composed of seven narrow leaflets ; dense racemes of yellow flowers in late autumn 2/6   3/6   5/6

E   „   **Fremontii.**—An exceedingly rare shrub from West U.S.A. for collectors of uncommon plants.   It grows 3—5 ft. high, and a warm, semi-shady position is recommended for it.   The pinnate leaves consist of three to seven glaucous leaflets, and make a good background for the dense erect racemes of yellow flowers borne during late autumn and early winter 10/6

E   „   **japonica.**—Japan.   A rare plant in gardens, distinguishable from B. (Mahonia) Bealei by its leaflets which are more numerous and narrower, gradually tapering to a long point.   They are yellow-green beneath and rounded at the base.   The 12—21 in. pendulous racemes of lily-of-the-valley scented yellow flowers are borne during the winter.   It is the most striking of the Mahonia section and has been known for many years as B. Bealei   7/6   10/6

E   „   **nepalensis.**—Nepal.   A beautiful tall shrub with pinnate leaves 2 ft. or more long ; 6—12 in. racemes of yellow flowers in March and April ; only suitable for mild gardens 10/6   12/6

E **Berberis nervosa.**—W. N. America. If given a semi-shady posi- | each.
tion, this rare dwarf shrub increases freely by underground
stolons. The 18 in. deep green, pinnate leaves assume
bronze-red tints from early autumn to late winter. The
end of almost every shoot carries an 8 in. erect raceme of
bright yellow flowers during March and April and these
are succeeded by large, ovoid, dark blue berries 2/6   3/6

E   „   **pinnata (fascicularis).**—California to Mexico. A pleasing deep green pinnate-foliaged shrub, 3—5 ft. high,
suitable for shady situations ; racemes of bright yellow
flowers are borne on the end of each shoot from February
to April 2/6   3/6

E   „   **trifoliolata.**—New Mexico. An exceedingly rare shrub,
3—6 ft. high, for gardens in the south and west, Ireland
and the west of Scotland. The spreading branches carry
leaves composed of three glaucous, spear-head-like
leaflets, each leaflet having conspicuous veins and four
wide, spiny teeth 7/6

E   „   **Wagneri (M. pinnata × Aquifolium).**—California,
N. Mexico. Distinct from all other Mahonias, growing
to 4 ft. ; leaves long, composed of seven to eleven leaflets,
grass-green, glaucous beneath, becoming bright red
throughout the winter ; flowers and fruit similar to
B. pinnata 3/6

E   „   **Mahoberberis Neubertii (Mahonia Aquifolium ×
Berberis vulgaris).**—An upright, slender branched
and open shrub, 4—6 ft. in height, with obovate purplish
leaves, the margins set with wide spiny teeth 3/6

E   „   „   „   **latifolia (ilicifolia of trade).**—An
unarmed open branching shrub, 3—5 ft. high, the
branches clothed with large purplish holly-like leaves,
glaucous beneath 2/6   3/6

Betula alba. (See **B. pubescens and B. verrucosa**). The
common weeping Silver Birch.

„   **albo-sinensis.**—W. Hupeh, China. A beautiful Birch,
of bushy habit. It should be kept to a single leader and
it will ultimately grow 25 ft. or more high. The outer
orange-yellow covering peeling reveals an inner orange-
red bark coated with grey bloom. The leaves are ovate-
acuminate and doubly toothed 7/6   10/6

„   „   **septentrionalis.**—This good form from W.
Szechuan, China, is a stronger grower and it has larger
ovate-acuminate leaves, prominently veined beneath.
The outer golden-yellow peeling bark reveals another
inner bark of orange-grey 10/6

„   **costata (ulmifolia var. costata).**—N.E. Asia. A pretty
birch, very rare in cultivation, with scattered white
lenticels on its branches. The 2—3 in. ovate-acuminate
or cordate leaves are doubly serrated 7/6   10/6

„   **Ermanii.**—N.E. Asia. This choice small tree carries
ovate-cordate metallic-green leaves. The bark exfoliat-
ing reveals another beneath, creamy-white ageing to
orange-brown 5/6   7/6

„   **japonica.**—The Japanese White Birch grows into a fine
tree, with slender spreading branches and silver-white
and orange-coloured bark. Its large, wavy, broad,
cuneate or deltoid-ovate-acuminate leaves are metallic-
green above and pale beneath 7/6   10/6

each.

Betula japonica mandshurica.—Manchuria. This rare form of the Japanese Birch quickly grows into a fine tree and it is usually in full leaf by the end of March. The leaves are broad at the base and unevenly serrated 7/6 10/6

 ,, ,, **szechuanica.**—W. China. A most beautiful and vigorous tree densely clothed with 2—4 in. triangular-ovate, dark green, deeply toothed leaves, glaucous beneath. The orange-brown papery bark peels to reveal a newer, silvery white bark, covered with grey bloom, beneath 7/6 10/6

 ,, **Koehnei (verrucosa × papyrifera).**— The upright growths become semi-weeping with age. Throughout the growing season, the bark is yellow-green but in early autumn it peels off, revealing another inner pure white bark 7/6 10/6

 ,, **lutea.**—N. America. The Yellow Birch is aptly named and it is one of the most attractive, though it is seldom seen in gardens. It is singularly beautiful in spring and early summer with its large, bronze-green, ovate-oblong leaves and again during the winter with its naked yellow bark 2/6 3/6 5/6

 ,, **Maximowicziana.**—Japan. In some soils, this grows into a lofty tree and its poplar-like leaves are perhaps the largest of the genus. Towards autumn the outer orange-brown papery flakes peel and reveal a silvery grey bark 3/6 5/6 7/6

 ,, **Medwediewii.**—Caucasus. This rare Birch is unlike any other during the growing season. It is tall, with stiff upright branches, and these are thickly clothed with dark green ovate-cordate, deeply furrowed leaves. The yellow-brown bark peeling reveals an orange-yellow inner bark which becomes silvery grey with age ... 5/6 7/6 10/6

 ,, **papyrifera.**—N. America. The Paper Birch with its conspicuous white-barked trunk quickly grows into a tall tree 3/6 5/6 7/6

 ,, ,, **kenaica.** — An uncommon small tree from the coast of Alaska. On young plants, the metallic-green ovate-cordate, pointed leaves are quite 4 in. long and 3 in. wide, but on adult plants they are much smaller. The outer creamy white covering peels to reveal a red-brown bark beneath 5/6 7/6

 ,, **pubescens.**—N. & C. Europe. The Common Silver Birch is distinct from B. verrucosa in having softer leaves covered with small hairs. It is also distinguishable by its ascending or spreading downy growths and the rugged, corky, base of its trunk 1/6 2/6 3/6

 ,, **verrucosa (pendula).**—Europe, Asia Minor. The common Weeping Silver Birch has silvery bark all the year round and is perhaps the most conspicuous land-scape tree we have. Its growths and broadly-ovate or diamond-shaped leaves have glandular warts. This and B. pubescens usually grow together, in their native habitat 1/6 2/6 3/6

 ,, ,, **dalecarlica (pendula laciniata).**—Sweden. The weeping cut-leaved Birch 3/6 5/6 7/6

Betula verrucosa Youngii.—This fine, wide, weeping-branched
tree with its silver bark is one of the most picturesque
trees and should be allowed plenty of room to develop 3/6
  The **Birches** are invaluable for the beautiful colouring of their bark in winter. However, during dry spells,
they rob the ground of moisture and so should not be
planted near any of the small-growing Ericaceae plants.
Prunus serrula tibetica, P. Maackii and many of the
Acers have conspicuous, coloured bark and associate
well with the various Birches.

each.

5/6 7/6

C **Bignonia capreolata.**—U.S.A. A rampant semi-evergreen
climber for a south or west wall ; flowers funnel-shaped,
orange-red, on the ends of the current year's growths, in
June 3/6 5/6

  „ **grandiflora.** (See **Campsis**).

EC **Billardiera longiflora.**—Tasmania. A delightful twining evergreen for sheltered walls ; flowers yellowish, pendulous,
succeeded by a mass of oblong dark blue fruits hanging
on thin stalks 2/6 3/6

EC „ „ **fructu albo.**—The white fruiting form is not as
beautiful as its parent 3/6

Boenninghausenia albiflora.—Mediterranean. An elegant
small shrub with rue-like foliage ; mass of feathery
white flowers from September to November ; quite
hardy here in open border 2/6

E **Boldoa fragrans.**—Mexico. An extremely rare evergreen with
pleasant fragrant round leaves, only suitable for south-
west favoured gardens ; loves semi-shade 10/6

E **Bowkeria Gerrardiana (triphylla).**—An evergreen with trifoliate
leaves and snow-white Calceolaria-like flowers ; a wall
shrub for mild gardens 3/6 5/6

E **Brachyglottis repanda.**—New Zealand. Handsome green
leaves silvery beneath ; masses of small fragrant creamy-
yellow flowers ; for favoured south-west situations. ... 3/6 5/6

Brooms. (See **Cytisus, Genista and Spartium**).

E **Bruckenthalia spiculifolia (Erica spiculifolia).**—Europe, Asia
Minor. A dainty little heath-like shrub for lime-free
soils ; erect racemes of rose bell-shaped flowers, which
attract bees, in June and July 1/6 2/6

Bryanthus. (See **Phyllodoce**).

Buddleja alternifolia.—Kansu, China. Slender arching branches
5 ft. long, wreathed with small lilac fragrant flowers
from June to August 1/6 2/6

  „ **auriculata.**—S. Africa. Quite hardy around the sea
coast of the south and west ; inland, a south or west
wall shrub ; masses of small cream-coloured flowers
with yellow throat, deliciously perfumed, during late
autumn 2/6 3/6

  „ **Colvilei.**—Sikkim. A rampant shrub reaching 15 ft. ;
large lance-shaped leaves and 6 in. pendulous panicles of
rose-coloured flowers ; not generally hardy 3/6 5/6

  „ **Davidii (variabilis) magnifica.**—The best form ;
growths 5 ft. long ; large panicles of violet-purple
flowers from July to October ; this beautiful shrub
should be pruned back every spring 2/6 3/6

  „ **Fallowiana.**—A rare species from China, with grey foliage
and panicles of beautiful fragrant blue flowers 3/6

	each.	

Buddleja Fallowiana alba.—White flowers with orange centre, deliciously scented. Both this and the type require a warm position inland 2/6 3/6

„ **globosa.**—A native of Chile. Attains a height of 15—20 ft. near the sea ; handsome with its heads of orange ball flowers from May to July ; should be pruned back every second year after flowering 1/6 2/6

„ **paniculata.**—A choice species from the Himalayas, only suitable for a south wall ; small panicles of violet scented lavender flowers in autumn and spring ... 3/6

E **Bursaria spinosa.**—New South Wales. A choice small-leaved evergreen for mild climates ; profuse panicles of small fragrant white flowers from August to October ; fruits red, pouch-like 5/6 7/6

Caesalpinia japonica.—A choice shrub from Japan, with Acacia-like leaves and erect, 4—12 in. panicles of canary-yellow flowers with red stamens. It grows 4—9 ft. high in the open in warm gardens, but much taller on a south or west wall 3/6 5/6

E **Calceolaria integrifolia.**—Chile. Planted at the foot of a south or west wall, it will produce its bright yellow flowers from early summer until late autumn 1/6 2/6

„ **violacea.**—Chile. Also requires wall protection ; a pretty shrub with pale violet flowers during summer 2/6 3/6

E **Caldcluvia paniculata.**—Chile. This exceedingly rare shrub is new to cultivation and in southern and western gardens it will attain a height of probably 10 ft. or more. The upright branches are furnished with attractive 2—4 in. opposite, lanceolate leaves which are dark green, serrated and conspicuously veined. Here, the many axillary panicles of small white flowers are produced in August, September and October 7/6 10/6

Callicarpa americana.—A medium-sized shrub with twiggy branches, from U.S.A. ; small grey-blue flowers ; berries violet-blue ; not perfectly hardy 2/6 3/6

„ **Bodinieri (Giraldii).**—China. A free-growing shrub 5—8 ft. high ; cymes of rose coloured flowers ; abundance of violet fruits whole length of branches ; foliage in autumn a pretty shade of violet-purple 2/6 3/6

„ **japonica.**—Japan. Of compact habit, not more than 3—4 ft. high, flowers pale pink ; fruits round, violet-blue 2/6 3/6

„ „ **angustata.**—A distinct form from Central China, of robust erect habit ; its handsome long foliage turns a clear yellow in early autumn 2/6 3/6

„ **koreana.**—Korea. Its small leaves are distinctly serrated ; worthy for its purple mottled foliage in autumn ... 2/6 3/6

Calluna vulgaris. (Placed under **Erica vulgaris** in order to have all the heaths together).

Calycanthus floridus (Allspice).—Virginia. Slow-growing, camphor-scented shrub, ultimately 4 ft. high ; 2 in. conspicuous red flowers from May to August ... 1/6 2/6 3/6

„ **occidentalis (macrophyllus).**— California. Strong-growing, quickly attaining 10 ft. ; large cordate leaves ; 3 in. crimson fragrant wax-like flowers in mid-summer 2/6 3/6

„ **praecox.** (See **Chimonanthus**).

E **Camellia cuspidata.**—W. China. This interesting, free-growing   each.
shrub 5—8 ft. high, is proving quite hardy in this dis-
trict. It is of pyramidal habit with twiggy branches
and ovate-lanceolate leaves. Pure white flowers, 1½ in.
across, are freely borne in the leaf axils during spring **5/6   7/6 10/6**

E   „   **japonica. Common Camellia** ... ...   —   —

E   „   „   **Adolph Audusson.**—This beautiful strong-
growing Camellia has large lustrous green leaves and
4—5 in. conspicuous, perfectly-formed flowers, composed of two rows of round bright crimson petals, borne
during April and early May **7/6 10/6 12/6**

E   „   „   **Apollo.**—One of the best Camellias for outdoor
cultivation. The upright branches are beautiful every
spring with numerous, perfectly formed, semi-double,
bright red flowers with yellow stamens **5/6   7/6 10/6**

E   „   „   **Arejishi.**—Japan.—An exceedingly rare and
attractive evergreen which suggests a new species. The
paeony-like 5 in. flowers, each with two rows of blood-
red wavy petals, look well resting on the 6 in. acuminated,
polished leaves in March and April **7/6 10/6 12/6**

E   „   „   **Campbellii.**—It forms a round compact bush and
is decorated with single or semi-double, well formed,
rose-pink flowers in April and May **7/6 10/6**

E   „   „   **Chandleri elegans.**—A magnificent Camellia of
spreading habit, with large handsome foliage and conspicuous semi-double bright pink flowers ... **5/6   7/6 10/6**

E   „   „   **Compton's Brow Pink.**—An admirable shrub
during March and April when its branches are laden
with 5 in. single, soft rose flowers. It is a strong grower
and has light green leaves **10/6 15/6**

E   „   „   „   **White.**—Its 5 in. perfectly
formed, white, single flowers each with a large cluster of
yellow stamens, are quite as beautiful as those of the
former **10/6 15/6**

E   „   „   **Devoniensis.**—This uncommon compact evergreen
has medium sized, oval, light green leaves which make a
good background for the numerous single or semi-
double, round-petalled, white flowers, borne during
March and April **7/6 10/6**

E   „   „   **Donckelaarii.**—One of the hardiest of all Camellias
for outdoor planting. Well formed semi-double deep
red flowers ; free flowering **5/6   7/6 10/6**

E   „   „   **Fred Sander.**—A good grower and quite dis-
dinct from any of the others of this section. It has deep
green leaves of medium size and refined 4 in. cerise-red
flowers with raised centres and containing 8—12 frilled
petals **7/6 10/6 12/6**

E   „   „   **Gloire de Nantes.**—This grand shrub is of good
habit and is densely clothed with medium-sized deep
green leaves. Its many substantial and conspicuous
rose-pink flowers are similar in shape to those of C. j.
Lady Clare **7/6 10/6**

E   „   „   **Kelvingtoni.**—It is perhaps the strongest grower
of the family and is of open habit. Its stout branches
are furnished with large, thick, olive green, pointed
leaves. The attractive semi-double flowers are flat,
4—6 ins. across, and composed of large crimson-red
petals **7/6 10/6**

E **Camellia japonica Lady Clare.**—One of the most beautiful of   each.
flowering shrubs during March and April. The flat,
5—6 in. semi-double bright pink flowers are a splendid
sight against the bold dark green leaves **5/6**   **7/6** **10/6**

E   „   „   **latifolia.**—One of the most reliable for general
planting in the open and the last Camellia to flower.
The 4—5 in. flowers, composed of two rows of deep red
petals, are freely borne during May **5/6**   **7/6** **10/6**

E   „   „   **magnoliaeflora.**—A worthy plant for a north-
west wall or a sheltered semi-shady corner ; pale green
foliage ; attractive shell-pink flowers, composed of two
rows of petals, their edges incurved **10/6** **12/6** **15/6**

E   „   „   „   **alba.**—Japan. A shrub of dense pyramidal
habit. 4—6 ft. high, handsome either in or out of flower.
Its pleasing olive-green acuminate leaves form a fine
background for the numerous 3—4 in. campanulate dainty
white flowers, borne from March to June   ... **10/6** **12/6** **15/6**

E   „   „   **Mathiotiana.**—An old variety, but still one of the
best ; 3—4 in. double, deep rose flowers **7/6** **10/6**

E   „   „   **nobilissima.**—A very useful shrub for general
culture inside or out. It is early flowering ; double
pure white blossoms are freely borne **7/6** **10/6**

E   „   „   **Preston Rose.**—A very hardy shrub, suitable
for general planting, bearing many pleasing, double,
imbricated, rose-pink flowers during March and
April **5/6**   **7/6** **10/6**

E   „   „   **Taroan.**—This new shrub grows 4—8 ft. high and
as much wide and is thickly clothed with shiny, round,
deep green leaves, 1¼—3 ins. long and shallowly
toothed. The many 4—5 in. bell-shaped bright red
flowers are borne from early March to mid-May   ...   **10/6**

E   „   „   **White Swan.**—An attractive form of good habit,
handsomely furnished with medium-sized deep green
pointed leaves. The profusely-borne 4—5 in. milk-white
flowers usually consist of seven fan-shaped petals. It
is easily distinguished as each bloom has a few petaloid
stamens **10/6**

E   „   „   **Yoibijin.**—A strong, bushy grower 6—10 ft. high,
and with leaves both rotund and elliptical-acuminate, the
latter being 2½—5½ ins. long. The large single flowers
are of a beautiful shell pink **10/6**

E   „   **oleifera.**—China. A rare and beautiful free-growing
species attaining 5 ft. or more in sheltered positions
around the south and west coasts and in similar climates.
Its richly scented, 5-petalled, white flowers start to open
in November and continue until February. Cut blooms
placed in water last some time. It is illustrated in
Nicholson's Dictionary of Gardening, page 251   ...   **10/6**

E   „   **reticulata.**—China. Often called the Queen of Camellias.
Once established it is a rampant grower but tender
in its youth. A sheltered semi-shady wall or an open
verandah is recommended. Each flower is five or six
ins. across, composed of two rows of glowing crimson-
rose-coloured petals **10/6** **15/6** **21/-**

E   **Camellia saluenensis (speciosa of gardens).**—Yunnan, China.   each.
Western gardens are indebted to the late Mr. G. Forrest
for this invaluable free-growing species. In foliage
it resembles C. Sasanqua. The 3—4 in. dog-rose pink
flowers, each with a cluster of maize-yellow stamens, are
profusely borne from March to the end of May **21/-**

E   „   **Sasanqua.**—Widely distributed in China. An open
twiggy-branched shrub, 5—10 ft. high. The obovate
leaves are leathery and purplish-green. The numerous
fragrant bright rose-coloured flowers are a cheerful sight
from October to April, according to position and
weather. In this district, on a north-west wall, there is a
specimen 8 ft. × 10 ft. **5/6**   **7/6 10/6**

E   „   „   **alba.**—A form with pure white, fragrant flowers,
paler foliage and not so strong a grower ... ...   **— —**

E   „   **Thea.**—The tea plant is quite hardy in sheltered gardens
in the South and West counties, and in similar climates.
From mid-October to spring, its slender twigs are crowded with 1—1½ in. spreading, 5-petalled, scented, white
flowers, borne in the axils of the 3—5 in. elliptical-oblong,
shallowly-toothed leaves **7/6 10/6**

E   „   **vernalis (Sasanqua × japonica).**—Japan. The leaves
and habit of this choice hybrid are characteristic of both
parents. It grows 6—10 ft. high by as much wide and
its 2½—3½ in. white flowers, sometimes suffused pink in
some soils, are borne from January to May according to
position and climate **10/6 15/6 21/-**
The **Camellia** is much hardier than is generally supposed. Many fine specimens can be seen growing in
the south, and in West Ireland and Scotland. The best
position is the woodland or amongst tall evergreens.
Camellias dislike a limy soil and full sun. A mulching
of ordinary leaf-mould and good rotten manure is very
beneficial.

C   **Campsis chinensis (Tecoma grandiflora).**—China, Japan.
A strong-growing, deciduous climber with pinnate leaves,
attractive pendulous, orange-scarlet flowers in August
and September **3/6   5/6**

C   „   **radicans (Tecoma radicans).**—N. America. Vivid scarlet and orange trumpet-shaped flowers in August ...   **2/6   3/6**
These climbing shrubs have long been known in our
gardens and especially in Italy and the south of France,
as **Bignonia grandiflora** and **B. radicans.**

Caragana arborescens.—A very useful, hardy shrub from
Siberia ; 3 in. pinnate leaves ; very pretty in May with
its yellow, pea-shaped flowers **1/6   2/6**

„   **pygmaea (gracilis).**—Caucasus to Himalaya. A graceful shrub, ultimately 4 ft. high, with pendulous, overlapping branches ; pretty bright yellow flowers in May   **3/6   5/6**

Carmichaelia australis.—New Zealand. Graceful, slender,
oval branches with minute foliage ; short racemes of
small lilac flowers, veined violet, covering the branches
from May to August, sweetly scented **2/6   3/6**

„   **Enysii.**—Cheeseman's Manual of the New Zealand Flora.
A tiny upright shrub, seldom more than 2 ins. high,
suitable for the rock garden or alpine house. It is
covered in May and June with small violet, scented
flowers **3/6   5/6**

Carmichaelia Enysii orbiculata.—New Zealand. This shrub   each.
is of dense habit, 6—9 ins. high, and is ideal for the rock
garden. The mass of violet flowers are borne in May
and June. Previously distributed as C. Enysii... ...   2/6   3/6
    "   **flagelliformis (arborea).**—New Zealand. A distinct
species with ½ in. wide, flat branches ; racemes of small
lilac-tinted purple pea-like scented flowers in June ...   2/6   3/6
    "   **grandiflora.**—New Zealand. Erect-growing shrub with
spreading branches ; leaves distinct, of three to five
large leaflets ; racemes of fairly large, purplish flowers
veined with violet, sweetly scented, from May to August   2/6   3/6
    "   **odorata.**—New Zealand. A shrub 3—10 ft. high, of
elegant habit, with pendulous branches ; abundance of
powerfully-scented small, lilac-tinted rose flowers, from
May to September 2/6   3/6
    "   **Petriei.**—New Zealand. A new species of erect habit,
with round wooded branches ; small clusters of violet-
purple, scented flowers in June and July 5/6
    The **Carmichaelias** are perfectly happy even in limy
soils, but they may not be quite hardy in the midlands.

Carniola mantica. (See **Genista tinctoria**).

E   **Carpenteria californica.**—California. A beautiful seaside
shrub, for the south and west, where it quickly attains
20 ft., and freely produces its 3 in. snow-white, fragrant,
anemone-shaped flowers during June and July. Inland
it requires a south wall 3/6   5/6
E   "   "   **Ladham's Variety.**—A beautiful form, as hardy
as the type, with larger, perfumed flowers   ...   ...   —   —

E   **Carpodetus serratus.**—New Zealand. An uncommon, graceful
shrub or small tree of pendulous habit ; small green
serrated leaves ; broad cymes of small fragrant pure-white
flowers ; only suitable for south-west gardens 3/6   5/6

Carriera calycina.—W. Hupeh, China. A rare member allied to
the Azaras, requiring a sheltered position ; flowers cup-
shaped, in panicles 6 in. long 10/6

Carya cordiformis (amara).—E. N. America. The leaves of
this small tree are cordate and composed of 5—9 ovate-
lanceolate and lanceolate-acuminate leaflets which are
irregularly toothed. It is quite as beautiful in autumn as
C. glabra 3/6   5/6
    "   **glabra (porcina).**—E. N. America. If given woodland
conditions, it quickly attains small tree size. Each leaf is
composed of 5—7 oblong-lanceolate, acuminated, serrated leaflets. It is much prized for its beautiful yellow
autumnal tints 3/6   5/6

Caryopteris clandonensis (Mastacanthus × mongolica).—
This charming natural hybrid is quite hardy and is as
free-growing as C. Mastacanthus. The 12—18 in. stems
are clothed with green, lanceolate toothed leaves and the
numerous electric blue, fringed flowers are borne from
early August till autumn frosts 2/6
    "   **Mastacanthus (incana).**—Japan, E. China. A small
shrub of spreading habit, 3 ft. high, smothered with
small heads of bright violet-blue flowers in September
and October 1/6   2/6
    "   **mongolica.**—Mongolia, N. China. The most beautiful,
but tender ; brilliant blue flowers, from July to October   —   —

		each.	

Caryopteris tangutica.—W. Kansu, China. Differs from C. Mastacanthus by its deeper blue flowers 2/6   3/6

E   **Cassandra (Chamaedaphne) calyculata.**—N. Hemisphere. An evergreen small shrub about 2 ft. high ; flowers white, lily of the valley-like in March and April, borne singly from leaf axils whole length of branches 2/6   3/6

Cassia corymbosa.—Buenos Ayres. Often seen in greenhouses, but it is quite hardy against a south or west wall in gardens around the south and west coast. It produces large clusters of Laburnum-like rich yellow flowers from June till autumn 3/6   5/6

E   **Cassiope fastigiata.**—Alpine Himalaya. An exceedingly rare small shrub reputed to be difficult to establish but it is quite easy in the Ericaceae border, with woodland conditions. The erect grey-green growths carry many white bells, ⅜ in. across, during April and May 7/6   10/6

E   „   **lycopodioides.**—Mountains of Japan. This little gem is quite happy in the woodland, where it never sees the sun before the evening. Its dense, prostrate, overlapping, grey-green growths form a cushion 1—2 ins. high, but 6—18 in. wide. Its lily-of-the-valley-like flowers are borne in May and June and often again in the autumn. A fine picture of a plant in flower appears in the Alpine Garden Society's Bulletin, Vol. 4, No. 1 (March, 1936), page 127 ... ...   3/6   5/6   7/6   10/6

E   „   **Mertensiana.**—A treasure from the Alpine regions of Alaska and California ; shrub not more than 1 ft. high ; flowers white, campanula-like, one-third of an inch wide, borne on side of branches from mid-May to August   2/6   3/6   5/6

E   „   **selaginoides (Hooker).**—This form from the Himalayas is a compact grower, 2—4 ins. high. The tiny, lanceolate, grooved leaves overlap the stems and give the plant a ridged appearance. The attractive pure-white globose-campanulate flowers are shallower than those of the following species 10/6

E   „   „   **(Kingdon Ward).**—W. China and Tibet. An attractive compact shrub, with erect grey-green twigs, 4—6 ins. high. These are beautifully decorated during April and May with many large nodding, bell-shaped 5-lobed, white, pink-tinged flowers. It is probably the best of this genus 10/6

E   „   **species.**—Japan. It is stronger growing than C. lycopodioides and it forms a thick flat mat 3—4 ins. high. Its twigs carry slightly larger lily-of-the-valley-like white flowers 5/6   7/6   10/6

  „   **stellariana.** (See **Harrimanella stellariana**).

E   „   **tetragona (Andromeda tetragona).**—A little shrub only a few inches high, from the Arctic regions ; flowers white, tinged red, nodding, bell-shaped, borne on the young stems during April and May 1/6   2/6   3/6

Catalpa bignonioides.—S. United States. A large tree and if uncrowded, of beautiful outline with wide spreading branches, and worthy of every garden. It bears in quantity broad panicles of white, bell-shaped, frilled flowers, yellow and purple within. Flowering during July and August, it is particularly welcome 2/6   3/6   5/6

E **Ceanothus Autumnal Blue.**—Hybrid. A first-rate robust shrub   each.
suitable for seaside gardens or for a south or west wall
inland. It carries big rugose leaves and large trusses of
china-blue flowers from June to October **8/6** **5/6**

E   „   **Burkwoodii (floribundus × Indigo).**—One of the best
hybrid shrubs raised within the past 10 years. It is not
quite hardy in the open here and so should be given a
S.W. or E. wall, according to locality. It bears 1—2½ in.
panicles of rich blue flowers from mid-summer till
autumn frosts. It grows and flowers freely in many
Gloucestershire gardens, where it is much admired 2/6 **3/6** **5/6**

  „   **Candolleanus.**—N. America. An extremely rare and
beautiful semi-evergreen shrub for gardens in the south
and west or for warm walls inland. Its deep green,
serrated, 2½—3½ in. leaves have prominent branching
veins and are tawny coloured beneath. The stems,
covered with tomentum, carry many 4—7 in. compound
panicles of cornflower-blue flowers. It is possibly the
best of the family and may be the correct C. azureus ... —   —

E   „   **cyaneus.**—California. This beautiful new Ceanothus has
numerous outward pointing spikes, up to 6 ins. long, of
bright blue flowers from early May to July. Here, it is
often severely cut by frosts even on south and west walls.
It is now known as C. tomentosus olivaceus (Jepson) ... **2/6** **3/6**

*E   „   **dentatus.**—California. This forms a thicket, 5—10 ft.
high, in seaside gardens. Few shrubs can equal it in May
and June when it bears round clusters of bright blue
flowers, held above the small dentated leaves **2/6** **3/6**

E   „   „   **Russellianus (Hort.)**—A dense branching shrub
suitable for a south or west wall. It is crowded with
2—4 in. panicles of light blue flowers in April and May **2/6** **3/6**

  „   **hybridus Arnoldii.**—Large foliage, strong grower, pale
blue flowers **2/6** **3/6**

  „   „   **Ceres.**—Panicles of bright pink flowers **2/6** **3/6**

  „   „   **Gloire de Versailles.**—Large panicles of rich
blue flowers; the hardiest and strongest grower; a
favourite **2/6** **3/6**

  „   „   **Henri Defosse.**—Elegant thyrses of indigo blue
coloured flowers; a poor grower **3/6**

  „   „   **Indigo.**—Indigo blue; also a poor grower ... **3/6**

  „   „   **Lucie Simon.**—Clusters of pretty light blue
flowers and glossy green leaves **2/6** **3/6**

  „   „   **Marie Simon.**—Attractive rose-pink flowers ... **2/6** **3/6**

  „   „   **Perle Rose.**—Bright rose. A good plant but
unfortunately a wretched colour in some soils **2/6** **3/6**

  „   „   **Richesse.**—Pure rose, but similar to Perle Rose
in some soils; dwarf habit **2/6** **3/6**

  „   „   **roseus carmineus.**—Good grower; flowers bright
carmine pink **2/6** **3/6**

  „   „   **Topaz.**—The foliage of this distinct hybrid reminds one of C. h. Indigo. It is, however, a much better
grower, and has light cobalt-blue flowers from July to
September **3/6**

The above **Ceanothus hybrids** flower from July until
autumn frosts, and are indispensable, for they flower
when flowering shrubs are not too plentiful. They
should be pruned every spring to obtain their full floral
beauty.

			each.
*E	**Ceanothus Lobbianus (thyrsiflorus × dentatus).**—California. Quite hardy around the south and west coast but requires a south or west wall inland. It is handsome during April and May with heads of bright blue flowers, held well above the crinkly deep-green leaves. Previously distributed as C. Veitchianus	2/6	3/6
*E	„ **papillosus.**—California. A rare evergreen for south or west walls in favoured spots ; shining deep green verrucose leaves ; terminal racemes of light-blue flowers	2/6	3/6
E	„ **rigidus.**—As a wall-shrub, fan trained, it has few equals ; its branches are wreathed from end to end with indigo blue flowers, in April and May	2/6	3/6
*E	„ **thyrsiflorus.**—California. In the south and west this is the second hardiest Ceanothus, often 15 ft. high ; clusters of pale blue flowers in May and June	2/6	3/6
*E	„ **Veitchianus (thyrsiflorus × rigidus).**—Previously distributed as C. floribundus (of trade). The hardiest of all the evergreen Ceanothus and plants 6—10 ft. high are often seen in gardens around the coast. It makes a splendid wall plant inland. The rigid branches, with small obovate leaves, are gay in early summer with bright blue flowers. Also known as **Ceanothus Brilliant**	2/6	3/6

The **Ceanothus** marked * were clearly described in the Gardeners' Chronicle, August 17th and 24th, 1935.

	Cedrela sinensis — China. An ornamental, fast-growing tree with bark peeling in long strips, and pinnate Ailanthus-like leaves 1—2 ft. long. The terminal panicles of white fragrant flowers are rarely seen 3/6	5/6	7/6

E	**Celmisia coriacea.**—New Zealand. This is probably the hardiest and handsomest of the genus and grows freely in a well-drained sunny position. It forms a rosette of many leathery tomentose leaves, silver-white beneath, 12—21 ins. long and 3—4 ins. wide. The attractive marguerite-like white flowers, held on 9—18 in. stalks, are produced freely from March to October	—	—
E	„ **holosericea.**—New Zealand. A charming rock plant ; long narrow leaves, reverse side snow-white ; daisy-like flowers with narrow, pure-white florets ; requires good drainage and full sun	2/6	3/6
	Ceratostigma minus (Pohillii).—W. China. A charming, small, twiggy compact shrub, profusely decorated with small deep blue flowers from May to October. Here, it is not hardy, but is a splendid plant for the alpine house		2/6
	„ **Willmottianum.**—A charming hardy Plumbago from Japan, of sub-shrubby character, 3 ft. high, will grow to 10 ft. on a sunny wall ; flowers bright sky-blue, freely produced from May to October		2/6
	Cercidiphyllum japonicum.—Japan. Forms a graceful small tree 10—15 ft. high. Its cordate leaves assume in autumn bright yellow and dark red tints... 2/6	3/6	5/6
	Cercis Siliquastrum.—Mediterranean. Better known as the Judas Tree, and treasured for its beauty and its curious legend. During April and May it is laden with small rose-pink pea flowers on naked wood. It loves full sun 2/6	3/6	5/6

Cherry.—Flowering and Ornamental. (See **Prunus**).

E **Chimaphila umbellata (japonica ?).**   This is still one of the   each.
rarest of the small-growing Japanese plants, but it is
quite content in soil suitable for Shortias, etc.   Its pretty
½—1½ in. grey-green leaves are unevenly serrated, in
whorls, and have cream-white midribs.   The nodding,
white or flesh-coloured, saucer-shaped flowers are in
terminal umbels of 1—3 ...   .   5/-   7/6

Chimonanthus fragrans (Calycanthus praecox).—China,
Japan.   A twiggy-branched shrub in the south and
west, 6—9 ft. high, on a sunny wall, 10 ft. or more, where
its flowering season is prolonged from November to
March ; flowers pale yellow, the inner petals striped with
dark purple, deliciously scented, on naked wood   ...   2/6   3/6

    „   „   **luteus. Hort.**—An exceedingly rare form which
should be planted against a south or west wall where it
will ultimately grow to 10 ft.   It is pretty when laden
with its pure sulphur-yellow flowers which are quite
distinct from those of the type and suggest a new species   10/6

E **Chiogenes hispidula (serpyllifolia).** — N. America.   The
Creeping Snowberry is an interesting plant and forms a
mat 1—3 ins. high.   The thread - like stems root into the
soil and are thickly set with tiny ovate leaves.   The
small 4-lobed white flowers are borne during May and
June, followed by white berries.   Like the Shortias and
Schizocodons, etc., it requires a cool position in the
south and west 3/6   5/6

Chionanthus virginica (Fringe Tree).—N. America.   One of
the most striking of N. American trees ; oblong leaves,
bright yellow in autumn ;   large loose panicles of
feathery petalled, snow-white flowers in June ; a good
grower if on its own roots   ...   ...   on own roots   3/6   5/6

E **Chloranthus brachystachys.**—China, Japan.   A rarity, suitable
for the south-west and similar districts.   The handsome
pale green leaves are oblong-acuminate, the margins set
with wide deep teeth ;   corymbs of many small white
flowers succeeded by brilliant bright red fruits, these
retained for many weeks 5/-   7/6

E **Choisya ternata (Mexican Orange).**—A distinct and useful
evergreen, forming a huge bush around the sea coast,
where it also makes a beautiful hedge ; in colder districts
it is useful as a wall plant.   Its floral season is from
March to May but in the south and west, it produces
many corymbs of white hawthorn-scented flowers during
the autumn 1/6   2/6   3/6

E **Cistus corbariensis (salvifolius × populifolius).**—S. Europe.
A very hardy, bushy shrub, attaining 3 ft., with ovate,
undulated leaves and white flowers, 1½ ins. across, with a
yellow stain at the base of each petal 1/6   2/6

E   „   **cyprius.**—A natural hybrid from Cyprus, much hardier
than its relative C. ladaniferus ; a tall shrub, 6—9 ft.
high ; buds in clusters, but flowers produced singly,
large, white, with blood-red blotch 1/6   2/6

E   „   „   **albus.**—Quite as strong-growing as the former,
with pure white saucer-shaped flowers.   It is a much
better plant than C. ladaniferus albiflorus 2/6   3/6

E   „   **florentinus.**—S.W. Europe.   A spreading small shrub ;
flowers white with a faint yellow blotch ; free-flowering   1/6   2/6

				each.
E	**Cistus glaucus (recognitus).**—Grows to 4 ft. ; long narrow undulated leaves ; white flowers with small crimson dash on each petal		1/6	2/6
E	„ **ladaniferus.**—S.W. Europe. A tender, tall shrub, 6 ft. high ; long narrow glutinous leaves ; single white flowers with red blotch on each petal		1/6	2/6
E	„ „ **albiflorus.**—Pure white frilled flowers, 3 ins. across ; also tender		2/6	3/6
E	„ **lusitanicus decumbens (Loretii).**—S. France. Semi-prostrate habit ; clusters of three to five large white flowers with maroon blotch on each petal		1/6	2/6
E	„ **monspeliensis.**—Mediterranean. An erect-branched shrub about 4 ft. high, with narrow green glutinous leaves and heads of 1 in. white flowers		1/6	2/6
E	„ **obtusifolius.**—Portugal. A compact shrub, 2 ft. high, with ovate-oblong leaves and small clusters of 1½ in. white flowers with a yellow stain on each petal ...		1/6	2/6
E	„ **platysepalus.**—S.W. Europe. An upright-growing shrub about 3 ft. high, with oblong wavy leaves and heads of 1½ in. white flowers with a small yellow blotch on each petal		1/6	2/6
E	„ **populifolius.**—S.W. Europe. Vigorous compact habit ; clusters of 2 in. white flowers with a slight yellow eye on each petal ; the hardiest of all Cistus here		1/6	2/6
E	„ **pulverulentus (crispus × albidus) (crispus) (Gauntlettii) (Sunset).**—Mediterranean. A compact shrub 3 ft. high, with grey, hairy, oblong leaves. It is the second best red-flowering Cistus		1/6	2/6
E	„ **purpureus (ladaniferus × villosus) (Cambridge form).**—One of the most striking ; lance-shaped, undulated leaves ; flowers 3 ins. across, bright red with a dark red blotch on each petal. Also known as Betty Taudevin		1/6	2/6
E	„ **rosmarinifolius (Clusii) (Halimiocistus).**—A twiggy compact shrub 18 ins. high, clothed with lanceolate, hairy leaves and decorated with small white flowers ...		1/6	2/6
E	„ **salvifolius.**—Mediterranean. A compact grower about 2 ft. × 4 ft. It is quite white with flowers each morning of its flowering season		1/6	2/6
E	„ **Silver Pink.**—A natural hybrid with silvery-grey foliage ; flowers in clusters, saucer-shape, of a clear bright pink, from early June to October ; a gem for the rockery.		1/6	2/6
E	„ **Skanbergii (monspeliensis × parviflorus).**—Greece. A delightful dense, twiggy, spreading shrub about 2½ ft. high, thickly clothed with lanceolate, green leaves, similar to those of the first parent. The petals of the many 1½ in. pale pink flowers are deeply notched ...		2/6	3/6
E	„ **wintonensis (Halimiocistus).**—Garden origin. A delightful shrub with small grey leaves ; clusters of silvery white 2 in. flowers " enriched with a purple zone " with yellow again at the base of each petal		2/6	3/6
	The **Cistus** flower during May and June and they live much longer on poor soils. They should be planted either in late spring or very early autumn.			
E	**Citharexylon spicatum.**—Previously distributed as C. Bessoniana. A semi-scandent evergreen suitable for south or west walls ; deep green leaves ; 3—5 in. racemes of small fragrant pale-violet flowers			3/6

Cladothamnus pyrolaeflorus.—B. Columbia. A rare little   each.
compact shrub of slow growth, 12—18 ins. high ; leaves
chiefly oblanceolate ; flowers 1 in. wide, of a rosy
colour, yellow margined, consisting of five petals ;
these are borne at the ends of the current growths during
June and July 3/6   5/6   7/6

Cladrastis lutea (tinctoria).—N. America. It is known as the
Yellow Wood and is usually seen as a small tree 15—25
feet high. Terminal panicles of white drooping pea-like
fragrant flowers are borne during July. In autumn the
pinnate leaves invariably fade to golden-yellow ... 3/6   5/-

EC **Clematis Armandii.**—C. & W. China. A noble evergreen with
large dark-green trifoliate leaves ; clusters of 2 in.
sweetly-scented, white, narrow-petalled flowers ;
requires a sunny sheltered wall 3/6   5/-

EC   „   „   **Apple Blossom.**—A beautiful climber during the
spring, with its pink flowers nestling among the bold,
green, bronze-tinted leaves ... ...   —   —

EC   „   **balearica.**—Balearic Islands. An evergreen with slender growths and polished bronzy-green leaves. The
creamy-yellow flowers are speckled with bright purple.
Being winter flowering, it requires a sheltered spot ... 3/6   5/-

C   „   **chrysocoma.**—Yunnan, China. This pretty shrubby
climber is not quite hardy. It carries trifoliate leaves and
white, tinged pink flowers, almost 2 ins. across... ...   3/6

EC   „   **cirrhosa.**—S. Europe. This slender climber differs from
C. balearica in its ovate-cordate, 3-lobed leaves and
unmarked creamy-white flowers, from January to April.
It requires a sheltered position 3/6   5/-

„   **Durandii.**—Hybrid. A magnificent semi-climber with
cordate leaves ; flowers 3—5 ins. across, beautiful dark
violet, with yellow stamens 2/6   3/6

C   „   **Flammula.**—Europe. A rampant climber with divided
leaves ; masses of pure white, sweetly-scented flowers
from August to October 2/6   3/6

C   „   **hybrid Beauty of Worcester.** Extra large, violet blue ⎫
C   „   „   **Blue Gem.** A pretty shade of pale blue ...   ⎪
C   „   „   **Fairy Queen.**   Pale pink with bright pink bars ⎪
C   „   „   **Gypsy Queen.** Rich dark velvet purple ...   ⎪
C   „   „   **Henryi.**—Large, creamy white ... ...   ⎪
C   „   „   **Jackmanii.**—Dark purple ... ...   ⎪
C   „   „   „ **superba.**—Dark violet, free flowering   ⎪
C   „   „   **Lawsoniana.**—Grey-blue ... ...   ⎬ 2/6   3/6
C   „   „   **Madame Grange.**—Dark red velvet, wavy petals ⎪
C   „   „   **Mrs. Hope.**—Beautiful lavender ... ...   ⎪
C   „   „   **Nellie Moser.**—Silvery-white with distinct pink ⎪
     bar   ⎪
C   „   „   **Perle d'Azure.**—Sky-blue, one of the best ...   ⎪
C   „   „   **President.**—Large, deep purple, autumn flowering ⎪
C   „   „   **The Queen.**—Light purple, large and free ...   ⎪
C   „   „   **Ville de Lyon.**—Bright red perfectly formed   ⎪
     flowers ... ...   ⎪
C   „   „   **William Kennett.**—Deep Lavender ... ... ⎭

„   **Jouiniana.**—Hybrid. Shrubby habit ; 1—2 ft. panicles
of small white suffused lilac flowers ; a good plant for
rambling over old stumps, etc. 2/6   3/6

C **Clematis macropetala.**—Siberia & N. China. If planted in a   each.
semi-shady position, or against a north wall in the south,
it will climb 6—12 ft. Its showy 2—4 in. flowers, borne
during May and June, have pointed petals and are violet-
blue, ageing to light blue 5/-

C ,, **montana.**—Himalayas, C. & W. China. One of the most
beautiful of climbers, with its wealth of starry, snow-white
flowers, during May 2/6   3/6

C ,, ,, **rubens.**—W. China. As free as the former, with
bright pink flowers 2/6   3/6

C ,, ,, **Wilsonii.**—A form from C. China with larger
white flowers, in July and August, sweetly scented ...   3/6

C ,, **orientalis.**—Persia to Himalaya. A widely distributed
species with glaucous grey foliage, and yellow flowers,
in August and September 2/6   3/6

C ,, **paniculata.**—Japan. A strong climber for rambling at
will ; a pretty sight during September and October,
with its mass of small white hawthorn-scented flowers   2/6   3/6

C ,, **Rehderiana.**—A choice climber from W. China with
6—9 in. pinnate leaves and 9 in. panicles of bell-shaped
primrose-yellow fragrant flowers, from August to
October 3/6   5/-

C ,, **Spooneri.**—W. China. A better climber, for general
planting, than the beautiful C. chrysocoma. It has three-
parted ovate or oval leaves, held on 3—4 in. stalks, and
its white flowers, 3 ins. wide, are carried on 4—7 in.
stems 3/6   5/-

C ,, **tangutica.**—W. China. A near relative to C. orientalis ;
grey-green leaves ; flowers rich yellow, freely produced,
and followed by a mass of feathery fruits of a silvery-
grey colour 2/6   3/6

C ,, **Veitchiana.**—W. China. One of a very few good flowering climbers for the autumn garden. Little distinguishes
it from C. Rehderiana. It is, however, a stronger grower
making trailing shoots up to 15 ft. long. From late
August to late October the numerous bell-shaped nodding flowers, primrose-yellow and scented, are a magnificent sight. Ideal for fences, old stumps and the like   3/6   5/-

Clerodendron Fargesii.—Szechuan, China. A large shrub,
10 ft. high ; young foliage purple ; flowers white,
star-shaped, fragrant, in August, succeeded in early
autumn by pretty porcelain-blue fruits 3/6   5/6

,, **foetidum.**—China. A sub-woody plant for the foot of a
south or west wall ; corymbs of many pink fragrant
flowers, from August to late autumn 3/6   5/6

,, **trichotomum.**—E. China, Japan. A beautiful shrub of
rounded form, 10—15 ft. high ; numerous fragrant
white flowers, from July to September, followed by dark
blue fruits 2/6   3/6

Clethra alnifolia.—N. America. An erect-growing shrub,
5—8 ft. high ; numerous racemes of many fragrant
creamy-white flowers ; valuable for late summer
flowering 1/6   2/6   3/6

,, ,, **paniculata.**—This vigorous form is one of the
best of July and August flowering shrubs. Almost every
shoot bears 6—8 in. branching racemes of fragrant
flowers. Its long and narrow leaves are mustard-
yellow tinted in autumn 2/6   3/6

Clethra alnifolia rosea.—A delightful form bearing branching racemes of rose-tinted flowers 2/6   3/6

   ,,   **barbinervis (canescens).**—China, Japan. A rare and choice species, 4 ft. high, with 4—6 in. panicles of fragrant white flowers, from July to September. The current growths and the midribs of its oval-obovate leaves are red. It is not quite as hardy as C. alnifolia 2/6   3/6

   ,,   **Delavayi.**—Yunnan, China. An upright, thin-habited shrub 8 ft. or more high, clothed with large rugose leaves. Many conspicuous spikes of large lily-of-the-valley-like flowers are borne from July to September. Unfortunately it is a difficult plant to establish in many gardens in this country 5/-

   ,,   **Fargesii.**—A choice species from C. China, attaining 8—12 ft. The pubescent leaves are ovate-oblong, and 6—9 in. terminal, erect and branching racemes of pearl-white scented flowers are borne during August and September. It is a valuable shrub for lime-free soils ...   3/6   5/6

   ,,   **tomentosa.**—U.S.A. A very distinct erect shrub ; tomentose leaves, with thick felt beneath ; 6 in. racemes of extra large fragrant white flowers in September 2/6   3/6

      All the **Clethras** delight in a moist lime-free soil and semi-shady position.

E **Clianthus puniceus.**—New Zealand. This magnificent shrub, commonly called "The Lobster's Claw" is best on a shady wall around or near the south and west coast ...   2/6   3/6

Colletia armata.—Chile. A curious shrub, ultimately 8 ft. high; small, white, scented flowers 2/6   3/6

   ,,   **cruciata (bictoniensis).**—Uruguay. Larger and more formidable-looking, with smaller white flowers. Both are autumn flowering and hardy in the south and west   2/6   3/6

Colquhounia coccinea vestita.—Nepaul. A shrubby member of the Salvia family, with orange scarlet flowers ; requires a sunny wall 2/6   3/6

Colutea orientalis (cruenta).—Orient. A compact small shrub, about 4 ft. high, with glaucous leaves and numerous coppery-red pea-shaped flowers from June to October ...   2/6   3/6

Comptonia asplenifolia.—N. America. An elegant and beautiful small shrub with dark green fern-like leaves which are attractively tinted in autumn. It hates sun and lime soils 2/6   3/6

Connemara Heath. (See **Daboecia cantabrica**).

E **Convolvulus Cneorum.**—S. Europe. This silver-foliaged, spreading shrub luxuriates by the sea ; inland it requires a hot sunny position ; a mass of silvery-white flushed pink flowers throughout the summer 1/6   2/6

E **Cordyline australis.**—New Zealand. A well-known tropical looking ornamental for seaside and favoured gardens. It is often grown in tubs and pots for summer effect, having sword-like leaves 3/6   5/6

E   ,,   **Banksii.**—New Zealand. This handsome ribbon-leaved plant is suitable for the south and west, near the sea ; inland it requires a favoured spot ; large drooping panicles of creamy-white scented flowers in May and June ; berries white 3/6   5/6

E   ,,   ,,   **erythrorachis.**—Differs from the former by having bright red midribs 5/-   7/6

		each.	

E **Cordyline indivisa.**—New Zealand. This distinct and rare tropical-looking plant, 5 ft. or more high, is only suitable for gardens in the south and west, etc. Its handsome leaves are 3—5 ft. long by 4—6 ins. wide, glaucous beneath, and their midribs are bright red or yellow ... **3/6** **5/6**

E **Corema album.**—An erect or semi-prostrate, grey-leaved pretty heath-like shrub from Portugal ; of botanical interest ; small round pink fruits, ageing to white **2/6**

Coriaria japonica.—Japan. An uncommon sub-shrubby plant, 3—4 ft. high, requiring good drainage and an open position. It is very striking during late summer with its ornamental 1 ft. racemes of coral-red globose fruits, ageing to amber and finally black **2/6** **3/6**

„ **terminalis.**—W. China. This species lives the life of a herbaceous plant. The 6—9 in. terminal racemes of black fruits are borne on the ends of annual growths, 2—4 ft. long and clothed with ovate-oblong leaves ... **2/6** **3/6**

„ „ **xanthocarpa.**—Himalayas. A particularly beautiful ornamental form having long racemes of yellow translucent fruits **3/6** **5/-**

Cornus alba.—N. Asia. A strong grower, 8 ft. or more high and as much wide. Its crimson-red stems, glaucous when young, look attractive throughout the winter, especially when planted by the edge of water. It will flourish in almost any kind of soil, and its leaves often tint beautifully before falling **1/6** **2/6**

„ „ **sibirica.**—Siberia. This exceedingly rare shrub is much smaller and seldom exceeds 3 ft. in height. It is very striking with its brilliant coral-red stems but unfortunately it does not grow well in every soil. It is a great success at Wisley and near Romsey and in gardens in Scotland. This and C. Westonbirt appear to be identical **3/6** **5/-**

„ **Baileyi.**—N. America. An erect brilliant red-stemmed shrub, 5—8 ft. high, decorated with pearl-white fruits, these being retained until spoilt by frost. Its ovate-lanceolate leaves become attractively coloured in late autumn. It is one of the best shrubs with coloured bark during the winter **2/6** **3/6**

„ **canadensis.**—Canada. A charming little species only a few inches high, with numerous erect 1 in. white tinted rose flowers from May to July, followed by bright orange-coloured fruits **1/6** **2/6**

„ **capitata (Benthamia fragifera).**—Himalayas, China. Around the south and west coast and sheltered spots, it forms a large bush or small tree of semi-evergreen character. During June and July, the imbricated branches are decorated with showy, sulphur-yellow bracts, succeeded by crimson, strawberry-like fruits 2/6 **3/6** **5/6**

„ **controversa (brachypoda.)**—China, Japan. A small-growing tree with its horizontal branches arranged in tiers ; wide cymes of blue-black fruits are borne on matured trees **5/6** **7/6**

„ **florida.**—E. North America. This fine plant, where it has a little shelter, quickly attains 15 ft. ; 2 in. conspicuous white cordate bracts (flowers) in May ; a magnificent autumnal with its glorious shades of orange and scarlet 2/6 3/6 **5/6** **7/6**

Cornus florida pendula.—A perfect weeping form of C. florida; quite as beautiful in flower ... ...   *each.* 5/- 7/6

„   „   **rubra.**—Attractive masses of bright rose-red bracts (flowers) in May and June. Its autumn foliage is even more striking than that of C. florida   3/6   5/6   7/6 10/6

„   **Kousa.**—Japan. This is an easy grower and one of the very best ornamentals for British gardens, especially if it is given a cool position. Specimens 5—15 ft. or more high, and as much wide, are a grand sight with their numerous 1—2 in. creamy-white, suffused rose bracts (flowers) during May, June and July. It is quite as   2/6   3/6 beautiful in autumn with its glorious coloured foliage   5/6   7/6

„   „   **chinensis.**—This interesting form from W. Hupeh, China, is freer growing and more erect in habit. Its spreading branches are effective during June with cream-coloured bracts (flowers), carried on 2—4 in. stiff wiry stalks. Here, the green leaves do not colour in the autumn and it is not a better ornamental than the type. These two plants should, if possible, be put against a background of taller trees 7/6 10/6

„   **Mas.**—Europe. Cornelian Cherry. A small tree of spreading habit, 10—20 ft. high ; invaluable in February and March with its profusion of small yellow flowers on naked wood ; large bright red fruits ; foliage turns bronzy-red in autumn ; one of the very best ornamentals on chalk soils 2/6   3/6

„   **Nuttallii.**—N. America. The most handsome of all the Cornus ; a small tree of free growth for a sheltered position, ultimately reaching 15—20 ft. ; of sturdy habit ; large creamy white bracts (flowers), flushed pink, often 4—6 ins. across, and honey-scented ; its foliage colours well in autumn. In these Islands, it is a difficult plant to establish in any position 3/6   5/6   7/6

E   „   **oblonga.**—Szechuan & Yunnan, China. An exceedingly rare and attractive evergreen growing 8 ft. or more high, for gardens in the south and west. The opposite narrow oval-acuminate leaves are lustrous green and wedge-shaped at the base. The many terminal pyramidal panicles of creamy-white flowers are delightfully scented   ...   10/6

„   **officinalis.**—Korea, Japan. A close relative to C. Mas ; similar yellow flowers and red fruits ; autumn foliage bronzy yellow 3/6   5/6

„   **paucinervis.**—C. & W. China. Short branched, slow-growing, of compact habit ; narrow oval leaves, prominently veined ; 3 in. corymbs of small white flowers followed by round black fruits 2/6   3/6

„   **stolonifera.**—N. America. This strong grower, 5—8 ft. high, is possibly the best red-stemmed dogwood we have for winter effect. It should be cut down yearly so as to obtain brighter coloured bark. Its leaves become magnificently coloured every autumn 1/6   2/6

„   „   **flaviramea.**—A useful shrub for winter effect, 3—6 ft. high, with yellow stems. This and C. alba should be cut down yearly to obtain a richer-coloured bark 1/6   2/6

Cornus suecica.—Britain, Asia and N. America. A fascinating
little plant less than 6 ins. high, related to C. canadensis.
The terminal umbels of four white bracts (flowers) are
borne in June. A semi-shady spot is recommended ... 2/6 3/6

each.

The **Cornus** dislike the sun shining on their roots.

E **Corokia buddleoides.**—New Zealand. A branching shrub, 12 ft.
high, suitable for walls in the south and west ; lance-
shaped leaves, white beneath ; numerous panicles of
small yellow flowers, followed by orange-coloured fruits 3/6 5/6

E „ **Cheesemanii (C. buddleoides × C. Cotoneaster).**—A
new and distinct natural hybrid from New Zealand,
5—8 ft. high, with twiggy spreading branches. The
young shoots and undersides of the leaves are covered
with silvery-white tomentum. The alterate leaves,
1—2 ins. long, are oblanceolate. The bright yellow
star-like flowers appear in May and are succeeded by
equally bright yellow hawthorn-like fruits 2/6 3/6

E „ **Cotoneaster.**—New Zealand. A charming small shrub
of greyish appearance, with zig-zag branches ; pretty
either with its yellow star-like flowers in May or its
round orange-red berries in autumn 1/6 2/6 3/6

E „ **macrocarpa.**—New Zealand. A conspicuous evergreen
for seaside gardens around the south and west coast ;
large grey foliage, white beneath ; small yellow flowers,
followed by quantities of brilliant orange-red berries,
retained for months 2/6 3/6

E „ **virgata.**—New Zealand. This very hardy shrub has
twiggy branches, and is of graceful habit. It also makes
a beautiful ornamental hedge, 4—7 ft. high. The yellow
star-like flowers, borne in May and June, are followed
by showy round bright orange fruits 1/6 2/6 3/6

Coronilla Emerus.—C. & S. Europe. A very hardy shrub, easy
to grow in almost any soil, and 4—5 ft. high although
when trained against a wall, it reaches 8—10 ft. The
leaves usually have seven small leaflets. Its Cytisus-
like, yellow tinged red-brown flowers are produced in
the axils of the leaves during April and May and again
in September and October 2/6 3/6

E „ **glauca.**—S. Europe. A dense, bushy, glaucous and
pinnate-leaved shrub for seaside gardens or for a south
or west wall inland. Its attractive rich yellow, pea-like
flowers are borne, according to its position, from June to
autumn. It should be planted out in spring 2/6 3/6

E **Correa Harrisii.**—Hybrid. Not a strong grower ; for south or
west walls in mild situations ; flowers tubular, dark
crimson 3/6 5/6 7/6

E „ **magnifica (speciosa).**—A beautiful shrub for a south or
west wall around the coast ; 6—10 ft. high ; the pendent
flowers, freely borne for eight months of the year, are
particularly graceful in outline, primrose with green
reverse 2/6 3/6

E **Cortaderia argentea Bertinii (Gynerium argenteum)
(Pampas Grass).**—Seldom more than 3 ft. high with
white plumes rising just above the leaves 2/6 3/6

E „ „ **Monstrosa.**—Undoubtedly the best white Pampas. This uncommon plant has elegant loose silvery
plumes on 3—5 ft. stalks. These, carried well above
the leaves, bend outwards with beautiful effect 2/6 3/6

E   **Cortaderia argentea pumila.**—Attains 4—5 ft. with many stiff
spikes of white plumes carried well above the leaves ...

each.
1/6   2/6

E   „   „   **Rendatleri.**—Pretty in late summer and autumn
with its 18—24 in. carmine plumes, ageing to bright
pink, on 7—10 ft. stalks 1/6   2/6   3/6

Corylopsis glabrescens. (Gotoana).—Japan. A rare species
with drooping clusters of yellow cowslip-like flowers
before the leaves, in March and April 7/6 10/6

„   **pauciflora.**—Japan. A charming shrub, 3 ft. high ;
dense twiggy short branches ; numerous drooping
spikes of primrose-yellow flowers, in March, sweetly
scented 3/6   5/6   7/6

„   **platypetala.**—China. Strong growing, open habit, 4—6
ft. high ; leaves roundish, glaucous beneath ; racemes
of 10-20 yellow fragrant flowers, in early spring ;
autumn foliage bright yellow 5/-   7/6

„   **sinensis.**—C. & W. China. An uncommon species, forming a small tree, 10—15 ft. high ; 2 in. drooping spikes
of ten to eighteen fragrant primrose-yellow flowers are
freely borne during April and May. In this district,
its handsome foliage assumes rich autumn tints 7/6 10/6

„   **spicata.**—Japan. A spreading branched shrub, 4—6 ft.
high ; leaves cordate, hazel-like, drooping spikes of
many yellow cowslip-scented flowers, in February and
March ; foliage bright yellow in autumn 3/6   5/6

„   **Veitchiana.**—C. China. This distinct species of open
bushy habit has stout growths usually covered with
small brown dots. The ovate leaves are metallic-green
above and glaucous beneath. The primrose-yellow
flowers, cowslip-scented, have red-brown anthers   ...   10/6

„   **Willmottiae.**—W. Szechuan, China. A quick, compact-
growing species, attaining 6—9 ft. ; branches during
March and April are covered with drooping racemes of
yellowish, fragrant flowers 7/6 10/6

„   **Wilsonii.**—C. China. An attractive, erect-growing large
bush or small tree, furnished with handsome obovate
leaves, glaucous beneath ; 3 in. racemes of primrose-
yellow flowers appear before the leaves 10/6

Corylus maxima atropurpurea.—The purple-leaved Filbert.
With its large rich purple foliage, it is a splendid
companion, throughout the growing season, to Berberis
Thunbergii atropurpurea and Rhus Cotinus foliis
purpureis 1/6   2/6   3/6

Cotoneaster acuminata.—A rare species from the Himalayas, of
erect habit, 10 ft. or more high ; large ovate-lanceolate
leaves, which colour well in late autumn 2/6   3/6

„   **adpressa.**—W. China. A dwarf, close-growing shrub
1 ft. high ; small round bright-red berries in early
autumn ; a really good rock garden shrub 1/6   2/6

E   „   **aldenhamensis.**—A chance seedling. A quick-growing
small tree with long, handsome, green foliage with grey
felt beneath ; the semi-pendulous branches are wreathed
in autumn with bright red berries ; a beautiful tree ... 2/6   3/6

„   **ambigua.**—W. Szechuan, China. A small shrub, 4 ft.
high ; striking autumn foliage, orange and scarlet ;
berries dark purple 2/6   3/6

E **Cotoneaster amoena.**—Yunnan, China. A compact small shrub, each.
3 ft. high ; small grey leaves ; branches studded in autumn
with bright red fruits, retained until mid-winter ... 2/6 3/6

„ **angustifolia.** (See **Pyracantha**).

„ **apiculata.**—W. Szechuan, China. The 4—6 ft. arching
branches are weighed down during the autumn with
bright crimson, sub-globose fruits 2/6 3/6

„ **bullata.**—W. China & Tibet. Few shrubs can equal this
species ; growths 5—8 ft. long, are a noble sight in
autumn, wreathed from end to end with corymbs of
large brilliant red fruits mingling with its oblong scarlet
leaves 1/6 2/6 3/6

E „ **buxifolia (rupestris).**—Nilgiries, Himalayas. A choice
shrub of rather rambling habit, less than 8 ft., with small
round glossy deep-green leaves. This species has the
largest fruits of the genus, abundantly produced and of
an intense scarlet, retained until December 2/6 3/6

E „ „ **vellaea.**—China. A pleasing shrub, 3—4 ft.
high, with procumbent branches ; pretty in autumn
with its mass of small red berries 2/6 3/6

E „ **congesta (microphylla glacialis).**—Himalayas. A
charming little shrub of close compact habit, for the
rock garden ; round bright-red fruits 1/6 2/6

E „ „ **procumbens.**—This new form is one of the most
charming of all rock-garden shrubs. Its quite flat, dense
growths advance slowly in many directions 2/6 3/6

E „ **conspicua.**—Gyala, Tibet, K.W. 6400. A beautiful new
species attaining 3—5 ft. Its interlacing branches carry
deep green, small, oval leaves and are downy beneath.
The large orange-red berries are plentifully borne all along
the branches throughout the winter months 2/6 3/6

E „ **Cooperi.**—An exceedingly rare and graceful species from
Bhutan. It grows to about 8 ft. and its whip-like
growths are clothed with 2—4 in. thin, obovate-lanceo-
late, light green leaves, glaucous beneath 3/6 5/6

E „ **Dammeri.**—W. Hupeh, China. A useful trailing shrub
only a few inches high, for the rock garden, tumbling over
large stones or for steep banks ; the round bright-
scarlet fruits are pretty throughout the winter, nestling
among the deep green leaves 1/6 2/6

E „ „ **radicans.**—A distinct form from W. China, with
bright green, ovate rugose leaves ; its branches are
perfectly prostrate and it quickly forms a mat 3 ft. or
more across 1/6 2/6

„ **Dielsiana.**—W. Hupeh, China. A beautiful slender-
branched shrub, 6—10 ft. high, wreathed with brilliant
scarlet berries and bright autumn foliage ; one of the
most prolific 1/6 2/6 3/6

„ „ **elegans.**—W. China. Quite distinct, pyramidal
habit, with thin flexible growths 2/6 3/6

„ **divaricata.**—C. & W. China. 5—6 ft. high, of graceful
spreading habit ; small green polished leaves and red
egg-shaped fruits ; few shrubs can equal this species
for its glorious scarlet autumn tints 1/6 2/6 3/6

E „ **excellens ?**—China. A tiny growing shrub with small
grey leaves and masses of pinkish-red berries, retained
well into the winter 1/6 2/6

			each.	
Cotoneaster Farreri.—Received here under this name. Distinct, with semi-pendulous growths and medium-sized ovate leaves ; it is covered in early autumn with round or pear-shaped bright red fruits			2/6	3/6
„ **foveolata.**—W. Hupeh, China. A choice species of pyramidal habit, 8—12 ft. high ; oval dull green leaves becoming vivid scarlet in early winter ; fruits red, finally black			2/6	3/6

E „ **Franchetii.**—Yunnan, China. Of rounded form, graceful arching branches clothed with silvery-grey leaves ; smothered throughout autumn with oblong orange-scarlet fruits **1/6** 2/6 3/6

„ **frigida.**—Himalayas. A popular tree, 15—20 ft. high, as is evident by the many hundreds seen in Bournemouth gardens ; mass of wide corymbs of large rich bright-red fruits retained till early winter **1/6** 2/6 3/6

„ „ **fructu-luteo.**—This small tree is particularly attractive from September to mid-winter, when its branches are laden with its uncommon yellow fruits ... 2/6 3/6

„ „ **Vicarii.**—A distinct form, with larger foliage, and as beautiful as the type in fruit. This is retained until the new year for birds are not partial to it. This and C. frigida montana appear to be the same plant ... 2/6 3/6

E „ **glabrata.**—W. China. This is the most conspicuous in foliage of all the Cotoneasters. The semi-evergreen leaves assume gorgeous tints. A good grower with corymbs of small orange-scarlet fruits, retained until the new year 2/6 3/6

E „ **glaucophylla.**—China. A rare species of good habit, 6—9 ft. high, with conspicuous foliage, bluish beneath. This is the last of the genus to flower, is hawthorn-scented, with corymbs of bright orange-red fruits retained till February 2/6 3/6

E „ **Harroviana.**—China. Of pyramidal habit, 8—12 ft. high with bright red stems ; one of the handsomest of the Cotoneasters in flower ; fruits bright red 2/6 3/6

„ **hebephylla.**—S.W. China. Of open habit ; a pretty picture in autumn with its 3—7 ft. branches wreathed from end to end with deep crimson hawthorn-like fruits ; height 8—12 ft. 2/6 3/6

E „ **Henryana.**—China. Of horizontal pendulous habit ; a useful shrub for many purposes ; its large leaves become bronzy-red towards the new year ; fruits bright crimson 2/6 3/6

„ **horizontalis.**—Himalaya & Szechuan, China. Of beautiful horizontal habit ; masses of bright red fruits ; rich orange and scarlet autumn colourings. This is always a charming shrub in whatever position it is placed. Its flowers and those of C. lucida are especially attractive to Queen wasps **1/6** 2/6 3/6

„ **hupehensis.**—C. & W. China. Seldom more than 5—7 ft. high. Its semi-pendulous branches are attractive in mid-autumn, with large bright red berries 2/6 3/6

„ **ignava.**—E. Turkestan. A dense, branched shrub, possibly not more than 4 ft. high, and somewhat like C. lucida in foliage. It assumes brilliant orange and scarlet tints in mid-autumn 2/6 3/6

E **Cotoneaster lactea.**—One of the most conspicuous of all Cotoneasters from China. A specimen, 15 ft. high, wreathed with 4—6 in. corymbs of dazzling red fruits, is a magnificent sight in late autumn	each. 2/6	3/6
„ **lucida (acutifolia. Lindley).**—Altai Mountains. Of compact upright habit, 6 ft. high, the dark green leaves assume striking autumn tints ; fruits round, black ...	1/6	2/6
„ **melanocarpa laxiflora.**—Asia. An uncommon shrub, 4 ft. high, with grey-green leaves and many flowers, succeeded by round black fruits	2/6	3/6
E „ **microphylla.**—Himalayas. A good shrub for covering walls. It is also a champion trailer for holding up banks, if its branches are pegged to root into the soil. Pretty during autumn and early winter, with large bright red fruits	1/6	2/6
E „ „ **cochleata.**—Cambridge Botanic Gardens. This uncommon evergreen shrub, with branches flat on the ground, can be easily counted as one of the best introductions of recent years. It is an admirable plant for the rock garden or for the edge of paths, etc. From July until Christmas, its large, glistening, carmine-red fruits are a beautiful sight	2/6	3/6
E „ „ **thymifolia.**—Quite distinct ; of dwarf compact habit, with tiny glossy green leaves and large round bright-red berries	1/6	2/6
„ **moupinensis.**—W. China. An erect grower, 8—12 ft. high. The large rugose leaves take on fine autumnal tints. Its black fruits distinguish it from C. bullata, with which it is often confused 1/6	2/6	3/6
„ **multiflora (reflexa).**—W. China. A too-little-known thin branching shrub, 5—8 ft. high, of elegant habit. It is as beautiful as the hawthorn of the hedgerow. The round, bright red fruits ripen in late summer ... 1/6	2/6	3/6
„ **nitens.**—W. China. This grows 6—9 ft. high. A pleasing shrub during late autumn, with its wiry growths weighed down with bright red fruits. The small leaves, well retained, assume bright scarlet tints ... 1/6	2/6	3/6
„ **obscura.**—W. China. Of spreading habit with rather large ovate foliage, with thick tomentum beneath. The leaves turn orange and blood-red in very late autumn ...	2/6	3/6
E „ **pannosa.**—S.W. China. An upright elegant shrub, 6—10 ft. high, with thin wiry dark red growths and ovate green leaves, white beneath ; a pleasing object throughout the winter, with its numerous dark-red fruits 1/6	2/6	3/6
„ **racemiflora nummularia.**—China. Of dense semi-weeping habit, with round grey leaves ; its fruits are dark red in late summer	2/6	3/6
E „ **rhytidophylla.**—W. China. Erect-growing with dark red branches ; some of the large handsome rugose leaves become brightly tinted in late winter ; corymbs of small orange-coloured fruits	2/6	3/6
„ **rotundifolia (disticha) (Hookeri of trade).**—Himalayas, S.W. China. A charming sub-evergreen species of erect habit, about 5 ft. high, with fish-bone-like growths, densely furnished with shiny box-like leaves. It is one of the first Cotoneasters to plant for its wealth of brilliant red polished fruits, retained until February 1/6	2/6	3/6

each.

E **Cotoneaster St. Monica.**—Hybrid.   This was found by the old
Swiss gardener in the gardens of St. Monica, Bristol.   A
handsome small tree with 4—6 in. elliptical-lanceolate,
red-veined leaves and with spreading branches weighed
down every autumn with large clusters of fruits,
carmine-rose ageing to vermillion 2/6   3/6

E   „   **salicifolia.**—W. China.   Of wide spreading habit, 12—20
ft. high ; its leaves, somewhat willow-like, are light
green and wrinkled ; berries small, orange-red.   The
true plant may not be in cultivation 2/6   3/6

E   „   „   **floccosa.**—C. China.   This form has pretty dark
green very narrow leaves covered beneath with a thick
fleece.   It attains 6—10 ft. and the weeping branches are
pretty in late autumn, laden with round bright red
berries 2/6   3/6

E   „   „   **rugosa.**—C. China.   A free-growing shrub of
semi-pendent habit ; leaves rugose and fruits coral-red.
It is one of the most freely fruiting Cotoneasters known.   2/6   3/6

E   „   **serotina.**—W. China.   A very distinct evergreen related
to C. lactea ; an unrivalled species for habit, foliage
and wealth of orange-red berries in early winter   ...   2/6   3/6

„   **Simonsii.**—Khasia Mountains.   Of compact habit ; few
shrubs are more beautiful as hedge plants.   In late
autumn and early winter, the branches are laden with
bright scarlet hawthorn fruits and brilliantly tinted
leaves 1/6   2/6

„   **tomentosa.**—European Alps.   Unquestionably a beautiful shrub, 4—6 ft. high, with large round leaves, covered beneath with thick felt, assuming autumn tints of red,
crimson, orange and gold and retained for many weeks.
Fruits brilliant red, ripe in October 1/6   2/6

E   „   **turbinata.**—C. China.   The foliage of this pyramidal
species is conspicuously grey-white beneath, effective
when exposed to the wind.   It is very late flowering
and the deep red pear-shaped fruits do not colour before
October.   A valuable and pleasing shrub at any time of
the year 2/6   3/6

E   „   **Wardii.**—S.E. Tibet.   Attains 6—9 ft. ; medium-sized
grey foliage, white beneath.   Its wealth of distinct
orange-red berries amongst the orange-scarlet foliage
is a magnificent sight 2/6   3/6

E   „   **Watereri (frigida × Henryana).**—This beautiful hybrid
is not quite so bushy as C. aldenhamensis but has slightly
larger leaves and fruits.   It is fast-growing, soon
attaining a height of 18 ft. or more and is a fine fruiting
ornamental 2/6   3/6

„   **Zabelii.**—C. China.   Arching branched shrub of loose
habit ; the light grey-green leaves are yellowish felted
beneath ; fruits pear-shaped, dull red 2/6   3/6

All the **Cotoneasters** are impartial to soil or site,
and are indispensable for the autumn garden, with their
varied tints and wealth of fruits.   Many are suitable,
and make admirable wall plants in cold districts, on
north and east walls.   The **Cotoneasters** and **Berberis**
are invaluable to the apiarist.

Crabs (flowering and fruiting).—(See **Malus**).

each.

Crataegomespilus grandiflora (Mespilus Smithii).—Graft hybrid. A small tree of round form, 10—15 ft. high, conspicuous during May, when the semi-pendent branches are wreathed with large, pearl-white flowers 2/6   3/6   5/6

Crataegus arnoldiana.—Massachusetts.—A small tree with a dense head of zig-zag branches armed with 3 in. thorns. The large white flowers are followed by ½ in. bright red fruits 3/6   5/6

„   **Carrierei.**—Hybrid. A beautiful thorn, having deep green glossy leaves, turning bronzy-red in late autumn, and white flowers about 1 in. across, succeeded by ¾ in. orange-red fruits, retained well into winter 3/6   5/6

„   **coccinea (rotundifolia).**—The scarlet fruiting Hawthorn of North America 2/6   3/6   5/6

„   **Crus-galli.**—N. America. Few small trees are more interesting than the Cockspur Thorn, with its flat head and spreading branches. The large white flowers, borne in June, are followed by ½ in. globose, red fruits, which hang until February. The polished green obovate leaves become gorgeously coloured in autumn in almost any kind of soil 3/6   5/6

„   **cupulifera.**—N. America. One of the very best for the autumn garden. A round-headed tree, 15 ft. high. Its lobed leaves turn blood-crimson 5/6   7/6

„   **Dippeliana (Leeana of Loudon).**—Hybrid. An uncommon small tree, 10 ft. high. The leaves are sharply lobed, and downy beneath, the flowers white with red anthers. It is pretty during autumn with yellow and red fruits 3/6   5/6

„   **Douglasii.**—W.N. America. This strong grower, of rounded habit, is not as good in flower and fruit as many other species, but its obovate-ovate, slightly-lobed leaves colour well every autumn 3/6   5/6

„   **Ellwangeriana.**—E.N. America. A strong grower, of tree size, with brown bark and large, ovate-rounded, slightly-lobed, green leaves. Its spreading branches are decorated in September with many polished, bright red fruits   3/6   5/6

„   **grignoniensis.**—A distinct and free-growing thorn. The leaves, with four to eight lobes, are bright green, colouring well in November and December. The thick, round, bright red fruits hang well into winter 3/6   5/6

„   **Holmesiana.**—N. America. It is related to C. coccinea but is a stronger grower and has much larger and deeper-lobed leaves. The large orange-red fruits are very pretty during the autumn 5/-

„   **macracantha.**—E. U.S.A. A handsome large shrub or small tree of dense habit. Its leaves, leathery and dark green, form a background to the large white flowers, with yellow anthers. It is conspicuous during autumn when laden with shiny, bright scarlet fruits 5/-

„   **orientalis.**—Orient. This much confused, choice ornamental attains small tree size in the south. The obovate leaves, held on ½—1 in. stalks, have 5—7, sometimes 9, narrow long, shining green lobes. Each lobe is jagged, finely serrated at the ends and glaucous beneath. The corymbs of 12 or more flowers are followed by ¾ in. depressed, globose, yellow-red fruits, which are attractive from early September to December   ...   5/-   7/6

Crataegus oxyacanthoides plena alba.—The double white
form of the common thorn 3/6   5/6

,,   ,,   ,,   **coccinea.** Paul's well known double
scarlet flowering thorn 3/6   5/6

,,   ,,   ,,   **rosea.**—Double pink flowers 3/6   5/6

,,   ,,   **punicea.**—Single crimson-red flowers 3/6   5/6

,,   ,,   **rosea.**—Single pink flowers 3/6   5/6

,,   **Phaenopyrum (cordata) (Washington Thorn).**—N.
America. A dense round-headed tree, 15—20 ft. high.
It is particularly beautiful during autumn with its
orange and scarlet-tinted leaves and large clusters of
bright scarlet fruits 3/6   5/6

,,   **pinnatifida major (Korolkowii).**—N. China. An effective tree, almost devoid of thorns, and with handsome
green, 7-lobed, prominently veined leaves resting on
brown-red branches. It is a splendid object when
laden with 1 in. globose-pear-shaped, glistening red,
speckled fruits 5/-

,,   **prunifolia (C. splendens. Hort.).**—Attaining 15—20 ft.,
it is particularly attractive during the autumn, when its
beautiful deep green leaves age to glowing crimson, and
the large fruits turn rich red 3/6   5/6

,,   **punctata.**—E. & N. America. A splendid thorn, attaining 15—30 ft. In early June the horizontal-spreading
branches are wreathed with large corymbs of flowers,
and again in autumn with large speckled deep red fruits   3/6   5/6

,,   **submollis.**—E. N. America. This species grows 20 ft.
or more high, with branches forming a broad round
head. It is pretty in early autumn with its heavy load
of shining bright orange-red fruits 3/6   5/6

,,   **succulenta.**—E. N. America. An uncommon species,
of upright habit, decorated with roundish obovate bright
green leaves and large white flowers in June, succeeded by
round, bright red fruits 5/-

,,   **tanacetifolia.**—Orient. An exceedingly rare small tree
with leaves 1—2 ins. long, held on ¼—½ in. stalks. They
are diamond-shaped and composed of 5—7 narrow, oblong lobes, wider at the base than those of C. orientalis.
Each lobe has 1—4 jagged teeth. The clusters of 6—8
fragrant flowers are succeeded by ¾—1 in. globose, orange
yellow suffused red fruits. From spring to autumn, the
current growths and leaves are covered with wool, giving
the plant a silvery appearance 5/6   7/6

The **Thorn** is a very hardy plant thriving well in
almost any soil. Many of the species are invaluable
for the richness of their autumn leaves and the grand
display of beautifully-coloured fruits.

Crinodendron. (See **Tricuspidaria**).

E **Cyathodes Colensoi.**—Mountains of Nelson and Canterbury,
New Zealand. This fascinating, rare shrub is of neat
habit, 3—9 ins. high, and densely clothed with tiny,
linear-oblong, blue-grey leaves. The terminal racemes
of 3—5 small flowers are followed by white or red drupe-
like fruits. It is a delightful companion for many of the
dwarf-growing Chinese Rhododendrons, Schizocodons,
Shortias, Phyllodoces, etc.... ... ...   —   —

E **Cyathodes empetrifolia.**—New Zealand. A heath-like creeping each.
shrub forming loose mats, with small creamy-white
flowers, deliciously scented, in May and June. It is
quite at home where ordinary heather will grow ... **1/6 2/6**

E „ **robusta.**—Chatham Islands. A rare and distinct shrub
for plant collectors, suitable for the south west. It has
dense small linear-oblong leaves and numerous inconspicuous flowers. In general character it resembles a
tiny pine **3/6 5/6 7/6**

Cydonia (Chaenomeles) cathayensis Wilsonii.—W. China.
This strong-growing shrub is attractive every spring
with its 1½ in. white, suffused pink flowers nestling
among the lustrous green leaves. It often bears huge
ovoid fruits but unfortunately it suffers from canker, in
our poor heathland soil **2/6 3/6**

„ **japonica.** Long been known as C. Maulei. Japan.
Forms a thicket of dense slender branches, only a few
feet high ; flowers orange-red shading to orange-scarlet,
in April and May. These are followed by numerous
golden apples, delightfully fragrant **2/6 3/6**

„ „ **Simonii.**—A charming semi-prostrate shrub,
not often seen in gardens, suitable for rock banks or as
a point plant in the rock garden. Its twiggy, spreading
growths bear numerous, perfectly formed, 2 in. geranium
scarlet flowers from March to June **2/6 3/6**

, „ **superba.**—This rare form is much slower growing
than the type. It is a splendid ornament for the rock
garden or for the front of borders. From March to June,
it is lit up with 1—1½ in. scarlet flowers **2/6 3/6**

„ **lagenaria (Chaenomeles japonica) (Pyrus japonica).**
—Japan. One of the most cherished of all wall shrubs in
early spring, with its profusion of large bright red to
scarlet flowers. It is better known under its old name of
Cydonia japonica **2/6 3/6**

„ „ **Abricot.** — Semi-double flowers, bright orange-
red ; dwarf habit ; one of the best **2/6 3/6**

„ „ **Aurora.**—This scarce shrub grows less than 3 ft.
high, and from early March to May, its thin branches
carry showy 1½ in. rose, suffused orange-red flowers ... **2/6 3/6**

„ **cardinalis.**—This splendid shrub was raised
at the same time as the beautiful C. l. Knaphill Scarlet.
The upright stems, with branching growths, carry
dense, 1½ in. glowing, salmon-red, suffused crimson,
cup-shaped flowers **3/6**

„ „ **Knaphill Scarlet.**—Many shrubs flower in May,
June and July, but none can surpass this, with its magnificent 2—2½ in. globular, rich orange-scarlet flowers.
A densely branched specimen, 3 ft. × 4 ft. and carrying
400 flowers was a glorious sight last year. It is also a
good shrub for the higher points on the rock garden.
It was raised about 1872, by the late Mr. Anthony
Waterer. Cydonia lagenaria Sunrise and this plant
appear to be identical **2/6 3/6 5/6**

„ „ **Moerloesii (Apple Blossom).**—A beautiful
shrub for the border or for planting against walls. Its
dense, 1½ in. apple blossom-pink flowers, carried from
early March until May, are very welcome and attractive **2/6 3/6**

each.

Cydonia lagenaria nivalis.—This strong grower is of open habit and attains 6 ft. or more in height. During the spring, its branches are wreathed with pretty 1½ in. pure white flowers and these are not disfigured by late frosts   2/6   **3/6   5/6**

„   **oblonga (vulgaris).**—C. Asia. The common Quince is worth a place in the autumn garden for its butter-yellow foliage. It will grow to 20 ft. and its white flowers, ageing to rose, are followed by fragrant golden-yellow fruits of excellent flavour when cooked 2/6   **3/6   5/6**

„   „   **lusitanica.**—Portugal. The Portuguese Quince has been known in English gardens since 1611. It is a strong grower and is decorated during May with 2½ in. rose-coloured flowers and again in autumn with large pear-shaped fruits 3/6   **5/6   7/6**

„   „   **Vranja.**—The neglect of the Bereczki Quince, a very hardy and attractive fruiting tree from Serbia, is difficult to explain. The flowers, a symbol of maiden beauty to native poets, stand above the oval leaves like dainty goblets ; their contents, mauve-tinted downy filaments. The fruits, like golden pears, are richly scented, whilst the leaves, shed late, rival them in wealth of gold. A plant to adorn any garden 5/6   **7/6 10/6**

The **Cydonias** are very hardy shrubs, thriving in almost any soil and situation and they are invaluable for planting against north walls. They seldom fail to give a fine display of flowers and fruits each year.

Cyrilla racemiflora.—South U.S.A. This rare shrub is quite happy and free-growing in the south under woodland conditions. It is of bushy habit attaining 5 ft. in lime-free soils. The Itea-like flowers are freely borne, and appearing in autumn are more valued. The shining green 3—6 in. oblanceolate leaves age to bright crimson from October to February 3/6   **5/6   7/6**

Cytisus   albus   (multiflorus).—Spain and Portugal. The common White Broom is much admired every spring when its 5—8 ft. slender branches are wreathed with small white flowers 1/6   **2/6**

„   „   **durus.**—Compact habit and not so strong-growing as the foregoing. The flowers are similar but produced later   2/6   **3/6**

„   „   **incarnatus (roseus).**—Slender branched, studded with small white, delicately rose-tinted flowers 2/6   **3/6**

„   **Ardoinii.**—Maritime Alps. A small decumbent shrub, less than 6 ins. high, with golden yellow flowers, in April and May 1/6   **2/6**

„   **austriacus Heuffelii.**—Hungary. A choice rock garden shrub resembling C. leucanthus in foliage and habit, but it has terminal clusters of bright yellow flowers from early May until the end of July **3/6**

„   **Battandieri.**—Morocco. This outstanding, newly intro-duced, small tree is as free-growing as the common Laburnum and has a blue appearance throughout the growing season. Its beautiful, three-parted, large, grey-blue leaves form a fine background for the mass of 5 in. erect racemes of golden-yellow, quince-scented flowers, borne during June. At Wisley, it was one of the few plants not injured by the frosts of May, 1935. It has received the highest awards of the Royal Horticultural Society. A.M. 16-6-31, F.C.C. 19-6-34   ...   ...   3/6   **5/6**

		each.
Cytisus Beanii (Ardoinii × purgans).—Of semi-prostrate habit, about 1 ft. high and twice as much in diameter. The prettiest of all dwarf Brooms in May ; flowers deep golden-yellow.	2/6	3/6
„ **Cornish Cream.**—A shrub, 4—6 ft. high, of open habit ; attractive throughout May with creamy-yellow flowers	2/6	3/6
„ **Dallimorei (albus × scop. Andreanus).**—A shrub 3—5 ft. high with short twiggy growths smothered in May with conspicuous rosy-pink shaded crimson flowers. It requires good soil		2/6
„ **decumbens (Genista prostrata).**—France and Balkans. A choice shrub for the rock garden, with its overlapping growths quite flat on the ground. The main shoots tend to grow in one direction and the twigs are nearly hidden by oblong-obovate, grey-green hairy leaves. During May and June, it produces many ½ in. rich yellow flowers	1/6	2/6
„ **demissus.**—Mt. Olympus. This rare decumbent alpine shrub was recently re-introduced. Its large, canary-yellow flowers, borne more or less from mid-May to mid-August, nestle among the trifoliate, hairy, grey leaves ...	3/6	5/6
„ **Dorothy Walpole.**—The wings are rich velvet crimson with deep rose standards ; probably a better grower than Dallimorei	2/6	3/6
„ **glabrescens.**—C. Europe. An ideal shrub for the rock garden or alpine house. Its short, stiff twigs are gaily decorated during May and June with fragrant, golden-yellow flowers		3/6
„ **kewensis (Ardoinii × albus).**—An ideal trailing shrub for the rock garden where it is allowed to ramble and tumble over at will. The long prostrate shoots are wreathed in May with sulphur-yellow flowers	2/6	3/6
„ **leucanthus (Schipkaensis).**—Balkan Mountains. A dwarf spreading shrub for the rock garden ; terminal clusters of creamy-white flowers from June to October	2/6	3/6
„ **Lyndhurst (albus × purpureus).**—A natural hybrid, of upright habit, 5—7 ft. high. Its slender growths are beautiful when carrying the pale rose-coloured flowers in May and early June		3/6
„ **Minstead (albus × Dorothy Walpole).**—A natural hybrid discovered growing by a huge specimen of C. albus, with C. Dorothy Walpole nearby. It is outstanding during April and May when its long, slender growths are covered with small rose-red flowers. It is as strong-growing as C. albus	2/6	3/6
„ **monspessulanus.**—S. & E. Europe, N. Africa. An upright-growing shrub, quickly attaining a height of 5—8 ft. and densely clothed with three-parted leaves. It is crowded with bright yellow flowers in spring and again in autumn. It is quite hardy in many gardens around Salisbury	2/6	3/6
„ **nigricans (Carlieri).**—C. Europe. A worthy shrub of compact habit, 3 ft. high. The 6—12 in. racemes are a mass of yellow flowers, from July to October	1/6	2/6
„ **Osbornii.**—Its habit resembles C. praecox, but it flowers much later. The flowers, abundantly borne, are canary-yellow	2/6	3/6

each.

Cytisus Porlock (monspessulanus × racemosus).—This valuable hybrid soon makes a large bush, 5—10 ft. high and it is hardy even in Wiltshire gardens. Its branches are thickly clothed with small trifoliate, silky leaves and the numerous, fragrant, golden flowers are borne, more or less, from April to autumn **2/6   3/6**

„   **praecox (purgans × albus) (Warminster Broom).**— One of the most beautiful of all May-flowering shrubs. A dense mass in early May with sulphur-yellow flowers **1/6   2/6   3/6**

„   „   **albus.**—A seedling form from C. praecox, of much stiffer habit and growing to 5 ft. It produces its mass of white flowers a little later **2/6   3/6**

„   „   **Buttercup.**—A seedling from C. praecox, of upright habit, soon growing 4—6 ft. high. The twiggy shoots produce golden-yellow flowers, of similar size to those of the parent, from April to October, but its chief floral beauty is during April and May **3/6**

„   **procumbens.**—S.E. Europe. A very hardy and useful shrub for many positions, including dry banks, etc. It is procumbent in youth, but ultimately forms a mass of interlacing branches 12—18 ins. high by 3 ft. across. It is crowded with bright yellow flowers in May and June **1/6   2/6**

„   **purgans.**—France, Spain, N. Africa. It has long been known in British gardens and is still one of the best of the family. It is of upright habit, 3—5 ft. high, and though it bears the majority of its deep golden-yellow scented flowers in April and May it usually carries some bloom until October **2/6**

„   **purpureus.**—E. Europe. An admirable pendent-branched small shrub clothed from end to end with pretty purple flowers, from May to July **1/6   2/6**

„   „   **albo-carneus (roseus or incarnatus of gardens).**—A dainty-growing shrub, barely 1 ft. high, clothed with small trifoliate leaves and slender branches, covered during May with bright rose, pea-shaped flowers. C. p. versicolor, with anaemic rose-coloured flowers, often has to do duty for this beauty   ...   **2/6   3/6**

„   **ratisbonensis (biflorus).**—E. Europe. Of open, bushy habit and greyish appearance, 3—5 ft. high. The bright yellow laburnum-like flowers are produced during May **1/6   2/6   3/6**

„   **scoparius (Common Broom).**—Europe. Large tracts in the south are a magnificent sight in May, when lighted up with the varied hues of its yellow flowers, which few of the named forms can equal **1/6   2/6**

„   „   **Andreanus.**—Rich crimson and bright yellow ; very striking when in full flower **2/6**

„   „   **Daisy Hill Splendens.** An improved form of the original plant Daisy Hill, and a better grower ; flowers sulphur-yellow with bright rosy-crimson keel **2/6   3/6**

„   **Dragonfly.**—A compact grower, having brown-red, suffused yellow, flowers **2/6   3/6**

„   **Firefly.**—A good grower with large fiery red, suffused yellow, flowers **2/6**

each.

Cytisus scoparius fulgens.—This is perhaps the best of all the coloured forms of the " scoparius " section. The conspicuous orange-yellow and bright crimson flowers fade to deep crimson and dark red. The colour contrasts are not so glaring as in most forms 2/3 3/6

" " **sulphureus (Moonlight Broom).**—Shorter and more compact, with pretty, pale sulphur-yellow flowers. A shrub not to be despised 2/6

" " **Sunlight.**—This is a splendid new form of C. scoparius, and worthy of wide cultivation. The 1 in. golden-yellow flowers, borne in May and June, fade to lemon-yellow 2/6 3/6

" **sessilifolius.**—S. Europe. Of graceful open habit, 3—5 ft. high ; many short racemes of bright yellow flowers in June 2/6 3/6

" **supranubius (Teneriffe Broom).**—Hardy around the south and west coast ; stiff erect branches and numerous small milky-white, rose-tinted flowers in May ; a pretty flowering shrub 3/6 5/6

The above **Brooms** are pot-grown. See also **Genistas.**

Æ **Daboecia azorica.**—Azores. This new Heath-like small shrub is a charming addition to the heather garden or Ericaceae border. The dense, small, bronze-green leaves make a perfect background for the egg-shaped, nodding, crimson-red bells, held on 3—6 in. slender stalks. It may not be hardy in the midlands 3/6 5/6

Æ " **cantabrica (polifolia) (Connemara Heath).**—Ireland, S.W. Europe. A compact-growing heath-like shrub, 12—18 ins. high, with spikes of globular, rosy-purple flowers from late June until late October 9/- to 15/- doz. 1/- 1/6

Æ " " **alba.**—A popular shrub with erect spikes of large snow-white globular flowers, held well above the green foliage ... ... 9/- to 15/- doz. 1/- 1/6

Æ " " **bicolor.**—In our heathland, iron soil, the pretty bicolor flowers revert and so the plant has been discarded — —

Æ " " **globosa.**—Spreading habit ; large pale purple globular flowers ... ... 9/- to 15/- doz. 1/- 1/6

Æ " " **purpurea.**—Very distinct ; dark green foliage contrasting well with the beautiful reddish-crimson flowers ; unfortunately forms with inferior colours are often seen under this name ... 9/- to 15/- doz. 1/- 1/6

The forms **alba** and **purpurea,** with their conspicuous flowers from late June to late October are worthy of every garden, either as dot plants or for edgings. As a drift in the heather garden they have few equals. However, they are for lime free soils only and should be pruned back every spring.
See also **Ericas** and **Phyllodoces.**

Æ **Danaë racemosa (Ruscus racemosus) (D. Laurus).**—Alexandrian Laurel. Asia Minor. A good shrub for growing in the shade ; the bright green foliage is effective at all seasons. Cut sprays placed in water last well 2/6 3/6

Æ **Daphne acutiloba.**—W. China. With long narrow leaves, it bears clusters of five to seven scentless white flowers in July and August. The scarlet berries are its attraction. 3/6 5/6

each.

Daphne alpina.—S. Europe. This rare shrub, about 1 ft. high, is clothed with ¾—1¾ in. oblanceolate, grey-green leaves. It is decorated during May and June with terminal clusters of 6—10, fragrant white flowers, which give place to orange-red fruits 5/–

E „ **arbuscula.**—Hungary. A gem, of mound-like habit, about 6 in. high. Its red-brown, short growths carry polished, green, grooved and revolute, linear-lanceolate leaves and terminal heads of 1 in. tubular, rose-pink flowers. Several specimens were much admired at the Alpine Society's spring show in 1936 ...   .   10/6

E „ **aurantiaca.**—This rare and beautiful Daphne from S.W. China is not easy to establish in the open but does well in a cold alpine house. Its twiggy growths carry ½—1 in. obovate-oblong leaves, glaucous beneath. It is conspicuous during May and June, and often again during the autumn, with many groups of ½ in. orange-yellow scented flowers 10/6

E „ **Blagayana.**—E. Europe. Of spreading habit with heads of twenty or more creamy-white fragrant flowers in March and April 3/6

E „ **Burkwoodii (Cneorum × caucasica).**—In habit and foliage this new hybrid strongly resembles D. collina neapolitana. It is free-growing and its many heads of richly scented, flesh-coloured flowers are produced over a long period. D. Somerset has the same parents and there is no appreciable difference between it and D. Burkwoodii 5/6   7/6 10/6

„ **caucasica.**—Caucasus. An uncommon shrub about 3 ft. high, for a cool position. The pale green oblanceolate leaves are 1½—3 ins. long ; clusters of tubular white scented flowers are borne during May and June at the end of the previous year's growths 5/–

E „ **Cneorum.**—S. Europe. This forms a spreading mass, usually less than 1 ft. high. The fragrant flowers are a mass of bright rose-pink during April and May and occasionally in autumn. Fine specimens are to be seen around the south coast, within reach of the salt air ...   2/6   3/6

E „ „ **alba.**—Jura Mountains. It forms tufts a few inches high, but several feet wide. Its charming white wax-like flowers are freely borne during May and June   7/6 10/6

E „ „ **eximea.**—The finest form yet seen, this superb variety is well over one-third larger in all its parts than the type, with a rich green foliage, and immense clusters of very fragrant blossoms which, breaking from ruby buds, are a deep-toned pink intensified by a glow of crimson   10/6

E „ „ **Verlotii.**—Dauphiny & Bavarian Alps. This charming form has longer and narrower leaves than the type. During the spring months, the ends of its slender twigs are gay with luminous, rose-red, scented flowers   5/6   7/6

E „ **collina.**—Italy. This exceedingly rare shrub of upright habit is quite hardy in many gardens. It has ½—1½ in. oblong, deep green leaves, rounded at the apex and densely covered on both sides with light brown hairs. The attractive heads of 10 or more rose-red, scented flowers are borne from March to June and often again during the autumn. It is often seen exhibited at the Alpine Society's shows as D. sericea 7/6 10/6

			each.
E	**Daphne collina neapolitana (Fioniana ? Hort.)**—A compact round bush, 18—30 ins. high, clothed with ash-green leaves. Its clusters of rose-pink flowers are borne from March to June and again during the autumn. One of the easiest of all Daphnes to grow	3/6	5/6
	„ **Genkwa.**—This rare Japanese Daphne is reputed to be difficult, but this is not true of plants on their own roots, in lime-free soil and semi-shade. Its dense, lilac-coloured flowers, borne on leafless twigs are a delight every spring. The oval-lanceolate leaves colour well before falling. Open ground plants are offered 3/6	5/6	7/6
E	„ **hybrida.**—Quite easy to grow and one of the hardiest. It attains 3—4 ft., is of open habit with medium-sized shining leaves and fairly large reddish-purple flowers which in spring and again in autumn scent the air for yards around. It is also known as D. Dauphinii ...	3/6	5/6
E	„ **Laureola.**—Europe. An easy grower on heavy soils, with very dark green foliage and yellowish scented flowers along the branches in February and March ; fruits egg-shaped, bluish-black	1/6	2/6
	„ **Mezereum.**—Europe, Siberia. Wreathed during February and March with fragrant purplish flowers followed by bright scarlet fruits, ripe in July	2/6	3/6
	„ „ **alba.** The white flowered form	2/6	3/6
	„ „ „ **grandiflora.**—A form with larger white flowers and yellow fruits	—	—
E	„ **odora.**—China, Japan. Perfectly hardy in the south and west if planted in a semi-shady recess ; powerfully fragrant large reddish flowers from mid-winter until late spring ; a most beautiful shrub ; also useful for cold greenhouse culture	3/6	5/6
E	„ „ **aurea marginata (japonica).**—Japan. Of more erect habit and hardier ; flowers pink ; leaves margined with yellow	5/6	7/6
E	„ **oleoides.**—S. Europe. Often asked for under D. buxifolia. A rare, slow-growing shrub ultimately attaining 2 ft. The oblanceolate leaves, dark blue-green, have yellow petioles. Terminal clusters of purple or rose-coloured flowers appear in May, and often again in September	3/6	5/6
	„ **papyracea (cannabina).**—Himalayas. This rare species is upright-growing, 18—24 ins. high, and is as hardy as D. indica. Its leathery, oblong-lanceolate leaves are 2—4 ins. long and wedge-shaped at the base. The tubular, pearl-white flowers, borne in March and April, give place to orange-red-coloured fruits	7/6	10/6
E	„ **petraea (rupestris) grandiflora.**—S. Tyrol. This precious shrub forms a hummock a few inches high and is the charm of every alpine gardener. Few plants are more beautiful in spring when its dainty, ½ in. linear leaves are almost hidden by the profusion of ½—¾ in. tubular rose-pink flowers. It is beautifully illustrated in the Alpine Garden Society's Bulletin, Vol. IV, No. 1, page 127 (March, 1936) 5/6	7/6	10/6
E	„ **pontica.**—Orient. A shade-loving shrub, 3 ft. high and wider across, with spreading branches. During April the abundant tubular yellow flowers emit an attractive perfume	3/6	5/6

each.

Daphne pseudo-mezereum.—This deciduous rarity from C. Japan is similar in habit, growth and foliage to D. Mezereum. Its thick-set growths carry clusters of green-yellow flowers, followed by oval, red fruits   ...   5/-   7/6

E   „   **retusa.**—China. This rarity of a difficult genus is one of the easiest to grow. It reaches 12—18 ins. in height, with thick short growths, and obovate or oval leaves up to 2 ins. long. The conspicuous clusters of rosy-purple flowers, white within, borne during May are deliciously scented 7/6   10/6

E   „   **sericea.**—Asia Minor. Horticulture is indebted to Mr. E. K. Balls for re-introducing this rarity. Its stiff growths are furnished with leathery, narrow-lanceolate, light green, pointed leaves, ½—2½ ins. long, and covered on the underside with silky, silvery hairs. During spring and early summer, it is lit up with terminal heads of rose-pink, sweetly scented flowers 10/6

„   **striata.**—European Alps. This rare prostrate shrub is seldom seen in British gardens. Its wiry growths carry tufts of oblanceolate leaves and heads of funnel-shaped rose-pink flowers 3/6   5/6

E   „   **tangutica.**—N.W. China. It is a free-grower, attaining a height of 3 ft. or more and as much in width, and has oval, oblong or oblanceolate, 1—3 in. leathery, dark green leaves. The attractive terminal umbels of closely packed, 1 in., rose-purple flowers, white suffused purple within, are borne from March to May. It is often seen labelled D. retusa from which, however, it is quite distinct 7/6   10/6

E **Daphniphyllum macropodum.**—A conspicuous evergreen from Japan, slowly attaining 8 ft., much more in the west. The stalks and midribs of the Rhododendron-like leaves are bright red 3/6   5/6   7/6

Davidia involucrata.—A noble tree from W. China, slow to start, but once it is established reaches a height of 50 ft. or more. Any ordinary soil suits it. The leaves are mulberry-like and scented when bruised. The outstanding feature of the tree consists of two white bracts of unequal size, enveloping the flowers, which develop in May 7/6   10/6

Decaisnea Fargesii.—W. China. A rare shrub, 5—10 ft. high, with pinnate leaves 2 ft. or more in length. The 12—18 in. drooping panicles of flowers are followed by greyish-purple pods of fruit, somewhat like broad beans   ...   2/6   3/6

Dendromecon rigidum.—California. The shrubby poppy thrives best against a south wall, where it will attain 8—20 ft., according to the district. The 2—2½ in. golden-yellow, buttercup-like flowers are freely produced for at least eight months of the year. Unfortunately the length of its life is uncertain and it may not be hardy in midland gardens 5/-   7/6

E **Desfontainea spinosa.**—Chile. This bright green, holly-like shrub, one of the most beautiful of all evergreens, requires a shady, sheltered spot where it soon forms a fine specimen covered with conspicuous red and orange tubular flowers from July to late autumn   2/6   3/6   5/6   7/6

Desmodium penduliflorum. (See **Lespedeza formosa**).   each.

Deutzia corymbosa.—Himalayas. A delightful small shrub with ovate leaves and 2—3 in. corymbs of snow-white hawthorn-scented flowers in July and August. Their beauty is enhanced by prominent yellow anthers   ...   2/6   3/6

   ,,   **discolor major.**—C. & W. China. A grand flowering shrub, 3 ft. high, slightly tender, with large flat milk-white flowers. It requires a sheltered position 2/6

   ,,   **gracilis.**—Japan. A well-known shrub for early forcing. Within reach of the sea, and in sheltered gardens, it forms a bush 3 ft. high. It is not satisfactory inland.   3 in. panicles of pure white flowers are borne in spring   ...   1/6   2/6

   ,,   **kalmiiflora (purpurascens × parviflora).**—A beautiful shrub 3 ft. high. The semi-weeping branches are laden with pink kalmia-like flowers during May. The true plant is offered. D. rosea (gracilis × purpurascens) has previously been distributed for this lovely plant.   2/6   3/6

   ,,   **longifolia.**—Szechuan, China. A unique species, 5—9 ft. high, of erect growth. It should be planted in semi-shade to obtain its full floral beauty. Conspicuous rich rose flowers, 1 in. across are borne during June   1/6   2/6   3/6

   ,,   ,,   **Veitchii.**—This Chinese form has more prominent, rugose leaves and slightly larger, kalmia-like, rose-coloured flowers 2/6   3/6

   ,,   **magnifica (scabra × Vilmorinae).**—A noble shrub, 6—8 ft. high. A beautiful object during June and July with large erect expanded panicles of double white flowers 1/6   2/6

   ,,   **macrocephala.**—Garden origin. A first-rate June-flowering shrub, reaching 5—8 ft. in height. Its erect branches are covered with extra large pure white flowers   1/6   2/6

   ,,   **Monbeigii.**—N.W. Yunnan. This attractive, wiry-branched, semi-pendulous shrub has small oval-lanceolate leaves, glaucous beneath. It grows 3—6 ft. high by as much wide. The numerous clusters, each containing numerous star-like pure white flowers are borne from May to July. A valuable shrub for any garden   1/6   2/6

   ,,   **parviflora.**—N. China, Manchuria. A plant of erect habit, 5 ft. high, carrying 2—3 in. corymbs of white flowers 1/6   2/6

   ,,   **pulchra (taiwanensis).**—A new arching-branched species from the mountains of Formosa, with leathery acuminated grass-green leaves, greyer beneath, and many white flowers during June and July 2/6

   ,,   **purpurascens.**—Yunnan, China. With thin flexible branches and corymbs of large round-petalled white flowers, daintily suffused rich crimson. This choice shrub requires a sheltered position 2/6   3/6

   ,,   **rosea (gracilis carminea) (gracilis × purpurascens)** —A hybrid of compact habit. Its slender semi-pendulous branches are wreathed with numerous bold, frilled, carmine flowers, shading to soft rose, in May   ...   1/6   2/6

   ,,   ,,   **campanulata.**—Garden origin. A good hardy form of rather erect habit, 3—4 ft. high, bearing large, open bell-shaped white flowers in May 1/6   2/6

   ,,   **grandiflora.**—A thin arching branched shrub, 4 ft. high, with 3 in. corymbs of many pink flowers, each ½ in. across, in May and June 1/6   2/6

			each.	

Deutzia scabra (crenata).—Japan, China. The true plant quickly grows 5—8 ft. high and is beautiful from mid-June to mid-July with upright 6 in. leafy panicles of scented Styrax japonicus-like flowers. It has 3—4 in. × 2 in. ovate-lanceolate leaves with upward-pointing teeth ... **2/6 3/6**

,, ,, **candidissima. (Pride of Rochester).**—An old favourite and a strong grower, with pure white double flowers **1/6 2/6**

,, ,, **latiflora.**—A magnificent shrub about 6 ft. high with erect panicles composed of fifteen to twenty single white flowers, each 1 in. or more across, in June ... **2/6 3/6**

,, ,, **longipetala.**—A hybrid of compact habit, 3 ft. high, with crowded panicles of extra large snow-white flowers, each having five long fringed petals and yellow anthers **2/6**

,, ,, **plena (crenata plena).**—Often seen in old gardens. Of upright habit, 5—7 ft. high, with a profusion of double flowers, white inside and rose-purple outside, during June **1/6 2/6**

,, ,, **staphyleoides.**—It grows 3—5 ft. high and has 3—4 in. lanceolate leaves with slender points. The panicles of magnificent, semi-pendulous white flowers, each with ¾ in. furrowed and shallowly serrated petals, are borne from mid-June to mid-July. One of the best shrubs raised during the last ten years **2/6 3/6**

,, **setchuenensis.**—C. & W. China. If planted in semi-shade, this graceful, thin-branching shrub will attain 6 ft. During May and June it freely produces 3—4 in. corymbs of white, ovate-petalled flowers, each ⅝ in. across **2/6**

,, **Sieboldiana.**—Japan. A small shrub of loose habit, rarely more than 3 ft. high. It bears cordate leaves and clusters of elegant small white flowers, in June **1/6 2/6**

,, **Vilmorinae.**—Szechuan, China. Vigorous, attaining 6—9 ft., with large dull-green rough leaves and clusters of fifteen to twenty-five snow-white flowers, 1 in. across. A beautiful shrub, but slightly tender **2/6**

,, **Wilsonii.**—China. A beautiful distinct May-June flowering shrub, 5—8 ft. high, with large corymbose panicles of snow-white flowers, 1 in. across **2/6**

The flowering period of all the **Deutzias** is prolonged if they are planted in semi-shade.

E **Dianella intermedia.**—New Zealand. A herb with 12—18 in. panicles of white flowers, shading to pale blue, each ½ in. across, rising from tufts of sword-like leaves, from July to October. These are succeeded by oblong dark-blue berries hung on thin threads **2/6 3/6**

E ,, **longifolia (revoluta).**—Australia. Leaves 2 ft. or more in length ; the loose panicles of deep blue flowers are followed by light blue ½ in. fruits, in August and September **3/6**

E ,, **tasmanica.**—Tasmania. 1—2 ft. iris-like leaves and 2 ft. panicles of loose bright blue flowers, ¾ in. across, followed by bright blue oblong fruits, which are a conspicuous ornament in autumn **2/6 3/6**

The Dianellas love semi-shade and are usually quite hardy throughout the south and west.

E **Diapensia lapponica obovata.**—A rare suffructicose alpine shrub from the meadows of the mountains of Japan. It forms close tufts 1 in. high but 12 in. or more wide, and is clothed with tiny obovate leaves. The singly borne, ¾ in. pure-white, 5-lobed flowers are held by 1 in. stalks above the foliage, during the summer. A treasure for the Ericaceae border or alpine house ... 3/6   5/6   7/6   10/6   *each.*

Diervilla florida (Weigela rosea).—N. China, Korea. The arching branches during May and June are garlands of deep rose flowers 1/6   2/6

„   „   **candida.**—Compact and upright in habit; wreathed with pure white flowers 1/6   2/6

„   **hybrida Abel Carrière.**—Bright rose, floriferous ... 1/6   2/6

„   „   **Bouquet Rose.**—Large wide satin-rose flowers in early May 1/6   2/6

„   „   **Conquête.**—Extra large rosy-pink flowers ... 1/6   2/6

„   „   **Descartés.**—Dark crimson ; often flowers again in late autumn 2/6

„   „   **Eva Rathke.**—Deep crimson ; a lovely shrub, but a poor grower 2/6

„   „   **Fleur de Mai.**—Carmine ageing to bright pink in early May 2/6

„   „   **Heroine.**—Pale flesh pink 1/6   2/6

„   „   **La Perle.**—Creamy white, suffused rose, throat distinctly marked, unique 2/6

„   „   **Othello.**—Clear pink, very showy; strong growing 1/6   2/6

„   „   **Saturne.**—Carmine red, ageing to bright pink ... 1/6   2/6

„   „   **Styriaca.**—Buds red, opening to bright rose tinged with crimson 1/6   2/6

„   **japonica.**—Japan. Strong-growing with distinct roundish leaves ; flowers rosy pink 1/6   2/6

„   **Middendorffiana.**—N. China. Japan. A beautiful shrub 3 ft. high with loose slender branches and terminal clusters of sulphur-yellow tubular flowers in April and May. It requires a sheltered position 2/6   3/6

Diostea juncea (Baillonia juncea).—Chile & Peru. This curious shrub makes long slender rush-like growths and attains a height of 15 ft. It is semi-weeping in habit and the small flowers, in spikes, are pale lilac with yellow throat. They are very sweetly scented and are borne from early June to late August 2/6   3/6

Dipelta floribunda.—One of China's best gifts to western gardens. It loves semi-shade, is stiff-branched and attains 8—9 ft. It bears fragrant pink tubular flowers, yellow throated, in May and June 3/6   5/6

„   **ventricosa.**—W. China. This species has longer acuminated leaves and 1 in. deep rose, tubular cask-like flowers with orange-coloured throats 3/6   5/6

„   **yunnanensis.**—W. China. A graceful shrub, 5 ft. or more high and as much wide, with opposite, ovate-lanceolate leaves. It bears short clusters of tubular, white suffused rose flowers with orange-coloured throats 3/6   5/6

Diplacus glutinosus. (See **Mimulus glutinosus**).

Disanthus cercidifolius.—Japan. A rare member of the Hamame-   each.
lis order with medium-sized cordate leaves, glaucous
beneath, becoming gorgeously coloured in autumn. The
somewhat insignificant flowers are dark red during
September and October. To appreciate the beauty of
this shrub, one must see the many specimens in the
humid atmosphere of Ireland. It has the distinction
of being the first plant to receive an A.M. on account of
its autumn foliage **3/6   5/6   7/6 10/6**

Discaria Toumatou.—New Zealand. An armed shrub allied to
the Colletias, bearing clusters of small white bell-shaped
flowers below every joint. It requires a sheltered
position and is not generally hardy **5/–**

E **Distylium racemosum.**—A rare evergreen from Japan, with
glossy green leaves and numerous small red flowers during March and April. In the open it attains 3—4 ft., but
10—15 ft. on a sheltered north wall, where it reaches
perfection **3/6   5/6   7/6**

E **Docynia Delavayi.**—W. China. A rare sub-species with
spreading branches armed with 2 in. prongs. The
elliptical-acuminate green leaves are margined with
minute blunt saw-like teeth. This requires a warm
situation to bring out its full floral beauty **3/6   5/6**

E „ **docynioides.**—S.W. China. An uncommon shrub of
spreading habit, 6—10 ft. high, which requires a south
or west wall to bring out its ½—1 in. white pink-tinged
Cydonia-like flowers. The ovate-acuminate leaves,
margined with minute double teeth are brightly
coloured throughout the growing season **3/6   5/6**

E **Drimys andina.**—Chile. This rare miniature shrub is new to
cultivation. It makes growths, 1—3 ins. long, yearly
and these are clothed with 1—3 in. oblanceolate leaves,
beautifully blue-grey beneath. It has not yet flowered   **—   —**

E „ **aromatica.**—Australia. A shrub attaining 5—10 ft.,
according to position, in the south and west. The
branches are dogwood-red and the narrow green leaves
are aromatic. Numerous creamy-white flowers are
produced during April and May **2/6   3/6**

E „ **colorata.**—New Zealand. Quite hardy near the sea and in
sheltered gardens in the milder parts of England, it
ultimately reaches 5 ft. in height. Its leathery, glaucous, ovate leaves are blotched and margined with
red **2/6   3/6   5/6**

E „ **Winteri.**—S. America. Around the south and west coast
it forms a huge bush, 10—15 ft. high, of Rhododendron-
like appearance, with ivory-white fragrant flowers during
May. A noble evergreen thriving with sufficient mois-
ture even on chalky soils **2/6   3/6   5/6**

E „ „ **latifolia.**—To appreciate this handsome evergreen, one must see the specimens in various gardens.
The flowers are much larger than those of the type.
The huge oblanceolate, green leaves are glaucous
beneath and 6—10 ins. long by 2—4 ins. wide **7/6 10/6**

Eccremocarpus scaber.—Chile. This fast-growing climber is   each.
a biennial in cold districts, but in warm gardens and
around the sea coast, it survives for a number of years.
Its growths are clothed with doubly-pinnate, Clematis-
like leaves. From June to October, it produces numerous 1 in. tubular orange-peel-coloured flowers. A
specimen on a sheltered trellis near here, is a splendid
sight every summer **2/6**   **3/6**

Edgeworthia chrysantha (Daphne chrysantha).—Himalayas,
China, Japan. This very hardy and sturdy shrub grows
to about 3 ft. high by 4—5 ft. wide. It should be in a
raised position so that one may enjoy its pendent clusters
of downy chrome-yellow, cowslip-scented, tubular
flowers. It is a fine substitute for the more difficult
Daphne aurantiaca **3/6**   **5/6**

Edwardsia. (See **Sophora**).

Elaeagnus argentea.—N. America. An attractive silvery foliaged shrub with thin erect growths, 4—8 ft. high. The
numerous small silvery-yellow flowers are fragrant during May and are followed by small silvery egg-shaped
fruits. It does best in a semi-shady position. **2/6**   **3/6**

E   „   **macrophylla.**—Japan & Formosa. A useful shrub of
rounded form, 6—10 ft. high, with large grey-green
leaves, conspicuously silvery beneath and effective
swaying in the wind. It bears small clusters of silvery
fuchsia-shaped flowers in October and November   ...   **2/6**   **3/6**

   „   **multiflora.**—China, Japan. Attains a height of about
6 ft., of open spreading growths ; small creamy-white
fragrant flowers during April and May. Attractive from
July to autumn with its heavy crop of oblong deep-orange
fruits **2/6**   **3/6**

Eleutherococcus. (See **Acanthopanax**).

Elliottia paniculata. (See **Tripetaleia paniculata**).

Elsholtzia Stauntoni.—China. A sub-woody shrub, 3 ft. high.
A useful autumnal with showy panicles of purplish-pink
flowers **1/6**   **2/6**

E **Embothrium coccineum.**—Chilian Honeysuckle or Fire Bush.
A tree up to 40 ft. high. This treasure requires a semi-
shady, sheltered position, preferably between evergreens
(rhododendrons) around the south and west coast. The
brilliant orange-scarlet honeysuckle-like flowers are
borne during May. A difficult plant to establish in
many gardens **3/6**   **5/6**   **7/6**

E   „   **longifolium.**—Chile. In most cool lime-free soils it is
easy and free-growing and quickly attains 12—20 ft.
It flowers 5—7 years after planting. It has narrow,
wavy, graceful leaves, 6—9 ins. long and its mass of
fiery flowers are borne from early May to late June.
It was grown in Irish gardens forty or more years ago **10/6** **15/6** **21/-**

E **Empetrum rubrum.**—Falkland Isles. A small spreading shrub,
6—12 ins. high, suitable for the Ericaceae border. The
wiry growths are packed with tiny, linear, grey leaves.
It has not yet flowered **2/6**   **3/6**

Enkianthus campanulatus.—Japan. The Enkianthus is much freer and happier if planted in semi-shade. This species grows 5—8 ft. high, of erect habit, with numerous racemes of bell-shaped creamy-white flowers veined with red. The foliage in autumn makes a glorious display of orange-yellow and fiery red ... ... **2/6**   **3/6**   **5/6**   each.

„   **cernuus.**—Japan. One of the rarest of all shrubs in cultivation. It has tiers of growths and ultimately reaches 4—6 ft. In May and June it bears many 2—3 in. racemes packed with cream-white, fringed flowers. The ¾—1½ in. obovate leaves turn a lively tint before falling. 1938 delivery **7/6**   **10/6**

„   „   **rubens.**—Japan. This superior shrub attains 3—6 ft. according to position. The erect stems, with spreading twiggy growths, bear numerous 3 in. tassels of rich deep red flowers in May and June. Its autumn foliage is also attractive **10/6**   **15/6**   **21/-**

„   **Palibinii.**—Japan. A beautiful compact-growing shrub, 5—8 ft. high. Towards the end of May, it is crowded with 2—4 in. racemes of rich red, bell-shaped flowers. It is one of the best for its glowing autumn tints ...   **10/6**

„   **pallidiflorus (campanulatus albiflorus).**—Japan. An attractive shrub of dense habit, with racemes of conspicuous bell-shaped flowers, pale primrose fading to nearly white. The autumn foliage is golden-yellow   **7/6**   **10/6**

„   **perulatus (japonicus).**—Japan. A rare species, with branches in tiers. It attains 6 ft. in height, bearing clusters of white pitcher-shaped flowers during April. One of the first six shrubs to plant for autumn colour ...   **7/6**   **10/6**

E   „   **quinqueflorus.**—Hong Kong, China. The most striking member of the genus but unfortunately it is only suitable for the south west, Ireland and the west of Scotland. The oval-obovate, long-pointed, leathery, metallic-green leaves are red tinted beneath and 2—4 ins. long. It produces clusters of ½ in. campanulate, bright pink flowers during the spring **10/6**

„   **recurvus.**—Japan. A recently - introduced shrub, 5—10 ft. high and with growths in tiers. Its slender branches are a pleasing sight in May and June, when carrying racemes of bell-shaped, pearl-white tinted pink flowers **5/6**   **7/6**   **10/6**

E **Epigaea asiatica.**—Japan. This treasure grows freely in woodland loam on the north side of a common Rhododendron hedge and hates the sun at any time of the year. From early March to mid-May it is decorated with many urn-shaped, bright rose-coloured flowers and these are protected by the 1½—3 in. hairy, ovate leaves, heart-shaped at the base **2/6**   **3/6**   **5/6**

E   „   **Aurora (repens × asiatica).**—This welcome hybrid, the second generation product of a cross made here in 1931, is intermediate in almost all respects between the parents and combines in one plant the best qualities of both. The tough, undulated, spade-shaped leaves, about 2 × 1½ ins., enhance, but do not hide the clustered buds which from mid-February to late April expand into flowers ½ in. wide, of the clearest dog-rose pink, the tips of the five wide-spreading petals almost carmine in their colouring. The inside of the cylindrical white throat is lined with hairs as in E. repens. 1938 delivery   **7/6**   **10/6**

E Epigaea repens.—The May Flower of North America. This choice creeping shrub forms a mat 6 ins. high. It loves woodland conditions, where it is quite happy. Here it is one of the freest-growing of all dwarf plants. Clusters of white sweet-scented flowers from early March to May   each.   2/6   3/6

E   „   „   **Apple Blossom (rosea).**—This form has rounder and deeper green leaves and its charming pink sweet-scented flowers are larger than those of the type   ...   5/6   7/6

Erica arborea.—Mediterranean region, Caucasus. A beautiful tree heath with greyish leaves, 6—15 ft. high in mild districts. The profusion of white flowers scents the air during March and April 1/6   2/6   3/6

   „   „   **alpina.**—Spain. A valuable form of pyramidal habit, 5—10 ft. high, with bright green foliage and white flowers. The hardiest of the tree heaths, it seldom gets injured by frost 1/6   2/6   3/6

   „   **australis.**—Spain, Portugal. A splendid shrub during April and May when smothered with its bright rose-coloured flowers. Unfortunately it is not suitable for the colder parts, especially the midlands 1/6   2/6

   „   „   **Mr. Robert.**—S. Spain. A worthy free-flowering tree heather with waxy snow-white flowers during April and May. It does better in partial shade. Height and habit similar to type 1/6   2/6   3/6

   „   **carnea.**—C. & S. Europe. Dwarf spreading habit ; covered during February, March and April with deep rosy-red flowers ...   .   9/- & 15/- doz.   1/-   1/6

   „   „   **alba.**—Discarded.

   „   „   **atrorubra.**—An attractive plant, having deep green foliage and dark carmine red flowers. It is the last of the series to flower   ... ...   10/6 & 16/6 doz.   1/-   1/6

   „   „   **Cecilia. M. Beale.**—A distinct improvement on E. carnea alba, stronger growing and of more erect habit. The freely borne flowers are whiter, larger and shown to better advantage...   ... ...   9/- doz.   1/-

   „   „   **C. J. Backhouse**   ⎫
      Creamy white flowers   ⎪
   „   „   **gracilis**   ... ...   ⎪
   „   „   **James Backhouse** ...   ⎪
   „   „   **King George**   ...   ⎪
   „   „   **Mrs. Doncaster** ...   ⎪
   „   „   **pallida**   ... ...   ⎪
   „   „   **Pink Pearl** ... ...   ⎬   9/- & 15/- doz.   1/-   1/6
   „   „   **praecox (rubra)** ...   ⎪
   „   „   **Prince of Wales** ...   ⎪
   „   „   **Queen Mary**   ⎪
   „   „   **Queen of Spain** ...   ⎪
   „   „   **rosea**   ... ...   ⎪
   „   „   **Thomas Kingscote**...   ⎪
   „   „   **Winter Beauty**   ...   ⎭

      Those bracketed are known as the **Backhouse Hybrids.**

   „   **Ruby Glow.**—A splendid addition to an already large family. This flowers at the same time as E. c. atrorubra. Its 6—9 in. growths are packed with carmine, ageing to light red flowers. These look pretty resting on the bronze-green leaves from March to May   10/6 doz.   1/-

each.

Erica Springwood.—Found on Monte Correggio, Italy. This robust-growing Heath annually makes trailing growths 6—12 ins. long. With its freely produced, large, oblong, white bells with yellow-brown anthers, it is an admirable addition to New Year flowering plants. Like the other members of the series, it is quite happy even in chalk soil. It is the purest white dwarf Heath we have **10/6 & 16/6 doz.**   1/—   1/6

„   „   **Pink.**—A seedling form, quite as vigorous as the former. From early January to the end of April, its trailing growths are crowded with beautiful bright rose-pink flowers, with protruding brown anthers **15/— doz.**   1/6

„   **Vivellii.**—Italian Alps. Foliage deep green, becoming bronzy-red in winter. From autumn to January the corolla of the flower is creamy white, the calyx deep carmine-red. Towards March the whole flower becomes vividly suffused brilliant carmine **10/6 & 16/6 doz.**   1/—   1/6

Erica carnea and its many varieties are invaluable for their winter display, when few other hardy flowers are seen. The whole set should be planted to obtain a continuous succession of bloom to fill the floral gap of a twelve months' heather garden. The colour of the flowers varies from light to very dark pink week by week. **E. c. Queen Mary** usually starts flowering the last week of October, to be followed by E. c. praecox. Experience proves that this section is quite at home planted near the sea and they also flourish and flower amazingly on the chalk downs around Salisbury. They are valuable to the apiarist on account of their flowering season.

„   **ciliaris.**—Dorset Heath. This covers a large area of common near Poole Harbour, where it is within reach of the salt air. Its beautiful pitcher-shaped, rosy-red flowers are abundantly produced from June to November. It is not an easy plant to establish in many inland gardens   ...   .   **10/6 doz.**   1/—

„   „   **alba.**—Pitcher-shaped white flowers   **9/— doz.**   1/—

„   „   **globosa.**—A beautiful natural form with grey-green growths and long erect spikes of pale rosy-pink flowers. It continues to flower from early July to autumn frosts   ...   .   **10/6 doz.**   1/—

„   „   **Maweana.**—Found in Portugal. A striking and attractive compact shrub, less than 1 ft. high, smothered with erect spikes of globular gay rosy-crimson flowers from July to the end of November ; a beautiful heather but seldom seen true to name   ...   ...   **12/— doz.**   1/3

„   „   **Mrs. C. H. Gill.**—Of compact habit, 12 ins. high, clothed with grey-green foliage. From June to September, it bears terminal erect crowded spikes of fifteen to thirty-five dark rose-coloured flowers   ...   **12/— doz.**   1/3

„   „   **Stoborough (Metcalfe).**—Known as long ago as 1875 but probably lost through forest fires. This fine form of our Dorset Heath bears numerous terminal tapering racemes of fifteen to twenty-five large flowers, cream-coloured in bud, ageing to pearl-white, from August to late October   ...   .   **12/6 doz.**   1/3

Erica cinerea.—N.W. Europe to Italy. In the south large tracts of barren, dry land are occupied by this species. Its purple blossom during summer and autumn is a magnificent sight ... ... **8/– doz.**   each. **9d.**

,,   ,, **alba.**—Of spreading habit, growing 12—18 ins. high, it is decorated throughout the summer months with 6—9 in. racemes of pure white flowers ... **9/– doz.**   **1/–**

,,   ,,   **minor.**—A tiny compact plant only a few inches high. The many umbels of pure white flowers are borne from early June to late October   **9/– doz.**   **1/–**

,,   ,, **Apple Blossom.**—A new natural form. Foliage light green, flowers white flushed with delicate pink **15/6 doz.**   **1/6**

,,   ,, **atrorubens.**—Possibly the most conspicuous summer and autumn flowering Heather we possess. It is a strong grower, of spreading habit. The 9—12 in. dark green sprays are richly decorated with ruby-red flowers, catching the eye from afar. It should find a place among the first twelve heathers ... **12/6 doz.**   **1/3**

,,   ,, **atrosanguinea.**—Later flowering with darker flowers than the well-known E. c. coccinea and of much dwarfer and more compact habit ... ... **12/6 doz.**   **1/3**

,,   ,, **carnea.**—This choice shrub should be included among the first eighteen Heathers. The profusion of large pale pink flowers resting on the semi-prostrate branches are a delight from early June to autumn frosts ... ... **12/6 doz.**   **1/3**

,,   ,, **C. D. Eason.**—During summer and autumn the sturdy branches are covered with umbels of luminous red flowers. Height about 1 ft. ... ... **15/6 doz.**   **1/6**

,,   ,, **coccinea.**—Of dwarf, compact habit, with very dark foliage. It is one of the most striking of all the heathers with its freely-produced scarlet-red flowers **12/– doz.**   **1/3**

,,   ,, **Frances.**—An effective natural form with dark bronze foliage and abundance of cerise red flowers on 9 in. branches ... ... **10/6 doz.**   **1/–**

,,   ,, **Knap Hill.**—From July to late October the red, suffused rose flowers almost hide the sturdy green growths. Height 9—15 ins. ... ... **15/6 doz.**   **1/6**

,,   ,, **lilacina.**—A distinct form of spreading habit, with bright green foliage. It is covered throughout the summer and early autumn with 6 in. sprays of delicate lilac-coloured flowers ... ... **15/6 doz.**   **1/6**

,,   ,, **Mrs. Dill.**—One of the most charming of all the cinerea section. A pygmy shrub 6 ins. high, of cushion habit, short stubby growths, dark foliage and a profusion of brilliant pink flowers ... ... **15/6 doz.**   **1/6**

,,   ,, **pallida.**—Dark foliage, 4—6 in. sprays of white flowers delicately tinged pale pink ... **10/6 doz.**   **1/–**

,,   ,, **purpurea.**—Deep green foliage, and 6 in. sprays of very dark red flowers. This and E. c. Apple Blossom make a good contrast ... ... **9/– doz.**   **1/–**

,,   ,, **rosea.**—A delightful plant, singly or in mass, smothered with 6 in. sprays of clear rose flowers, and a good grower ... ... **9/– doz.**   **1/–**

each.

Erica cinerea Rose Queen.—A first-rate shrub that has merited its introduction. It has the longest flowering period of all the cinereas and the 6—12 in. sprays of glowing rose-pink flowers are very striking amidst the dense tumbling growths ... ... **12/6 doz.** ... 1/3

„   „   **schizopetala.**—A compact grower, about 1 ft. high with bronze-tinted stems and leaves. The main feature of this plant is the split corolla. It bears numerous light purple flowers and when in bloom may easily be mistaken for a shrubby Thyme. It is of interest to the botanist and collector of the uncommon **2/6**

Erica cinerea and its many natural forms are free-flowering from May until late October and are worthy of wide cultivation.

„   **darleyensis (E. carnea × mediterranea).**—Garden origin. Of cushion-like habit, growing 18 ins. high, this variety is smothered in most seasons from early November till the end of April with rosy bells ; a useful plant, but not so bright in colour as many of the carnea hybrids ... ... **9/– doz.** ... 1/–

„   **hybrida Dawn (Tetralix × ciliaris).**—Natural Hybrid. Forms a thicket of wiry growths 1 ft. high. The umbels of fifteen to twenty-five dark rose flowers are borne on 3 in. erect stems ... ... **10/6 doz.** ... 1/–

„   „   **Gwen.**—Natural Hybrid. A pretty semi-prostrate plant, its young growths copper-coloured. It bears short umbels of pale rose flowers from July to October **9/– doz.** ... 1/–

„   „   **H. Maxwell (Tetralix × ciliaris).**—Natural Hybrid. One of the most useful heathers we possess for dry or moist soils. It is particularly attractive from July to October, carrying many heads of fifteen to twenty-five large cylindrical rose-red flowers well above the foliage **10/6 doz.** ... 1/–

„   **lusitanica (codonodes).**—Spain, Portugal. From Christmas, in mild seasons, until June, this noble tree heather is always a welcomed shrub, especially in March, when the lower branches are white with bloom and the buds pink above them **1/6** 2/6 3/6

„   **Mackayi.**—Connemara & N.W. Spain. Natural Hybrid. A pretty shrub of dwarf habit ; umbels of bright pink flowers during July and August ... ... **9/– doz.** ... 1/–

„   „   **plena (E. Crawfurdii).**—A very pretty shrub from July to September with its mass of full double delicate pink flowers ... ... **9/– doz.** ... 1/–

„   **mediterranea.**—S.W. France, Spain. An erect-growing shrub with slender branches covered with scented bronzy-red bells from March to May. Height 5—10 ft. ... ... **12/6 & 16/6 doz.** 1/3 1/6

„   „   **alba.**—Grows 2—3 ft. high, of compact pyramidal habit, smothered from early February to May with fragrant pure-white flowers. This beautiful shrub grows and blooms freely in the north where summer conditions are much cooler than with us **10/6 doz.** ... 1/–

„   „   **Brightness.**—An ideal compact shrub, 18 ins. high, with grey-green foliage and bright rosy-red flowers from January to April ; much darker if planted in semi-shade ... ... **10/6 doz.** ... 1/–

			each.
Erica	**mediterranea hibernica (glauca).**—W. Ireland. Glaucous grey foliage ; the bells are light grey tinged with rosy-red ; height 2—4 ft. ... ... **9/- doz.**		1/-
,,	,, **hybrida.** (See **darleyensis**).		
,,	,, **superba.**—One of the very best shrubs for the spring garden, of compact habit, 3—4 ft. high by as much wide, becoming smothered from February to April with pink flowers... ... ... **10/6 & 16/6 doz.**	1/-	1/6
,,	,, **W. T. Rackliff.**—It is more compact and much easier to grow than E. m. alba. The larger pure-white bells are carried from January to May ... ... **16/6 doz.**		1/6
,,	**Pageana.**—Native of Heathlands, Caledon, S. Africa. It is advisable to experiment with this outstanding shrub in order to prove its hardiness. Here a 2 ft. specimen is quite happy, planted on the S.W. side of a Rhododendron hedge. From April to June, the compact growths look attractive with the scented, buttercup-yellow, waxy bells	3/6	5/6
,,	**spiculifolia.** (See **Bruckenthalia**).		
,,	**Stuartii (Mackayi × mediterranea).**—A natural hybrid found in Galway in Ireland ; long pinched flowers with deep rose lobes from June to September **9/- doz.**		1/-
,,	**terminalis (stricta.)**—S. Europe. Though shy flowering inland, a beautiful shrub around the coast, flowering from early July to late November ; numerous heads of 4—8 soft rose flowers. Height 3—6 ft. **10/6 doz.**		1/-
,,	**Tetralix.**—A native shrub of rather spreading habit, 9—18 ins. high, with dense heads of four to sixteen cylindrical rose-coloured flowers from June to October ... ... **9/- doz.**		1/-
,,	,, **Lawsoniana.**—Quite a dwarf, of compact habit. It carries heads of nine to eleven pretty pale pink flowers from June to late autumn ... ... **9/- doz.**		1/-
,,	,, **mollis.**—With frosty-grey foliage and growth tips powdery white. Its handsome heads of globose snow-white flowers are borne from June to late October. The true plant is illustrated in A. T. Johnson's book on Hardy Heathers ... ... **9/- doz.**		1/-
,,	,, **Pink Glow.**—This variety is of branching habit, with ash-grey foliage and many loose terminal heads of glowing pink flowers ... ... **10/6 doz.**		1/-
,,	,, **rubra.**—A choice dwarf shrub for autumn, whether planted singly or in mass. The umbels of dark red flowers are borne above the deep ash-grey foliage **9/- doz.**		1/-
,,	,, **Ruby's Variety.**—The dainty cylindrical waxy flowers, on 3 in. stalks, are white, ageing to pale pink. Each bell has a purple lip ... ... **10/6 doz.**		1/-
,,	**umbellata.**—W. Mediterranean Region. A delightful shrub of grey-green appearance, 6—12 ins. high, but much wider. Its many decumbent growths carry tiny leaves and also heads of small pink flowers from April to autumn frosts. It is not hardy in midland gardens	1/6	2/6
,,	**vagans.—Cornish Heath.**—A spreading shrub up to 18 ins. high. The season's growths become leafy racemes from 6—12 ins. long of globular, pinkish rose-coloured flowers from July to October ... ... **9/- doz.**		1/-

each.

Erica vagans alba.—Dense short growths ; a free-flowering white form ... ... **9/– doz.**   1/–

„ „ **carnea.**—A compact shrub with flesh-pink flowers ... ... **9/– doz.**   1/–

„ „ **grandiflora.**—Carries 9—15 in. racemes of rose-coloured flowers from June until the autumn frosts ; very profuse ... ... **9/– doz.**   1/–

„ „ **Lyonesse.**—This charming plant has 4—9 in. sprays of conspicuous pure-white flowers with protruding brown anthers,borne from July to autumn frosts **10/6 doz.**   1/–

„ „ **Mrs. Maxwell.**—One of the finest of nature's gifts in the whole of the Heath family, from the Serpentine district of Cornwall. Its 6—12 in. branches are smothered with deep cerise flowers from July to the end of October ... ... **10/6 doz.**   1/–

„ „ **rubra.**—Many forms are offered under this name. This one has compact semi-prostrate branches, terminating in a leafy raceme 6—9 ins. long and crowded with deep red flowers ... ... **10/6 doz.**   1/–

„ „ **St. Keverne (kevernensis).**—An exquisite flowering shrub with 6—12 in. branches furnished with bright rose-pink flowers from July to the end of October ... ... **9/– doz.**   1/–

„ **Veitchii.**—An accidental hybrid between arborea and lusitanica. The beautifully-scented pinkish-white flowers exhibit characteristics of both species. Height 3—6 ft. **1/6   2/6   3/6**

„ **vulgaris (Calluna vulgaris) (Ling).**—It is reputed to hate limy soils, but it can be found thriving in many places on the chalk downs about Salisbury... ... ... **9d.**

„ „ **alba.**—Better known as the White Heather of Scotland ... ... **9d.**

„ „ „ **pilosa.**—The slender 9—18 in. growths carry grey-green leaves and are thickly set with pure white flowers, from June to autumn **9/– doz.**   1/–

„ „ „ **rigida.**—This accommodating shrub, with rigid bright-green growths, covers and roots into the soil as its grows, ultimately forming a carpet barely 9 ins. high. During the summer and early autumn it is simply white with flowers ... ... **9/– doz.**   1/–

„ „ „ **tenella.**—The slender erect green branches are clothed from end to end with pearl-white flowers from July to October, height 9—15 ins. **9/– doz.**   1/–

„ „ **Alportii.**—A useful autumn-garden plant. Its many tall and erect growths are crowded with crimson flowers, set amidst its dark green foliage **9/– doz.**   1/–

„ „ **aurea.**—During the growing season the short straggly growths are golden-yellow, ageing with the cold winds of winter to brighter gold, tinted with red **9/– doz.**   1/–

„ „ **Co. Wicklow.**—This accommodating Heath is only a few inches high and is of dense, flat habit. It is one of the most pleasing members of the family, having garlands, 3—6 ins. long, of large double clear-pink flowers from July to winter ... ... **12/6 doz.**   1/3

each.

Erica vulgaris cuprea.—This compact-growing plant is very striking in the Heather garden during the winter and spring months. Its pale yellow-growing foliage assumes brilliant copper-bronze and bright red tints. Height 9—15 ins. ...　...　...　...　...　**9/- doz.**　1/-

„　„　**flore pleno.**—Of dwarf spreading habit with deep green foliage. The branches are wreathed from July to the end of September with double pale pink flowers **9/- doz.**　1/-

„　„　**H. E. Beale.**—A grand addition to a large genus, from the New Forest. It is a strong grower of open habit reaching a height of 1—2 ft. The spreading growths are gaily decorated with extra-large double silvery-pink blossoms from early August to late October. One of the first twelve heathers to plant, succeeding even on clay soils　...　**10/6 & 16/6 doz.**　1/-　1/6

„　„　**J. H. Hamilton.**—A new Heather, 12 ins. high but much wider, found on Mt. Maughan, Yorkshire. It has semi-prostrate interlacing growths and is one of the most distinct of the family. From July to winter its slender 3—6 in. twigs are roped with delightful rose-pink, full double flowers ...　...　...　**16/6 doz.**　1/6

„　„　**Kuphaldtii.**—Found by Herr Kuphaldt at Oldenburger Moor, Germany, in 1930. An exquisite Heather about 4 ins. high and 12 ins. or more across. During the summer and autumn it is wreathed with E. vulgaris-coloured flowers and resembles a miniature waterfall　...　...　...　...　...　**9/- doz.**　1/-

„　„　**Serlei.**—In its good form it is the best summer and autumn-flowering white Heather. It is of pyramidal habit and if left unpruned, will attain a height of 3—5 ft. Its feathery branches are a mass of flowers of outstanding whiteness and merit　...　...　...　**10/6 doz.**　1/-

„　„　**tenuis.**—Of semi-prostrate habit with thread-like growths. These are covered during the summer and again in late autumn with purple-red flowers　**9/- doz.**　1/-

„　**Watsonii (E. ciliaris × Tetralix).**—A rare natural hybrid with racemes of pitcher-shaped rose-coloured flowers from July to the end of October ...　...　**9/- doz.**　1/-

„　**Williamsii.**—Discarded as it is not attractive.

Collections of Heathers to flower all the year round can be supplied at **50/-, 70/- & 100/- per 100.**

All Heathers are evergreen and they will grow in most lime-free soils, a few are indifferent to it. It is advisable, however, to work leaf-mould into heavy staples before planting.

Winter-flowering heaths (except tree heaths) should be clipped over immediately after flowering. Summer and autumn ones should not be pruned before March or April. The various hues of foliage and dead flowers harmonize beautifully throughout the winter ; at a distance some might easily be taken for heaths in flower.

See also **Bruckenthalia, Daboecia** and **Phyllodoce.**

Erinacea pungens.—S.E. Europe, N.W. Africa. A spiny compact shrub, not more than 1 ft. high. It requires full sun to produce the blue-grey pea-shaped flowers but unfortunately these are seldom seen, even in the south **3/6　5/6　7/6**

E **Eriobotrya japonica (Loquat).**—A noble large dark green glossy   each.
foliaged shrub or small tree from Japan and China. The
hawthorn-like scented flowers are rarely seen in the
open. Hardy around the south and west coast   ...   3/6   5/6

Erythrina Crista-galli.—Brazil. A sub-shrub requiring a south
or west wall. It bears 3—5 ft. racemes of bright scarlet
sweet-pea-like flowers during the whole of the summer   3/6   5/—

E **Escallonia hybrida Alice.**—This new and distinct shrub grows
3—4 ft. high. Its thin growths are pretty from April
to August, when laden with 3—6 in. spikes of rich rose-
red flowers, held above the 1—2 in. obovate polished
green leaves 1/6   2/6

E   „   „   **C. F. Ball (macrantha × Ingramii).**—This
variety grows to a large bush of branching habit, with
bright carmine-red flowers from May to late autumn ...   1/6   2/6

E   „   „   **Donard Beauty.**—A charming bushy shrub
about 4 ft. high. The slender pendulous branches are
profusely decorated throughout the summer with rich
rose-red flowers 1/6   2/6

E   „   „   **Donard Brilliance.**—The 3—4 ft. open, branching growths are particularly beautiful when laden with
rich, red tinted crimson, flowers from mid-May to July.
Height 6 ft. or perhaps more 2/6

E   „   „   **Donard Gem.**—One of the prettiest of all the
Escallonias. It is a compact grower, 3—4 ft. high. The
short sprays of large pale pink flowers, sweetly scented,
are freely produced in May and June and again in autumn   1/6   2/6

E   „   „   **Donard Seedling (langleyensis × virgata).**—
The semi-weeping growths are studded during June and
July with showy pale pink flowers, fading to white,
delightfully hawthorn-scented 1/6   2/6

E   „   „   **edinensis (rubra × virgata).**—An invaluable
shrub 4—6 ft. high, with thin arching branches wreathed
from end to end with pretty pink flowers during summer   1/6   2/6

E   „   „   **exoniensis (pterocladon × rubra).**—A perfectly
erect-growing shrub that soon forms a windscreen near
the sea. It has glossy green leaves and large panicles of
white, tinted rose, flowers from June to October   ...   1/6   2/6

E   „   „   **Ingramii (macrantha × punctata).**—This
forms a bold evergreen 10 ft. high, with handsome dark
foliage and racemes of large rich red flowers during summer and autumn. Along the coast, or within nine miles
of it, it quickly makes a first-class ornamental hedge or
wind-break 1/6   2/6

E   „   „   **Iveyana (montevidensis × exoniensis).**—
A natural hybrid, in foliage resembling E. exoniensis,
of strong, bushy habit, bearing numerous 6 in. panicles
of many honey-scented, white-tinged pink flowers from
July to autumn. Bees are attracted by its flowers   ...   1/6   2/6

   „   „   **langleyensis (punctata × virgata).**—The 4—6
ft. pendulous branches are laden during June and July
with bright rosy-carmine flowers 1/6   2/6

E   „   „   **Slieve Donard.**—The slender arching branches,
4 ft. or more in length are a pleasing sight from mid-
May to late June and again in autumn. Its flesh-coloured
fragrant flowers age to deep pink 1/6   2/6

each.

E **Escallonia macrantha.**—Chile. A favourite shrub for forming hedges by the seaside. It makes a splendid wall shrub with its large glossy leaves and numerous bright rosy-red flowers from July to November 1/6   2/6

E   „   **montana.**—A small shrub about 18 ins. high, from Chile, suitable for rock gardens. The flowers are deep red, from June to October 1/6   2/6

E   „   **montevidensis.**—A choice species from Montevideo, only hardy in gardens abutting on the sea ; a wall shrub inland. It bears 9—18 in. panicles of large pure-white flowers in autumn 2/6   3/6

E   „   **organensis.**—A rare species from Brazil, of rounded habit, suitable for sheltered gardens in the south-west. It bears rose-pink, wax-like flowers 2/6   3/6

E   „   **revoluta (coquimbensis) (mollis).**—A semi-scandent shrub, 10 ft. or more high, for a south or west wall, with grey-green obovate leaves and flowers a pretty shade of pink in autumn 2/6   3/6

E   „   **rubra (microphylla).**—Chile. A twiggy dense compact small foliaged shrub attaining 3—4 ft., smothered with loose panicles of red flowers during late summer and autumn 1/6   2/6

  „   **virgata (Philippiana).**—A splendid species from Valdivia, of graceful appearance, with small green leaves and abundance of sweet-scented, white star-like flowers from June to September 1/6   2/6

E   „   **viscosa. (glutinosa).**—Chile. A strong-growing, loose-habited shrub with its branches and obovate leaves clammy. The 5—6 in. panicles of white flowers are produced from July to late autumn 2/6

E **Eucryphia cordifolia.**—Chile. Perhaps the most beautiful of all the Eucryphias, though unfortunately tender. The pure white flowers are sweetly scented and borne throughout September and October   ...   **3/6**   5/6   7/6

  „   **glutinosa (pinnatifolia).**—Chile. An erect branched shrub 12—15 ft. high, decorated during August with a profusion of 2 in. wide pure white hypericum-like flowers. The pinnate foliage becomes brightly tinted during late autumn...   ...   ...   **3/6**   **5/6**   7/6   10/6

  „   „   **plena.**—Hort.—Differs from the former in having extra petals, which do not add to the beauty of the flower **3/6**   5/6   7/6

E   „   **intermedia.**—This lovely hybrid of E. lucida and E. glutinosa (pinnatifolia) originated in the garden at Rostrevor House, Co. Down, and has oblong shining leaves which may be either solitary or trifoliate. The flowers, Anemone-like, chalice-shaped, of snowy purity, are almost 2 ins. wide and appear in quantity in late August and September, borne in opposite pairs on short stiff stalks from the leaf axils, their broad and overlapping petals crowned by the galaxy of pink-tipped thread-like stamens radiating from the heart. It was deservedly awarded an A.M. on September 1st, 1936 and it is a fitting memorial to a famous Irish Gardener and his garden. There is a good illustration in The Gardeners' Chronicle for September 12th, 1936 (page 190). Previously distributed as E. Rodgersii...   ...   .   7/6 to 21/-

E **Eucryphia lucida (Billardieri).**—Tasmania. A slender quick-   each.
      growing species ultimately attaining 10 ft. The oblong
      leaves are dark green and glossy, the flowers white and
      cup-shaped, filled with pink anthers. The refined
      beauty of this shrub and the almond scent of its many
      flowers combine to place it amongst the most beautiful,
      and flowering in August, the most valuable we possess 5/6   7/6 10/6

E   „   „   **Milliganii.**—Tasmania. This rare compact al-
      pine form is much smaller in all its parts than the type.
      It is a slower grower, making not more than 3—6 ins. of
      growth yearly   ...   .   15/6 21/—

E   „   **Moorei.**—Tasmania. A rare small tree of elegant appear-
      ance with branches in tiers, furnished with pinnate
      leaves composed of eleven to thirteen leaflets, glaucous
      beneath. Many 1—1½ in. saucer-shaped white flowers
      are produced in the leaf axils during the autumn. It
      requires a warm sheltered position   ...   ...   10/6 15/6 21/—

E   „   **nymansay.**—This distinguished natural hybrid between
      E. glutinosa and E. cordifolia appeared at Nymans,
      Sussex. More vigorous than either parent and more
      vertical in growth it promises to make a fine tree. The
      foliage suggests E. glutinosa but is evergreen, whilst
      the flowers combine the merits of both parents. No
      good garden should exclude this bonny foundling 5/6   7/6 10/6
          The **Eucryphias** love woodland conditions in lime-
      free soils.

E **Eugenia apiculata (Myrtus Luma).**—Chile. A particularly
      handsome shrub or small tree for the south-west. It
      develops rapidly, its bark is cinnamon-red, its leaves
      dark and shining, whilst its white flowers scent the air
      from July to September 2/6   3/6

E   „   **Chequen.**—Mountains and woods, Chile. An uncommon
      hardy aromatic shrub of compact habit and attaining
      8—15 ft. Its grey-brown branches are densely clothed
      with opposite ½—1½ in. bullate, ovate-acute, wavy
      leaves, olive green above, paler beneath. During the
      summer, it produces many globose pure white flowers,
      each ¾—1 in. in diameter. Previously distributed as
      Raphithamnus chilensis 2/6   3/6

   Euonymus alatus.—A slow-growing stiff-branched shrub from
      Japan and China, covered with corky wings. The
      medium-sized leaves change in autumn to pink and
      crimson. One of the best of autumn shrubs   2/6   3/6   5/6

      „   „   **apterus (subtriflorus).**—C. & W. China. This
      choice variety has spreading branches and is of looser
      habit, growing a few feet high but much wider. The
      leaves are thinner but quite as beautiful during the
      autumn as those of E. alatus 3/6   5/6

      „   „   **coloratus.**—This seedling form is of upright
      habit. The bronzed growing leaves take on deep red and
      scarlet tints 2/6   3/6   5/6

      „   **Bungeanus.**—N. China, Manchuria. An uncommon
      shrub with slender dark branches, ultimately reaching
      10 ft. or more in height. In most seasons the large ovate
      pointed leaves are richly coloured. The pale yellow
      fruits, tinged with pink, are not borne regularly 3/6   5/6

Euonymus europaeus.—Europe to W. Asia. The native Spindle wood of the hedgerow, effective in late autumn with its mass of pink fruits and orange seeds ... ... 1/6   each. 2/6   3/6

    ,,   ,,   **aldenhamensis.**—A fine free-fruiting form ...   2/6   3/6

    ,,   ,,   **atropurpureus.**—About 5 ft. high and erect in habit, with dark purple-growing foliage. It is conspicuous in autumn with its glowing scarlet tints ...   2/6   3/6

    ,,   ,,   **fructu albo.**—The white fruiting form attractive in autumn long after the leaf fall 2/6   3/6   5/6

    ,,   ,,   **intermedia (macrophylla).**—Previously distributed as E.c. fructu coccineo. This upright-growing shrub, 4—7 ft. high, should be among the first twelve fruiting ornamentals. The rigid branches are a perfect sight when carrying the extra-large, rose-red fruits, which age to brilliant red and are retained long after the 4 in. ovate-elliptical leaves have dropped. Cut sprays placed in water will last six weeks or more ... 2/6   3/6   5/6

    ,,   **Farreri (Farrer species No. 708).**—A Chinese trailing species that barely rises one inch from the ground ...   2/6

E   ,,   **grandiflorus.**—N. India, W. China. An uncommon evergreen probably not more than 5 or 7 ft. high in most gardens. Its lanceolate or elliptical deep green leaves are 2—5 ins. long. During May and June it bears groups of 4-petalled, 1 in. primrose-yellow flowers, followed later by red and black fruits 7/6   10/6

    ,,   **lanceifolius.**—A handsome and distinct semi-evergreen laurel-like species from China. A proportion of its foliage becomes gold and crimson tinted in autumn—fruits bright rose, very fine and decorative 3/6   5/6

    ,,   **latifolius.**—S. Europe, W. Asia. A spreading shrub, 10—15 ft. high. One of the most beautiful subjects in autumn with its large dark red leaves and rosy-red fruits hanging on 3 in. threads long after the leaves drop 2/6   3/6   5/6

E   ,,   **nanus.**—A delightful small shrub 2 ft. high, from the Caucasus, decorated in summer with pretty pink fruits, and is best in semi-shade 1/6   2/6

    ,,   **oxyphyllus.**—Japan, Korea. This distinct rarity is a fast grower quickly reaching 8—12 ft. It is one of the very best for the autumn garden, with its mass of crimson fruits and blood-red ovate-oblong, long-pointed leaves 3/6   5/6   7/6

    ,,   **pauciflorus.**—Manchuria, Korea, N. China. A rare shrub probably growing to 8 ft. or more in height. The current season's shoots are dogwood-red, ageing to light brown the second year. Its long-pointed obovate leaves assume buff-yellow, pink and crimson tints. The fruits borne this year for the first time, are bright rose, tinted crimson 3/6   5/6

E   ,,   **pendulus.**—Himalaya. A handsome species forming a small tree. During spring the attractive young foliage is crimson. It requires a mild situation. Previously distributed as E. fimbriatus, which is a deciduous species 3/6   5/6

    ,,   **phellomanus.**—Kansu & Shensi, China. An exceedingly rare shrub, about 6 ft. high, with corky-winged branches. Its leaves are similar in outline, but much larger, than those of E. alatus and they colour well every autumn. The fruits are rose-red 5/-   7/6

Euonymus planipes.—A worthy species from Japan, forming a large bush of upright habit, 6—10 ft. high. It is conspicuous in autumn with its large magnificently-coloured leaves and numerous rosy-red fruits suspended on 3 in. threads ... ... 2/6 3/6   each. 5/6 7/6

E „ **radicans.**—Japan, Korea. This forms a thick evergreen mat, useful for covering bare places in the shade or sun. It is also good as a climber on north walls 1/6 2/6

E „ „ **coloratus.**—A choice plant worthy of every garden. Its trailing growths, 2 ft. or more in length, are clothed with large ovate evergreen leaves. From October to April they are handsomely coloured from the suffusion of the dark crimson reverse. The veins are pale yellow, pink and crimson tinted 2/6 3/6

E „ „ **minimus (Kewensis).**—A tiny-leaved, compact creeping plant under 3 ins. high, but given some support it will climb several feet. It is useful for the rock garden 1/6 2/6

„ **sanguineus.**—China. A choice shrub of open habit, with dark red wood. The large leaves are dark green above, dark crimson beneath, assuming in autumn a riot of vivid crimson and scarlet tints ; fruits dark red. One of the most beautiful of autumn ornamentals ... 2/6 3/6 5/6

„ **Sieboldianus.**—China and Japan. An exceedingly rare species, 6—10 ft. high, with slightly corky branches clothed with 4—6 in. elliptical-oblong, net-veined, serrated leaves which become richly coloured every autumn. From August to December, it carries ribbed, obovoid, red-crimson fruits 7/6

E „ **Wilsonii.**—A rare evergreen shrub from China, proving quite hardy in the open border ; fruits hedgehog-like, seeds yellow coated 3/6 5/6

„ **yedoensis.**—Japan, Korea, China. An upright-growing shrub 5—10 ft. high, pretty in autumn with its brightly coloured foliage and wealth of rosy-red fruits, retained long after the foliage drops 2/6 3/6 5/6

„ „ **Koehneanus.**—C. China. This excellent form is quite as free-growing as the type. The numerous rose-crimson fruits, with orange seeds, hang long after the beautifully coloured obovate-oblong leaves have dropped 7/6
The deciduous **Euonymus** are also known as Spindle-woods and occupy a high position among fruiting and autumn-colouring shrubs. They will thrive in a variety of soils, including those containing lime.

E **Eupatorium micranthum (Weinmannianum).**—Mexico. A compact and rapid-growing evergreen, 3—5 ft. high, suitable for seaside gardens or sheltered corners inland. Large flat corymbose heads of small white sweetly-scented flowers are borne from August to November 1/6 2/6

Euphorbia sikkimensis.—China. A choice sub-shrub, dying down in the winter, for a warm corner. The annual 3—6 ft. growths are densely clothed with brilliantly coloured, ageing to light green, lanceolate leaves. It is attractive from spring until the autumn frosts 3/6

E „ **Wulfenii.**—Dalmatia. An attractive shrub either in sun or semi-shade ; long narrow bluish leaves and large heads of many small green-yellow flowers from January to May 2/6 3/6

Exochorda Giraldii.—W. China. Of bushy, rather upright   each.
habit, 6—8 ft. high. The young foliage is prettily tinged
with pink and with age the leaf stalks become red.
Racemes of 1½ in. flowers are borne in May 3/6
    „   „   **Wilsonii.**—C. China. This species grows 8—12 ft.
high, and as much in width. It is of a compact branching habit, carrying numerous 6 in. racemes of pure-white
delicately almond scented flowers in May 3/6
    „   **Korolkowii.**—A distinct erect-growing species from
Turkestan, attaining 8—12 ft. ; 4 in. racemes of flowers
in mid-April 2/6   3/6
    „   **macrantha (Korolkowii × racemosa).**—A hybrid
growing 9—12 ft. high with many showy 4 in. racemes of
six to ten pure white flowers. It is one of the most beautiful of spring-flowering shrubs 3/6   5/6
    „   **racemosa.**—C. China. Very bushy in habit. The
branches bend with the wealth of white flowers in May.
Commonly known as the Pearl Bush 2/6   3/6
E **Fabiana imbricata.**—Chile. An evergreen heath-like branching
shrub, 6—10 ft. high, quite at home around the south
and west coasts in semi-shade. It is wreathed from
early May to late summer with narrow tubular white
flowers 2/6   3/6
Fagus Engleriana.—A rare fast-growing species from W. China.
The large young leaves are bluish, ageing to pale green
above and glaucous beneath, fading again to deep yellow
in autumn 5/6   7/6   10/6
    „   **sylvatica.**—The native common Beech 1/6   2/6   3/6
    „   „   **atropurpurea Riversii.**—It is unfortunate that
inferior purple-leaved forms are made to do justice for
this beautiful richly-coloured, broad-leaved tree 3/6   5/6   7/6   10/6
E **Feijoa Sellowiana.**—Brazil. Foliage deep green, silvery beneath.
It bears attractive 2 in. flowers with many protruding
crimson stamens, during late summer and autumn. It is
usually planted against a south or west wall, but noble
specimens growing in chalk soil can be seen in the open 2/6   3/6   5/6
Fendlera rupicola.—S.W. United States. A twiggy-branched
shrub, slowly reaching 3 ft. The white rose-tinted
flowers are borne during May and June. A satisfactory
shrub if grown on a south wall 3/6   5/6
Forsythia Giraldiana. Farrer species 388. An uncommon
slender, spreading shrub, 5—8 ft. high and as much wide.
The many dainty bell-shaped yellow flowers are produced
before those of F. ovata and are followed by bronze-tinted,
ovate-acuminate leaves 2/6   3/6
    „   **intermedia (suspensa × viridissima).**—A shrub
6—9 ft. high, with small clusters of golden-yellow flowers
in late March 1/6   2/6
    „   „   **primulina. (Rehder's Manual of Trees and
Shrubs).**—This splendid shrub makes annual growths
3—7 ft. high and they are especially attractive during
March and April with their dense large lemon-yellow
flowers, with revolute lobes 2/6   3/6
    „   „   **spectabilis.**—A highly desirable shrub of rampant
growth worthy of any garden. The extra large flowers
are so densely borne that a specimen makes a cloud of
golden yellow during March and April. Height 6—10 ft. 1/6   2/6

		each.	

Forsythia intermedia vitellina.—Strong and erect in habit, it produces a mass of deep yellow flowers during April ... 1/6 2/6

„ **japonica.**—Japan. A rare shrub, new to cultivation, which may not grow more than 4 ft. high. The elliptical acuminate leaves are 2—4 ins. long and half as much wide and have four or more pairs of prominent branching veins. It has not yet flowered 7/6

„ **ovata.**—Korea. The best form is compact-growing, seldom more than 4 ft high and it is probably the prettiest of the family. The branches bear charming campanulate bright yellow, scented flowers during February and March, even in severe weather 2/6 3/6

„ **suspensa.**—China. A first-rate spring-flowering shrub for training on a wall or allowed to ramble at will in the open ; flowers golden-yellow at the end of March ... 1/6 2/6

„ „ **Sieboldii.**—Introduced from Japan in 1833. Of much bushier habit and not so tall-growing, with pendulous branches reaching to the ground. Its conspicuous golden-yellow flowers were much admired when exhibited at Vincent Square in April, 1935 ... 1/6 2/6

Fothergilla Gardenii (alnifolia).—Virginia to Georgia. Introduced in 1765. A slow-growing twiggy-branched shrub of compact habit, 3 ft. high, bearing terminal spikes of fragrant white flowers on naked wood during March and April. The alder-like leaves assume dark red and fiery-scarlet tints and are retained for many weeks during autumn 2/6 3/6 5/6

„ „ **glaucophylla.**—Introduced from Georgia. An uncommon small shrub for the Ericaceae border, woodland walks, etc. The ovate-oval leaves are conspicuously blue-green above and blue-grey beneath. They are covered on both sides with minute hairs and are crowned with 4—7 shallow or deep dents. Its spikes of white, sweet-scented flowers and its autumn tints are quite equal to those of the former 5/-

„ **major.**—Georgia. Introduced 1780. This rare shrub of upright habit attains a height of 5—9 ft. and is handsomely clothed with oval-obovate or cordate leaves. These are blue-grey beneath and for many weeks during the autumn, assume brilliant yellow tints. The numerous, erect, cylindrical spikes of white, sweet-scented flowers are larger than those of F. monticola. During the growing season, it closely resembles Parrotiopsis Jacquemontiana 10/6

„ **monticola.**—N. Carolina to Alabama. Introduced 1899. This attractive shrub, 3—5 ft. high, and as wide, should be found in every garden. Beautiful in spring with its cream-coloured burnet flowers and in summer with its fine mulberry or hazel-like leaves, glaucous beneath, autumn brings its climax. It is then and for many weeks a wonder of sunset shades in orange, scarlet and crimson ... ... 5/6 7/6 [10/6

The **Fothergillas** dislike heavy soils. They grow freely in sandy loam and preferably in semi-shade.

Fremontia californica.—A semi-evergreen from California, quickly attaining 10—15 ft. or more, of pyramidal habit. The numerous bright yellow flowers, borne from May to October are 2½ ins. wide. This beautiful shrub is quite hardy in sheltered gardens in the milder parts of England. A poor soil is recommended to produce short growths, and consequently more abundant flowering **5/- 7/6**

                                                   each.

E Freylinia cestroides.—S. Africa. It has narrow foliage and small orange-yellow scented flowers in loose panicles in autumn ; only suitable for Devon, Cornish and similar gardens **2/6 3/6**

Fuchsia magellanica (macrostemma).—Peru, Chile. A beautiful summer and autumn flowering shrub with bright scarlet calyx and purple petals. The type of the garden race **1/6 2/6**

    „   „   **corallina.**—(Garden Origin). A form with attractive leaves and showy flowers with bright red sepals and purple petals. Few finer wall plants exist **1/6 2/6**

    „   „   **gracilis.**—A beautiful shrub from July till autumn frosts defeat it. The 3—5 ft. elegant branches are loaded with red and purple flowers ... ... **1/6 2/6.**

    „   **Riccartonii.**—Hybrid. The hardiest of all Fuchsias and probably the most attractive late summer and autumn-flowering ornamental we have. It is used as a boundary hedge in many places in the south and west of England and in Ireland. It is a magnificent sight with its mass of pendent crimson-red and purple flowers   **12/6 to** **1/6 2/6** **21/- doz.**

E Galax aphylla.—N. America. An elegant, dwarf, very hardy shade-loving herb with bright green cordate leaves, becoming towards autumn and remaining until spring a dark bronze, changing ultimately to bright crimson. It bears spikes of many small white flowers on 12—18 in. stalks from June to the end of August ... ... **1/6 2/6.**

E Garrya elliptica.—California. In its male form, a beautiful shrub for seaside gardens ; inland it requires shelter or the protection of walls. The foliage resembles that of the evergreen oak and the showers of drooping catkins, 9—15 ins. long, are at their best in mid-winter **2/6 3/6 5/6**

E   „   **macrophylla.**—Mexico. One of the most attractive evergreens. It forms a bush 10 ft. × 8 ft. The large oblong leaves are lighter green, grey beneath. It is rather tender in its youth and the flowers have little beauty **5/- 7/6**

E   „   **Thuretii.**—Hybrid. A quick-growing evergreen, hardy in the south and west, of upright habit, with large oblong dark green glossy leaves. Very shy flowering **2/6 3/6**

E Gaulnettya Wisleyensis (Gaultheria × Pernettya).—Wisley. A bushy shrub growing 1½—2½ ft. high, with the previous year's growths packed with 1½—2½ in. racemes, each of 6—15 pearl-white lily-of-the-valley-like flowers from early May to June. The large fruits are purple-black. Seedlings have reverted **7/6**

E **Gaultheria adenothrix.**—Introduced in 1915. We are indebted
to Japan for this dainty 6—12 in. shrub, ideal for the
Ericaceae border or alpine house. The zig-zag short
growths are furnished with dense leathery 1—1½in.
ovate-pointed dark green leaves. Many nodding,
white, suffused pink, globe-shaped flowers, almost ½ in.
wide and held on ½—¾ in. stalks, are borne from April
to September and are followed by hairy, crimson fruits 2/6   each.   3/6   5/6

E   „   **antipoda.**—Tasmania, New Zealand. A very hardy,
erect, compact shrub, 1—2 ft. high. It is clothed with
½ in. brown-green, orbicular leaves. The ends of the
branches carry 2—3 in. erect panicles of many pearl-
white flowers and these are succeeded by red or pearl-
white fruits 2/6   3/6   5/6

E   „   **caudata.**—W. China. The thick arching branches attain
3—5 ft. and carry bold, reticulated, ovate-acuminate,
olive-green leaves, neatly serrated and glaucous beneath.
Many 1—1½ in. racemes of 9—13 small, globose, green-
white flowers are borne in the leaf axils during May and
June. It is not hardy in the midlands 10/6

E   „   **Cumingiana.**—Formosa. This rare species is new to
cultivation and makes a pleasing shrub 9—15 ins. high.
It has thin, arching, zig-zag, red growths, neatly furnished
with leathery, ovate, long-pointed, glossy green leaves,
1—2½ ins. long. The many 1 in. racemes of 3—7 pretty
bell-shaped, deeply-lobed, green-white crimson flushed,
¼ in. flowers are borne from early June to autumn and
followed by peppercorn-like, chocolate-red fruits.
It will not prove hardy in the midland counties   ...   7/6

E   „   **cuneata.**—A choice compact species, 9 ins. high, from
China, with reddish stems and pale green polished
leaves. The 3 in. sprays of small lily-of-the-valley-like
flowers are succeeded by pure white fruits 2/6   3/6

E   „   **depressa.** — New Zealand. One of the gems of this
beautiful genus. The close tufts of short, erect, wiry
stems are densely clothed with small orbicular crenulated leaves, dark red beneath. Its tiny white flowers
are followed by numerous ½ in. bright red fruits   2/6   3/6   5/6

E   „   „   **fructu albo.**—Similar to the former but with ½ in.
pure white fruits 3/6   5/6

E   „   **depressa** × **Pernettya macrostigma.**—Bigeneric
Hybrid. A fascinating little shrub, probably not more
than 6 ins. high, with erect thread-like stems carrying
tiny, linear, bronze-red leaves. The white pernettya-
like flowers are followed by small ridged fruits, held in
fleshy calyces 7/6

E   „   **fagifolia (oppositifolia × antipoda).**—New Zealand.
This choice natural hybrid grows 1½—2 ft. high and is
densely clothed with ¼—½ in. orbicular, crenulated
leaves, polished on both sides. Its tiny flowers are
followed by white or red fruits. It might easily be mistaken for a small Nothofagus 2/6   3/6

E   „   **fragrantissima.**—India, Malaya. An uncommon species
having red stems and oblong dark green leaves, grey
beneath. The revolute margins have wide shallow
teeth. The short axillary racemes of drooping white
flowers are followed by pearl-white or pale blue fruits ...   5/-

E   „   **furiens.** (See **Pernettya ciliaris**).

E **Gaultheria Griffithii.**—Himalayas. Of drooping habit, 3—4 ft. each.
high. The oblong-acuminated light green leaves, paler
beneath, have shallow saw-like double teeth. It bears
many short racemes of small lily-of-the-valley-like
flowers. In our climate the fruits rarely mature ... 7/6

E „ **hispida.**—New Zealand. A choice species of erect habit,
1—2 ft. high with leaves 1—2½ ins. long and dark green
turning bronzy-red throughout the winter. It is pretty
in late summer with its many white fruits 2/6 3/6

E „ **Hookeri.**—Himalayas. A noble evergreen shrub, 2—3 ft.
high, with large deep green reticulated leaves and numerous white lily-of-the-valley-like flowers ; quite hardy
planted under high evergreens in the south and west ... 5/- 7/6

E „ **humifusa (myrsinites).**—A dwarf and compact little
rarity from British Columbia, seldom more than 1 in.
high, with small round wavy leaves. The campanulate,
white suffused pink flowers are succeeded by scarlet
fruits... ... ... 3/6 5/6

E „ **Merrilliana.**—Formosa. A rare species, recently introduced to cultivation, which grows 6 in. high and 18 ins.
or more wide. Its dense wiry stems carry ½—1 in. oval-
obovate, leathery, shining leaves, with few conspicuous
red veins beneath. It is one of the handsomest of the
genus with its large white or pink fruits 7/6

E „ **Miqueliana.**—A compact-growing shrub from Japan, under
1 ft. high, with pale green leaves and round white flowers.
It bears in quantity pure white corrugated fruits during
July and August. Previously distributed as G. pyro-
loides 1/6 2/6 3/6

„ **moupinense.** (See **Vaccinium moupinense**).

E „ **nummularioides.**—Himalayas. A pretty creeping shrub
for clothing banks or flat spaces, given shade and moisture. The stems, as well as the underside of its cordate
leaves, are clothed with brown hairs. The small pink
flowers from every leaf axil are followed by conspicuous
black fruits 1/6 2/6

E „ „ **nummularifolia (minor).**—Himalayas, W. China.
This distinct form has small leaves, longer growths
and redder hairs. It is also prostrate and in spite of
its refusal to flower with us, is one of the most attractive
of this genus 2/6 3/6

E „ „ „ **minuta** F. 2522.—W. China. This neat
and attractive member has thread-like, brown, hairy
growths and tiny ovate-elliptical, spine-tipped green
leaves and it lies flat on the ground like Mitchella
repens. The many chocolate, red-tinged, lily-of-the-
valley-like flowers are borne singly, in the axils of the
leaves, from June until October 2/6 3/6

E „ **oppositifolia.**—New Zealand. A rarity not generally
hardy. The terminal 6 in. panicles of twenty to forty
white flowers are succeeded by as many showy white
fruits. The polished green leaves are invariably opposite 2/6 3/6

E „ **ovatifolia.**—British Columbia. A charming small species
with short procumbent hairy branches and pale green
leaves. Its pink-tinted flowers in May are followed by
flattish bright red fruits. It is illustrated in Stewardson
Brown's Alpine Flora of the Canadian Rocky Mountains 2/6 3/6

E **Gaultheria procumbens.**—N. America. A splendid carpeting each.
shrub in shade, under 6 ins. high. Its leaves are dark
green turning to reddish in winter. Its many nodding
pink flowers during July and August are followed by
bright red fruits during autumn and winter 1/6 2/6

E „ **pyrolaefolia.**—Sikkim. Hooker 1849. This little treasure forms a mat by producing underground stolons.
The 1 in. obovate-round, reticulated, bright green,
serrated leaves are borne singly or in whorls, on 1—3 in.
stems. Leafy 1 in. racemes of tiny pale pink egg-shaped
flowers are borne from mid-May to July. It may easily
be mistaken for Salix reticulata. Previously distributed
as G. reticulata 5/-

E „ **rupestris.**—New Zealand. A choice shrub, 9—18 ins.
high, with short, spreading, thread-like growths. The
ovate leaves, closely set, are variable in size and are
blotched with red on both sides 3/6 5/6

E „ **Shallon.**—N. America. This forms a dense thicket up to
5 ft. high. The leaves are broadly ovate, dark green, and
the pretty pinkish egg-shaped flowers in May are
followed by pleasantly-flavoured purple fruits. One of
the few shrubs to enjoy themselves under the drip and
shade of high trees 1/6 2/6

E „ **sinensis (Species K.W. 8562).**—One of Kingdon Ward's
best finds. It forms a compact shrub 6 ins. high and
18 ins. or more wide and its slender dense stems carry
pleasing green, ½ in. obovate, minutely toothed leaves.
It bears an abundance of ¼ in. globose-campanulate,
deeply lobed white flowers, these followed by ½—¾ in.
fig-shaped, saxe-blue fruits 2/6 3/6 5/6

E „ „ Forms with pink and white fruits ... ...   — —

E „ **tetramera.**—S. & W. China & Tibet. A pleasing compact
shrub seldom exceeding 2 ft. in height, although it grows
to 4 ft. in width. It has dense, dark green netted leaves
and numerous small white flowers. During late summer
and autumn, its branches bear pear-shaped, light blue or
violet-coloured fruits. Previously distributed as G.
Forrestii but this plant is not yet in commerce ... 2/6 3/6

E „ **thibetica (Species K.W. 6845).**—This treasure grows into
a tuft 6 ins. high. Its thread-like stems are clothed with
tiny, linear, crenulated and polished leaves not more
than 1/16 in. apart. The ¼ in. chocolate-red, bell-shaped
flowers, held in green calyces, are succeeded by violet blue
fruits 7/6 10/6

E „ **trichophylla.**—Himalayas. A charming low evergreen,
4 ins. high, quickly forming large mats. It has tiny
leaves and single pinkish bell-shaped flowers. The form
offered has large bright blue fruits 1/6 2/6 3/6

E „ **Veitchiana.**—C. China. Under ideal woodland conditions, this beautiful shrub will grow to 3 ft. high and as
much through. Its large oblong leaves and crowded
racemes of white flowers are followed by abundance of
bright blue fruits 2/6 3/6

E **Gaultheria Wardii.**—S.E. Tibet. A most distinct and attractive   each. species for sheltered gardens, where it will grow to a height of 3 ft. or more. The elliptical-lanceolate, long-pointed, grooved leaves and the stems have dense light brown hairs. The racemes of pitcher-shaped white flowers are borne on the previous year's growths and are followed by blue fruits covered with white bloom   3/6   5/6

E   „   **yunnanensis (Franchet). (G. laxiflora. Diels).**—An uncommon shrub of elegant arching habit, 2—4 ft. high, but it is not so hardy as many of the other members of the family. The alternate leaves, 3—4 ins. long, are drawn out to a long point. The short racemes of loose bell-shaped, green-white flowers are borne at the ends of the shoots in August and September 10/6

    All the **Gaultherias** are free-growing if planted in semi-shade. The best home for them is along woodland walks, in lime-free soils.

Gaya Lyallii. (See **Hoheria Lyallii**).

Gaylussacia baccata (resinosa).—N. America. A rare shrub, 3—5 ft. high. The obovate green leaves are distinct in having numerous prominent resin dots beneath ; racemes of six to eight pale red flowers in June 5/-   7/6

E   „   **brachycera.**—Pennsylvania to Georgia. A rare, pleasing, small shrub under 1 ft. high. The young box-like leaves are vivid crimson, ageing to dark shining green. The cylindrical contracted flowers are white striped with pink and are borne during May and June. It loves a semi-shady position in the south 3/6   5/6

  „   **frondosa (glaucum).**—U.S.A. A choice slender-branched shrub a few feet high. The young growths and obovate leaves are glaucous, becoming conspicuous bluey tinted. 2—3 in. racemes of small bell-shaped flowers are borne in June and July 7/6   10/6

  „   **ursina.**—N. & S. Carolina. A great favourite for the autumn garden. Of open branching habit, 4—7 ft. high, with 2—4 in. obovate-oval leaves. Numerous showy campanulate milk-white, red-tinged flowers are produced at the ends of the branches from early May to late June 5/-   7/6

    All the **Gaylussacias** love woodland conditions in lime-free soils, and are unequalled during autumn and winter for their gorgeous foliage.

EC **Gelsemium nitidum.**—A choice slender climber from N. America, that needs a wall in semi-shade. It bears 2 in. oblong shining green leaves and sweet-scented yellow jasmine-like flowers in Spring 3/6

Genista (See also **Cytisus**).

  „   **aethnensis (Etna Broom).**—Sicily. A fast-growing hardy graceful shrub 10—15 ft. high. The rush-like growths in July and August are covered with a cloud of golden yellow pea-shaped flowers 1/6   2/6   3/6

  „   **anxantica.** (See **G. tinctoria anxantica**).

  „   **cinerea.**—S. W. Europe. Attains 5—8 ft. The long silky twigs are wreathed with bright yellow flowers from July to September. A rare and choice shrub. This and G. virgata were the two most outstanding shrubs at Wisley last June and July 3/6

each.

Genista dalmatica.—A rare alpine shrub, 4—9 ins. high, from Dalmatia. The dense tufts of gorse-like growths are smothered in June and July with racemes of golden-yellow flowers 2/6

„ **germanica.**—Europe. An attractive small shrub 2—3 ft. high, of open habit, armed with small spines and bearing numerous 2 in. racemes of yellow flowers in June   ...   2/6

„ **hispanica (Spanish Gorse).**—Rarely growing more than 2 ft. high and of rounded cushion form. It is hidden with bright yellow flowers in May and June ; indispensable and suitable for many positions 1/6   2/6

„ **januensis (triquetra of Waldstein).**—Italy & S.E. Europe, 1826. An ancient but ideal prostrate shrub for a pan in the alpine house or for a ledge on the rock garden. Its triangular growths carry many bright yellow flowers during May and June 2/6   3/6

„ **pilosa.**—Europe. It seldom exceeds 4 ins. in height and is an ideal shrub for the rock garden or for crazy pavings, etc. The thread-like growths, densely packed with tiny leaves and green bracts, lie flat on the ground and the rich yellow flowers are freely borne during May and June 1/6   2/6   3/6

„ **radiata.**—C. & S. Europe. An uncommon compact shrub with spike-like growths, distinctly jointed. Terminal heads of deep yellow flowers are borne from April to June. One of the best for dry soils 1/6   2/6

„ **sagittalis.**—Europe. The perfectly prostrate branches are wide winged, never rising 6 ins. high. A pretty shrub in late June with its erect racemes of bright yellow flowers 1/6   2/6

„   „   **minor (delphinensis).**—Dauphiny, S.E. France. A singular little beauty for the alpine house or for a choice position on the rock garden. The tiny, short, winged growths are barely 1 in. high and they carry racemes of bright yellow flowers in May and June. A beautiful illustration of this plant was given in the New Flora and Silva, Vol. IX, No. 1 (October, 1936), page 55   3/6

„ **tinctoria anxantica.**—Naples, S. Italy. It was discovered in 1818 but is still rare in British gardens. The thin slender branches lie on the soil and it is an ideal shrub for the rock garden or for a pan in the alpine house. It is quite pretty and has much larger flowers than those of the type 1/6   2/6

„   „   **humifusa.**—A fascinating alpine shrub, 1—4 ins. high, but much wider. Its annual 2—4 in. wiry growths are densely clothed with glistening, downy, elliptic-lanceolate green leaves, ¼—½ in. long. The extensions of its growths are crowded with bright yellow flowers   1/6   2/6

„   „   **mantica (Carniola mantica).**—Grows to 3 ft. and bears 6—12 in. racemes of bright yellow flowers on the current season's slender growths. A good late summer flowering shrub 2/6

„   „   **plena.**—Europe. Compact, semi-prostrate in habit and less than 18 ins. high. Plants are mounds of orange yellow flowers in July and August 1/6   2/6

Genista Villarsii.—Dalmatia, S. & C. Europe. This exceedingly   each.
rare and small prostrate shrub makes 1—4 in. tiny whip-
cord-like growths annually. The ends of its shoots bear
many yellow flowers during May 3/6   5/6

„   **virgata.**—Madeira. This forms a large shrub 10 ft.
or more high, of compact habit. It is exceptionally
beautiful with its mass of bright yellow flowers, borne
during June and July 2/6   3/6

Ginkgo biloba.—E. China. Cultivated in Japan. The Maiden-
hair Tree develops into a handsome specimen and it
grows freely in many gardens overlaying chalk. It
should be given a place for its beautiful mellow yellow
tinted autumn foliage 3/6   5/6

Gordonia Altamaha (pubescens).—Altamaha River, Georgia.
1770. It is as lovely as it is rare and will stand many
degrees of frost. In the south and west counties, providing it is given a semi-shady position in a soil where
Rhododendrons are happy, it will make 18—30 ins. of
growth each year. On healthy plants obovate undulated
leaves, with uneven blunt teeth and bright red midribs, are 8 ins. long and 3½ ins. wide. They assume the
richest autumn tints of any hardy shrub. The cup-
shaped or Camellia-like white flowers, borne in August
and September, are 2—3 ins. across and are held firmly
on stout stalks 15/6   21/-

E   „   **axillaris (anomala).**—W. China & Formosa. An uncommon evergreen which has proved hardy in the West,
south of Ireland and the west of Scotland. It has
attractive, oblanceolate-oblong, pointed leaves, 6 ins.
or more long. The beautiful single, white, Camellia-
like flowers are produced from November to May, according to position and climate 10/6 15/6 21/-

Gorse. (See Ulex).

E   **Grevillea alpina (alpestris).**—S. Australia. This compact shrub
is 1—2 ft. high and quite hardy in many gardens within
reach of the sea air, in the south and west. Almost every
short twig bears clusters of red-yellow flowers for quite
eight months of the year, according to position and
climate 2/6   3/6

E   „   **rosmarinifolia.**—New South Wales. A beautiful shrub
for the south and west and similar places. The showy
rose-red flowers nestling among the narrow leaves are
borne from late winter onwards. It does well in seaside
gardens. 2/6   3/6

E   „   **sulphurea.**—New South Wales. Of more upright habit
and with much shorter leaves than the former. The
chrome-yellow flowers are borne from May to July. It
is best in semi-shade 2/6   3/6

E   „   **thyrsoides.**—This differs from G. rosmarinifolia by its
more upright habit, narrower leaves and rich crimson-
red flowers 2/6   3/6

E   **Griselinia littoralis.**—New Zealand. One of the most useful of
all evergreens for the seaside where it makes a splendid
hedge. Isolated it will attain large size 2/6   3/6

E **Guevina Avellana.**—Chile. A large shrub or small tree in warm   each.
humid climates such as the south-west and north of
Ireland. It has handsome pinnate leaves and carries
long axillary racemes of white flowers, growing well in
semi-shade and under high evergreens. The seeds are
edible 5/-   7/6 10/6

Gymnocladus dioica (canadensis).—N. America. The Ken-
tucky Coffee Tree is one of the most beautiful of all
ornamentals. The bi-pinnate leaves are 3 ft. long and
2 ft. wide. When unfolding they are bright pink,
and during autumn become clear yellow 3/6   5/6

Gynerium argenteum (Pampas Grass).—(See **Cortaderia
argentea).**

Halesia carolina (tetraptera).—N. America. One of the most
beautiful of all hardy flowering shrubs and worthy of
every garden. In semi-shade it soon grows 6—10 ft.
high, of spreading habit. In May and June it is hung
with silvery white snowdrop-like flowers. It is not good
on chalky soils 2/6   3/6

„   **monticola.**—S.E. United States. Known since 1897,
but it is still rare in British gardens. This splendid
species quickly attains tree size if it is given woodland
conditions. Its branches, with their peeling bark, are
a fine sight during May and June, when decorated with
drooping 1 in. pure white flowers. A beautiful plate of
this rarity appears in Bean's third volume of Trees and
Shrubs 5/6   7/6

Halimodendron halodendron (argenteum).—Known as the
Siberian Salt Tree. This is an elegant shrub 4—6 ft.
high, with small pinnate green leaves. The branches
in June and July, are studded with pale pink cytisus-like
flowers. Very hardy but not good on chalky soils ...   3/6   5/6

Hamamelis japonica.—The type plant is very rare. It forms a
large spreading shrub of many twiggy shoots, up to 10 ft.
high. The sweetly-scented flowers begin to appear
early in January, and by February the plant is gay with
pale yellow flowers 3/6   5/6   7/6

„   „   **arborea.**—Japan. Of open habit, 10—15 ft.
high though in some gardens it reaches 25—35 ft. This
is a very beautiful shrub from November to the end of
March with scented flowers, like gold thread, contrasting
well with the deep claret of the calyx. It makes a fine
plant on a north or east wall 3/6   5/6   7/6

„   „   **flavo-purpurascens (rubra).**—Japan. A variable cultivated form. The one offered has reddish-gold-
coloured flowers. Its autumn foliage is particularly
good 5/6   7/6

„   „   **Zuccariniana.**—Japan. Not strong growing,
but distinct in habit and foliage. The lemon-yellow
flowers are freely produced in March 3/6   5/6   7/6

„   **mollis.**—C. China. The most conspicuous in foliage and
perhaps the handsomest of a fine family. The tomentose leaves are dark green, ripening to golden-yellow,
whilst the flowers may begin to unfold in December and
continue until March. Their fragrance adds another
charm 3/6   5/6   7/6 10/6

Hamamelis vernalis.—S. Central U.S.A. A slender-branched shrub of good habit, 6 ft. or more high. The deliciously scented red flowers are borne on the bare branches, during the new year. Its glaucous green leaves, bright green beneath, assume attractive shades of yellow in autumn 3/6   5/6   7/6

   " **virginiana.**—N. America. Not so attractive as its eastern relatives, it is not without merits of its own. The flowers open in autumn before the leaves fall and are of a similar colour, but borne in great profusion. The plant is well worth its place 2/6   3/6   5/6

     The **Hamamelis** love woodland conditions in the south, where they grow freely. They bloom when flowers are scarce and are good for cutting.

E **Harrimanella stellariana (Cassiope stellariana).**—Japan. A delightful and very hardy dense prostrate plant, 1—3 ins. high, with wiry stems packed with light brown Empetrum-like leaves. It requires similar conditions to the Epigaeas, Schizocodons and dwarf Rhododendrons. From April to July, it produces in quantity, dainty ¼ in. rose-coloured or creamy-white bells with crimson calyces held on 1—2 in. stems. It was one of the most attractive of the rarities exhibited at the Alpine Garden Society's Show, April 20th, 1937. ... ... 3/6   5/6   7/6

Heath. (See **Daboecia** and **Erica**).

Hedysarum multijugum.—S. Mongolia. A shrub of zig-zag habit, but beautiful in autumn with its reddish pea-shaped flowers 2/6   3/6

E **Helichrysum rosmarinifolium (Ozothamnus).**—Victoria, Tasmania. This attractive plant grows quite freely in gardens near the sea in the south and west, quickly attaining 5—8 ft. It is smothered from June to August with small white flowers, richly scented 2/6

Helwingia japonica.—A hardy botanical shrub from Japan. The flowers are borne on the midribs of the green leaves. It succeeds in semi-shade 3/6   5/6

Hippophae rhamnoides (Sea Buckthorn).—Europe, Temp. Asia. A very attractive shrub in autumn, especially near the sea, with its silvery foliage and branches hung with orange-coloured fruits which are not relished by birds. Almost any soil suits it. Male and female plants are supplied 2/6   3/6

Hoheria Lyallii.—A beautiful quick-growing shrub or small tree, with glaucous leaves. The extensions of its branches are laden in July with white cup-shaped flowers, suggesting cherry blossom. They are also sweetly scented. Perhaps the finest plant New Zealand has sent us 2/6   3/6   5/6

   "   **ribifolia.**—New Zealand. A beautiful shrub 8 ft. or more high. The downy leaves give it a blue-grey appearance. From mid-June to early September the handsome 1 in. cherry-like white flowers are borne in profusion. Unfortunately it is only suitable for south-west and similar gardens 5/6

E   "   **populnea.**—New Zealand. Only suitable for the milder districts and is of erect habit with its leaves broadly ovate and toothed. The flowers are pure white and borne in bunches during September and October ... 3/6   5/6

E **Hoheria sexstylosa (lanceolata).**—New Zealand. Usually it requires a sheltered wall, but in milder districts it grows into a large bush. During July and August the branches are wreathed with snow-white flowers. The leaves are lance-shaped and bright shining green. It grows and flowers freely on S. and W. walls N.E. of York — each. 2/6   3/6   5/6

EC **Holboellia hexaphylla (Stauntonia hexaphylla).**—Japan, Korea. A handsome climber, the compound leaf bearing three to seven leathery ovate leaflets, grey beneath and distinctly reticulated. The flowers are white, tinted with violet and fragrant. It requires a south or west wall 3/6   5/6

EC „ **latifolia (Stauntonia latifolia).**—Himalayas. A wall climber for the southern counties. Once established, it soon forms a conspicuous evergreen, 15 ft. or more high, twining as it grows. The prominent flowers, staminate white, pistillate purple, are sweetly scented. To encourage the flowers it should be kept spurred 2/6   3/6

Hydrangea arborescens grandiflora.—Ohio. An upright-growing shrub about 4 ft. high, that does exceedingly well in many gardens in the midlands. It is invaluable from early July to late September for its many heads of sterile pure white flowers 1/6   2/6

 „ **aspera.**—Himalaya, China. Of stiff habit, 3—6 ft. high. Its large, oblong-toothed leaves are highly ornamental together with its porcelain-blue sterile flowers from August to autumn 5/-

 „ **Bretschneideri.**—A large spreading shrub from China, 3—5 ft. high, with oblong leaves. It starts to flower as Viburnum tomentosum Mariesii is fading and is often, when in flower, mistaken for this plant... ... ...   2/6   3/6

EC „ **integerrima.**—Chile. This little known self-climber is as vigorous as Pileostegia viburnoides and is useful for low walls, rocks, etc. Its leathery 1—4 in. elliptical-ovate, green leaves are net-veined and bluntly serrated, and have yellow-white midribs. It blooms from June to autumn, each inflorescence being 6 ins. × 3½ ins. and containing small pale yellow fertile flowers with occasionally a few creamy-white bracts. In the south it loves shade 7/6

 „ **involucrata.**—Japan. A striking, compact shrub, 18 ins. high for the south and west. The sterile flowers are bluey-white, whilst the fertile ones are brilliant blue, blooming from August to late autumn 2/6   3/6

 „ **opuloides (Hortensia) (macrophylla).**—China. This and its many varieties do not naturally give blue flowers in all soils. In many gardens in the south and west bushes 3—5 ft. high and as much through are a magnificent sight with their many heads of brilliant blue flowers from August to November 2/6   3/6

 „ „ **Mariesii.**—Japan. It is one of the most attractive late summer and autumn flowering shrubs and loves a semi-shady position, in the south and west. The many 2½ in. conspicuous sterile bracts may be white, pink or bright blue, according to soil 2/6   3/6

		each.
Hydrangea opuloides nigra (cyanoclada).—Manchuria. This hardy plant grows 3—5 ft. high and as much wide. From June to autumn its erect black stems carry cobalt blue fertile flowers, surrounded by 2 in. rose-red bracts	2/6	3/6
„ **paniculata (vera).**—Japan. This choice but neglected shrub is much confused with the following variety. It grows 3—5 ft. and is pretty from mid-July to late autumn with its showy white, ageing to bright pink, sterile flowers	2/6	3/6
„ „ **grandiflora.**—Japan. A shrub 3—5 ft. high. To obtain the massive panicles of white sterile flowers from July to October, it should be pruned every spring	2/6	3/6
C „ **petiolaris (Climbing Hydrangea).**—Japan. A rapid self-climber which, when once established, soon attains a height of 10—15 ft. It is suitable for walls, tree stumps and banks in any aspect. The sterile flowers are white along the margins of 6—10 in. flat corymbs during summer	2/6	3/6
„ **quercifolia.**—A choice species from N. America, with large, deep green, five to seven-lobed leaves, beautifully autumn tinted. It bears 6—8 in. erect panicles with many white sterile flowers scattered on the margin. It does best in semi-shade	2/6	3/6
„ **serrata acuminata (Hortensis acuminata).**—Japan. This distinct shrub attains a height of 2—4 ft. and has ovate-oval-acuminate, puckered, metallic-green leaves, coarsely toothed. The sterile bright pink or pale blue flowers are borne along the margins of the wide corymbs	2/6	3/6
„ „ **rosalba (Hortensis Lindleyi) (H. japonica).**— This beautiful shrub has upright stems, 3—5 ft. in height and loves a semi-shady position in the south. The wide corymbs of bright rose-red flowers are borne from June to August. In heathland soils its flowers are often blue-tinted	2/6	3/6
„ **strigosa.**—W. Hupeh, China. This beautiful species grows freely in woodland gardens in the south and west. Its bristly, rather angled branches carry 3—8 in. oblanceolate-oblong, hairy leaves. The 6—8 in. corymbs of small white fertile flowers are edged with 1 in. sterile purple-blue bracts (flowers)		5/-
„ **villosa.**—W. Szechuan, China. Closely related to H. aspera. The handsome lanceolate leaves are tomentose and grey on the under-side. The compound umbel of porcelain-blue starred about with lavender florets, achieves a harmony that is surprising	3/6	5/6
„ **xanthoneura.**—W. China. An upright-growing shrub 6—10 ft. high with attractive foliage. The stout growths are chestnut brown and marked with conspicuous lenticels	2/6	3/6
„ „ **Wilsonii.**—W. China. With light brown bark and not so strong a grower. The margins of the wide corymbs during late summer and autumn are decorated with white sterile flowers ageing to deep pink	2/6	3/6
E **Hymenanthera angustifolia.**—Tasmania. An uncommon dense stiff-branched shrub, 3—5 ft. high, with small oblong green leaves. It is covered from September to late winter with small white fruits	2/6	3/6

E **Hymenanthera chathamica.**—Chatham Island. An erect-growing shrub 4—8 ft. high, only suitable for the south and west. It bears distinct pale green lanceolate leaves and the small flowers are succeeded by many white fruits in autumn ... ...   each. 3/6   5/–

E   „   **crassifolia.**—New Zealand. A good shrub for seaside gardens, where it grows to 6 ft. It is smothered during autumn and winter with white fruits 2/6   3/6

Hypericum aureum.—U.S.A. A wiry-branched shrub 4 ft. high, with bluey-green leaves and terminal clusters of scented orange-yellow flowers in late summer and autumn 2/6

E   „   **calycinum (Rose of Sharon).**—Orient. A favourite among dwarf evergreens for growing under the shade of trees. To obtain its beautiful bright yellow flowers from June to October it should be cut to the ground in early April.   **10/6 & 16/6 doz.**   1/–   1/6

E   „   **chinense.**—China, Japan. A spreading branching shrub, 18 ins. high, worthy of a sheltered spot. It bears cymes of five to seven flowers of bright yellow, 2½ ins. across, with protruding stamens 2/6

   „   **fragile.**—Greece. A beautiful dwarf shrub with overlapping branches, covered in summer with 1 in. bright yellow flowers, looking like a cushion of yellow ... 1/6

   „   **Hookerianum (oblongifolium).**—Himalayas. A distinct erect-growing shrub 3—5 ft. high, beautiful from August to autumn frosts with its handsome clusters of 2 in. cup-shaped bright yellow flowers 1/6   2/6

   „   **Leschenaultii.**—Mountains of Java. This choice shrub is of upright habit and has foliage resembling that of H. Hookerianum. It is quite hardy in coastal gardens but requires a sheltered position inland. The many 2—3 in. brilliant yellow flowers are freely borne from July to autumn frosts 2/6

E   „   **Moserianum.**—As a dwarf shrub, 1 ft. high, it has few equals, either planted singly or in mass. The 2½ in. golden-yellow flowers are freely borne from July to autumn frosts 1/6

   „   **olympicum.**—Greece. An upright grower, 9—15 ins. high. The dense wiry stems are neatly clothed with glaucous, narrow leaves and carry heads of attractive deep yellow flowers during the summer months ... 1/6   2/6

   „   „   **pallidum.**—Quite a pretty form with heads of large pale yellow flowers 1/6   2/6

   „   **patulum Forrestii.**—S.W. China. A much better plant than the type. Of bushy habit, 2—3 ft. high and as much wide. The young foliage from spring to mid-summer is bright red ageing to green and turning again in autumn gold, crimson and red. Numerous 2 in. bright yellow flowers are borne from early July to autumn frosts ... 1/6   2/6

   „   „   **grandiflorum.**—A Chinese form, 3 ft. high and much superior to H. patulum. Its branches are weighted from August to October with quantities of 3 in. bright yellow flowers 1/6   2/6

Hypericum Rodgersii.—Mt. Victoria, India. This beautiful erect-growing shrub attains 5—10 ft. in Irish gardens and is undoubtedly the best hardy member of the genus as yet. It produces 2—3 in. buttercup-yellow flowers from early summer until autumn frosts 2/6

Idesia polycarpa.—China, Japan. It is perfectly happy in many south and west gardens and with age grows into a small tree. It carries large, cordate, dark green leaves, glaucous beneath. The many attractive, drooping 4—12 in. panicles of deep red pea-like fruits are held for many weeks during the autumn 3/6   5/6

E **Ilex Aquifolium.**—Europe, W. Asia. The common Holly is one of the noblest of our woodland trees. It makes a particularly attractive hedge and given a free foot run, will grow 9—18 ins. yearly ... ...   1/6 to 5/-

E „ **crenata nummularia (crenata Mariesii).**—Japan. A thicket of thin short twigs, densely clothed with tiny glistening, ovate-orbicular, crenulated leaves. It is an ideal plant for the rock garden 3/6   5/6

E **Illicium anisatum (religiosum).**—Japan. A low compact-growing shrub 3—6 ft. high, with pleasantly aromatic oval leaves. It grows well in semi-shade and bears 1 in. yellowish flowers in summer. Hardy in all but the coldest parts 3/6   5/6   7/6

E „ **floridanum.**—N. America. Not so hardy as I. anisatum. It grows 6—10 ft. high in the warmer parts and has larger, leathery, aromatic leaves. The many flowers are brownish-crimson. It loves semi-shade ...   —   —

Indigofera decora.—Korea, N. China. Exceedingly rare in cultivation and grows 6—9 ins. high. It is ideal for the rock garden. The brown-red stems carry 2—3 in. pinnate leaves composed of 7 elliptical, green leaflets, glaucous beneath. They make a fine background for the 1—3 in. racemes of rose-pink pea-like flowers from the end of May to late September. It dies to the ground every winter 5/-

„ „ **alba.**—China, Japan. This charming sub-shrub makes yearly growths about 12 ins. high and it is ideal for the rock garden or for the front of borders. It is furnished with 6—9 in. pinnate leaves and 6—9 in. racemes of pure white pea-like flowers from the end of May to late September. It dies to the ground every winter   3/6

„ **Gerardiana.**—Himalayas. Planted in the open it is sub-shrubby, and on a south or west wall it will grow to 6 ft. A splendid shrub from June to September with panicles of twenty-five to thirty small rosy pea-shaped flowers   1/6   2/6

„ **hebepetala.**—Himalayas. It grows 2—3 ft. high, with 6—9 in. pinnate leaves, racemes of 3—9 in. crimson and rose-coloured flowers during July and August 5/-

„ **Kirilowii (macrostachya).**—China, Japan. An exceedingly rare sub-shrub, dying down during the winter in cold districts and worthy of every garden. The 2—3 ft. annual growths carry Robinia-like, pinnate leaves. Each plant produces successively from 15 to 40 6—9 in. erect racemes of bright rose-coloured pea-like flowers, from early June till autumn frosts. They are as beautiful as those of Robinia hispida. It is illustrated in Bot. Magazine, T. 8580 ... ...   3/6

Indigofera pendula.—W. China. A spreading shrub growing   each.
5—10 ft. high in sheltered gardens. Its hairy branches
carry 8—10 in. pinnate leaves, each having up to 27
leaflets. The 6—18 in. pendulous racemes of many pea-
like, rose-purple flowers are borne from July to the end
of September 5/–

„   **Potaninii.**—China. A choice border shrub with erect
stems. The side branches are covered with short
panicles of many rose-coloured flowers from early July
to August 2/6   3/6

E **Itea ilicifolia.**—C. China. A bushy shrub 4—6 ft. high, with
glossy green, holly-like leaves and many 9—15 in.
drooping racemes of small scented white flowers during
July and August. It is not generally hardy and loves
semi-shade 2/6   3/6   5/6

„   **virginica.**—An uncommon, perfectly hardy woodland
shrub, 3—5 ft. high from East U.S.A. The leaves are
oblong, light green, and it bears numerous 3—6 in.
cylindrical racemes of sweetly scented, creamy-white
flowers from July to September. Its foliage colours well
in autumn. Cut sprays last some time 2/6   3/6

Jamesia americana.—West. N. America. A choice compact-
growing shrub, rarely more than 3—5 ft. high, with
oval hairy leaves and terminal panicles of pretty pure-
white flowers in June and July 3/6   5/6

C **Jasminum nudiflorum.**—China, Japan. An always welcome
shrub for its bright yellow flowers on naked shoots 3—5
ft. long, from mid-winter to April. It will grow in any
soil and practically anywhere 1/6   2/6

C „   **officinale.**—Persia & N.W. India. A rampant semi-
evergreen, but by hard pruning can be kept in bush
form. Its well-known and deliciously scented white
flowers are produced from June to autumn frosts ...   1/6   2/6

E „   **Parkeri.**—N.W. India. This dense twiggy evergreen
grows from a few inches to 1 ft. high and is ideal for the
rock garden or for a pan in the alpine house. The
tubular yellow flowers are ½—¾ in. long and ½ in. wide
and are freely borne during June. Good specimens
can be seen at the Alpine Society's shows 2/6   3/6

EC „   **primulinum.**—China. The most beautiful of all outdoor jasmines but not quite hardy, though worthy of a
warm sheltered wall. The 1½—2 in. soft yellow flowers
are freely borne from May to early autumn 2/6   3/6

EC „   **revolutum.**—N.W. Himalayas. Of loose, shrubby
growth, with large green leaves and many fragrant yellow
flowers in late summer. This climber attains 9—12 ft. on
a west wall 2/6   3/6

E **Kalmia angustifolia.**—East N. America. A neat little shrub
2—3 ft. high, densely clothed with rather small leaves.
The profuse terminal clusters of saucer-shaped rosy-red
flowers are produced from mid-May to July on the ends
of the previous year's growths 1/6   2/6   3/6

E „   „   **ovata (nitida).**—N. & S. Carolina. A plant
attaining 4 ft., of erect habit, with opposite dark green
oblong leaves, bluey beneath. The terminal clusters
of saucer-shaped rose-coloured flowers, with many
stamens protruding, are produced during June ... 2/6   3/6   5/6

each.

E **Kalmia angustifolia rubra.**—A beautiful form with densely packed clusters of darker red flowers produced more or less from mid-May to September **1/6** 2/6 3/6

E   „   **carolina.**—Vancouver to S. Carolina. This compact rarity is almost unknown in British gardens. It may not exceed 18 ins. when fully grown. The pubescent growths are densely clothed with oblong-lanceolate, revolute, grey-green leaves, $\frac{1}{2}$—$1\frac{1}{2}$ in. long and $\frac{1}{4}$—$\frac{1}{2}$ in. wide. Many pink or rose-red flowers, $\frac{1}{2}$ in. across are produced during May and June. It is closely related to K. angustifolia **5/6** 7/6 10/6

  „   **cuneata.**—An extremely rare shrub from N. America, 2—3 ft. high, with erect growths. The obovate green leaves assume a glorious colour in autumn. It bears clusters of cup-shaped creamy-white flowers during June and July and these are much admired by visitors to the nursery **3/6** 5/6 7/6

E   „   **latifolia.**—N.America. One of the most beautiful of all flowering shrubs. The numerous large clusters of many saucer-shaped deep rose flowers against the glossy green foliage during June are exquisite **2/6** 3/6 5/6

E   „   **polifolia (glauca).**—East N. America. A very beautiful shrub of rather spreading bushy habit, 1—2 ft. high. The terminal flat clusters of $\frac{1}{2}$ in. saucer-shaped pale rose flowers are produced in late April and May **1/6** 2/6 3/6

E   „   „   **microphylla.**—Colorado, California. This uncommon shrub slowly forms a tuft a few inches high. Its 1—3 in. stems are furnished with ovate-obovate or elliptic-oblong, slightly revolute leaves. The thread-like stalks carry pretty saucer-shaped pink flowers in April and May. It is beautifully illustrated in the New Flora and Silva, Vol. VIII, No. 3 (April, 1936), page 169 ...   7/6

In the south and west the **Kalmias** love the shade of distant trees.

E **Kalmiopsis Leachiana.**—This plant is extremely rare in nature and we are grateful to the author for finding it at 5,000 ft. on Big Craggy, Curry County, America. It is a compact shrub, about 6—12 ins. high, with twiggy stems carrying Kalmia polifolia-like leaves. The beautiful $\frac{1}{2}$—$\frac{3}{4}$ in. saucer-shaped rose-pink flowers are held upright on 1—2 in. thread-like stalks and are freely borne from April to June 7/6 10/6

Kerria japonica.—China. The slender branches are wreathed with bright yellow single flowers in April and May. Height 3—6 ft. 1/6 2/6

  „   „   **pleniflora.**—It has long been grown in gardens and it is a fine shrub from April to September when its branches are crowded with conspicuous double yellow flowers. It grows and flowers freely on exposed north walls in many Yorkshire gardens 1/6 2/6

Koelreuteria paniculata.—China, Korea, Japan. This slow-growing ornamental tree needs full sun to bring out its beauty. The attractive pinnate or partially bipinnate leaves are 1—2 ft. in length, turning bright yellow in autumn. The terminal pyramidal panicles of yellow flowers are 12 ins. or more in length, borne in July and August 3/6 5/6

		each.

Kolkwitzia amabilis.—C. China. A choice shrub 3—5 ft. high, of many slender twiggy branches. The weigela-like flowers are pink with a yellow throat and are borne during May and June 2/6 3/6

Laburnum Adamii.—A graft hybrid which grows to a small tree, producing many racemes of yellow and purple flowers on the same branch during May 2/6 3/6

„ **alpinum (Scotch Laburnum) (Longest and Latest).** Usually a small tree, 10—15 ft. high, with trifoliate leaves and pendulous racemes, 1 ft. or more long, of many golden-yellow flowers. It is the last Laburnum to flower and is worthy of wider cultivation 2/6 3/6

„ **anagyroides (vulgare) (Common Laburnum).**— Europe. A well-known and beautiful tree for any position 1/6 2/6 3/6

„ „ **autumnale (semperflorens).**—Flowers freely in late May and again in late September, when the flowers are much deeper coloured 2/6 3/6 5/6

„ **Vossii (alpinum × anagyroides).**—An erect grower, forming a stiff head and bearing conspicuous 18 in. racemes of rich yellow flowers from the end of May to the middle of June 2/6 3/6

„ **Watereri (alpinum × anagyroides).**—Bears handsome large glossy leaves and numerous 1 ft. slender racemes of yellow flowers in early June 2/6 3/6

EC **Lapageria rosea.**—Chile. A magnificent climber for cool green-houses though fine specimens are to be seen in the south-west on north walls. The rich rosy-crimson wax-like pendulous bells are a beautiful sight from August to autumn frosts. Thrives best in soil rich in humus 10/6 12/6

E **Laurelia aromatica.**—Chile. A noble rare shrub, 10—15 ft. high, hardy in the extreme south and west and in Ireland. The handsome oval-oblong dark green serrated leaves are pleasantly aromatic 5/- 7/6 10/6

E **Laurus nobilis.**—Mediterranean region. A useful hardy aroma-tic-leaved shrub. It grows freely and makes a fine specimen with shelter. In the south and west it makes a fine hedge 2/6 3/6 5/6

„ **regalis.** (See **Umbellularia californica**).

Laurustinus. (See **Viburnum tinus**).

E **Ledum glandulosum.**—West N. America. This plant was first discovered in 1826 and it is said to be difficult to grow. Here, in an Ericaceae border, it is easy and quite happy and may possibly attain a height of 3 ft. or more. The downy stems carry aromatic, oval-ovate or elliptic green leaves, ½—2 ins. long by ¼—⅜ in. wide. They are grey beneath and covered with shining scales. It produces 2 in. clusters of ½ in. cup-shaped, white flowers in May and June 3/6 5/6

E „ **groenlandicum (latifolium) (Labrador Tea Plant).**— N.America, Greenland. A very hardy, semi-shade-loving shrub, 2—3 ft. high, with narrow aromatic leaves. It is pretty from April to June with terminal clusters of numerous small white flowers 1/6 2/6 3/6

E „ „ **compactum.**—Dwarf and compact with smaller clusters of flowers 1/6 2/6 3/6

E Ledum minus.—Japan. This distinct and rare member forms a compact shrub 12—18 ins. high and has erect, felted stems. The rugose, aromatic, revolute, linear leaves are ½—1½ ins. long and about ⅛ in. wide. Many terminal clusters of small white flowers are produced during May and June ... ...   each. 7/6 10/6

E „ **nipponicum.**—Japan. This rare and compact shrub grows 6—12 ins. high and is an attractive addition to the Ericaceae garden. It is covered with red-brown downy hairs and the ½—2 in. ovate or oblong, pointed, crenulated, leaves are bright green above and blue-grey beneath. Its many heads of dainty white flowers are borne during May and June 5/6 7/6

E „ **palustre.**—Arctic Regions. A small shrub of thin habit with narrow recurved leaves having rusty tomentum beneath. It bears small terminal clusters of white flowers in April and May 1/6 2/6

E Leiophyllum buxifolium.—East U.S.A. A pleasing cushion-like shrub with small glossy box-like foliage. It is furnished with terminal clusters of rosy-pink flowers, ageing to white, during May and June, and loves semi-shade 1/6 2/6 3/6

E „ „ **var. Hugeri (of Schneider).**—N. & S. Carolina. This forms a cushion 6—9 ins. high, with longer leaves than the type. It is pretty during May and June with heads of pink ageing to white flowers 2/6 3/6

E „ „ **prostratum (Dendrium prostratum).**—High Mountains of Carolina and Tennessee. This little-known charming, slow-growing, prostrate shrub becomes 3—6 ins. high but 2 ft. across. It is ideal for the Ericaceae border or for a pan in the alpine house. It has dense thyme-like leaves and numerous clusters of small pink flowers, ageing to white 3/6 5/6

E Leptospermum baccatum.—Australia. Received here as L. Nairnii. It has distinct and dark green slightly recurved leaves, silvery beneath, and white flowers with a faint crimson base 2/6 3/6

E „ **Liversidgei (thymifolia).**—Australia. A distinct species having branches thickly covered with tiny green leaves and white flowers 2/6 3/6

E „ **pubescens (lanigerum).**—Australia, Tasmania. A slender branching shrub with its sharply pointed leaves and young growths covered with downy hairs, giving a silvery appearance. It has white flowers 2/6 3/6

E „ **scoparium.**—New Zealand. An upright-growing shrub, smothered during June with white flowers 2/6 3/6

E „ „ **Chapmanii.**—Upright in growth with compact branches. It is a beautiful shrub from May to July when laden with bright pink flowers. The hardiest of all the coloured forms 2/6 3/6

E „ „ **Nichollsii.**—New Zealand. The slender branches with bronzed leaves are wreathed during June with showy crimson-red flowers 2/6 3/6

E „ „ „ **gloriosa.**—A seedling from L. Nichollsii, with larger flowers of a beautiful shade of pink. It is as good a plant as the tender L. Boscawenii 2/6 3/6

each.

E **Leptospermum scoparium prostratum.**—Prostrate-growing, and a useful rock garden shrub in the south and west. It is much hardier than the erect forms of L. scoparium ... 2/6 3/6

E   „   **stellatum.**—Australia. The hardiest and best white-flowering species, slightly scented and of upright growth 2/6 3/6
    All the **Leptospermums** are invaluable for seaside gardens in the south and west.

Lespedeza formosa (also incorrectly known as Desmodium penduliflorum).—N. China, Japan. An invaluable sub-shrub but herbaceous during winter ; leaves tri-foliate, handsome in autumn ; slender pendulous racemes, 2—3 ft. in length, of rosy-purple pea-shaped flowers 1/6 2/6

E **Leucopogon Fraseri.**—New Zealand. An Erica-like creeping shrub, erect in growth but very dwarf in stature. The tiny leaves are pointed and stiff to the touch and become bronzed during the winter. Its small white flowers are very sweetly scented and are succeeded by berries, having the appearance of little apricot beads 1/6 2/6

E **Leucothoe Catesbaei (Andromeda Catesbaei).**—Virginia to Georgia. This beautiful semi-pendulous shrub has few equals. The lustrous bold green foliage assumes throughout the winter, magnificent crimson tints. Flowers pitcher-like, in short racemes, whole length of branches in May 1/6 2/6 3/6

E   „   „   **Rollisonii.**—A distinct compact form, not more than 2 ft. high, with narrow willow-like leaves which are bronze-tinted more or less the whole year. It is quite as pretty as the former when in flower 2/6 3/6

E   „   **Davisiae.**—California. An exquisite rare evergreen of neat habit, seldom more than 3 ft. high. It has ovate leaves and pitcher-shaped flowers, in erect racemes at the end of every shoot during June and July ... 2/6 3/6 5/6

  „   **Grayana.**—Japan. A very rare small shrub reaching possibly not more than 3 ft. with us. The stout red growths are furnished with medium-sized ovate leaves, ageing to bright red in autumn. The terminal racemes of ivory-white flowers, suffused pink, are borne during May and June 10/6

E   „   **Keiskei.**—One of the many good plants given to us by Japan. Its zig-zag slender growths are dark red. The large leathery leaves are ovate-acuminated, serrated and bright crimson on both sides, ageing to dark red during winter. From May to September it is decorated with terminal racemes of ¾—1 in. nodding, cylindrical pure white flowers. Height 1—2 ft. 2/6 3/6

E   „   **populifolia (acuminata).**—S. Carolina to Florida. 1765. One of the rarest members of the natural order Ericaceae. It develops into an attractive bush about 3 ft. high and with curved branches. It is very similar in foliage to Nothofagus Dombeyi and N. Moorei. The short racemes of flowers, three-tenths to half an inch long, are borne from April to June 10/6

  „   **racemosa.**—U.S.A. An erect shrub about 4 ft. high, with orange and bright red foliage in late autumn. One-sided 4 in. racemes of cylindrical white flowers are borne in June 3/6 5/6

E **Ligustrum japonicum.**—Japan, Korea. This handsome ever-   each.
green grows to a height of 4 ft. or more and is quite as
wide. It carries large, black-green, polished, ovate-
oblong leaves which form a beautiful background to the
many terminal panicles of white scented flowers, borne
from early July to late September 2/6   3/6

E   „   **lucidum (japonicum macrophyllum of gardens).**—
China, Korea, Japan. An old inhabitant of British castle
and monastry gardens and one which should be more
popular. It is still one of our best evergreens and it is
laden every August and September with 6—8 in.
panicles of white flowers. Introduced in 1794 ...   ...   2/6   3/6

„   **sinense.**—China. An elegant deciduous shrub of great
beauty, ultimately forming a semi-weeping specimen,
6 ft. × 6 ft. or more according to soil and position.
The masses of 3—4 in. loose panicles of white scented
flowers are borne during July. This shrub is well
illustrated in W. J. Bean's Trees and Shrubs, Vol. II, page
28   ...   .   2/6   3/6

„   **vulgare flore luteo.**—This unique and rare form of our
hedgerow privet has masses of clusters of buff-yellow
or primrose-coloured flowers from early June to mid-
July. It attains 5 ft. × 5 ft. or more according to soil   3/6

Limonia trifoliata. (See **Aegle sepiaria**).

Lindera Benzoin.—U.S.A. Of botanical interest. A rare
hardy shrub of slow growth with pungent aromatic
leaves   ...   .   —   —

Lippia citriodora (Aloysia citriodora).—S. America. The
lemon-scented Verbena has been grown in gardens for
many years and it is much valued for its scented leaves.
Inland, it should be planted against a south or west wall.   1/6   2/6

Liquidambar formosana (acerifolia).—China, Formosa. A
small-growing tree, 10—20 ft. high, with maple-like
dark red leaves ageing to deep green and brightly tinted
again in autumn. Here it is susceptible to spring frosts   5/6   7/6

„   „   **monticola (Rehder and Wilson).**—China. This
rare small tree of pyramidal outline is a good grower and
is proving hardy in gardens this side of Birmingham.
The beautiful leathery, crenulated leaves are rich bronze-
red in their youth, ageing to green, with red veins.
They are 4—5 ins. long and 4—7 ins. across and have
three deeply cut lobes, often with two smaller ones at
the base 7/6

„   **orientalis.**—West Asia. This very hardy tree is rare in
cultivation. Slow to develop, with rugged branches,
it ultimately reaches 25 ft. or more in height. The
leaves, of maple type, have five deep oblong lobes and
these again two or five deep teeth. The autumn foliage
is bright yellow 5/6   7/6 10/6

„   **styraciflua.**—East U.S.A., Mexico. One of the most
beautiful of all trees, but requires shelter from cutting
winds. The maple-like leaves are gorgeously coloured
in autumn 2/6   3/6

Liquidambar styraciflua levis.—This very hardy and stately   each.
small tree has been grown at Abbotsbury for 40 years or
more as L. orientalis.   The thick spreading branches
and main stem are devoid of corky bark.   The huge,
aromatic, deeply 5-lobed leaves are bronze coloured
during the growing season.   They age to green, becoming
magnificently coloured during autumn.   Previously distributed as L. species **5/6   7/6 10/6**

Liriodendron Tulipifera.—East U.S.A.   The tulip tree is a
handsome ornamental of beautiful outline and thrives
in almost any soil, including chalk.   The upright, tulip-
like green-white flowers, with orange-coloured base,
are produced in quantity during June and July.   It is
also attractive during the autumn when the large
leaves with truncate bases, change to rich yellow   **2/6   3/6   5/6**

E **Lithospermum prostratum.**—S. Europe.   Prostrate growing,
4-12 ins. high, and forming a spreading mass with abundance of rich blue flowers from early spring to summer   **1/6**

E   „   „   **Heavenly Blue.**—A charming form with numerous sky-blue flowers **1/6**
Both these indispensable plants are quite happy in
soils which suit heathers ; for rock gardens, banks, etc.

E **Litsaea japonica (Tetranthera japonica).**—China, Japan.
An exceedingly rare evergreen for the south and west,
attaining 10 ft. or more in height.   Inland it requires
a south or west wall.   The 6—9 in. dark green leaves
are strongly lemon-scented **7/6 10/6**

E **Loiseleuria procumbens (Azalea procumbens).**—Arctic and
Alpine Europe.   Better known as the creeping Azalea.
Here in a woodland border it is one of the easiest growers
of all the rare Ericaceae.   It rarely attains more than 4 ins.
and it bears in May many terminal clusters of pale rose-
coloured flowers **2/6   3/6   5/6**

E **Lomatia ferruginea (pinnatifolia).**—Chile.   A shrub of
graceful outline with handsome divided bronze-green
leaves, glaucous beneath.   The Grevillea-like flowers
are rosy-red and white, on short stalks.   It is only
suitable for mild parts.   Fine specimens are to be seen
in Cornwall and in south and north Ireland   **5/-   7/6 10/6**

E   „   **fraxinifolia.**—Australia.   This attractive shrub is new
to cultivation and will grow 3 ft. or more high in these
Islands.   Its brown-red stems carry many ornamental,
leathery grey bipinnatifid leaves, irregularly cut and
toothed, and 8—10 ins. long by 6—9 ins. across.   The
creamy white Grevillea-like scented flowers are borne
from early May to late July **7/6 10/6**

E   „   **longifolia.**—Australia.   A rare, sparingly branched shrub
3—6 ft. high, with narrow leaves, 6—12 ins. long, deep
green and widely toothed.   It is reasonably hardy under
high evergreens in the south and west **3/6   5/6   7/6**

E   „   „   **glaucophylla.**—Australia.   An elegant shrub,
3—5 ft. high.   It is furnished with attractive 6—12 in.
narrow leaves, blue-grey above and glaucous beneath ...   **7/6 10/6**

E   „   **obliqua.**—A handsome shrub, 4—8 ft. high, with leathery
ovate leaves.   It requires a warm sheltered position   **7/6 10/6**

E **Lomatia siliaefolia.**—New South Wales. This is the pgymy of   each.
the genus and is of mound-like habit, 9—18 ins. high.
Its short stiff stems carry wide, bipinnatifid green leaves.
The Grevillea-like white scented flowers are produced
in May and June **5/- 7/6**

E   ,,   **tinctoria.**—Australia. This shrub attains a height of
3 ft. or more and its erect stems carry bipinnatifid, grey-
green leaves, 3—5 ins. long and 2—3 ins. across. Every
growth produces a 4—9 in. panicle of Grevillea-like
white scented flowers from early May to late July.
Previously distributed as L. siliaefolia **3/6 5/6 7/6**

The Australian **Lomatias** are much hardier than is
generally supposed, especially if they are planted near
larger evergreens. L. tinctoria has often stood 18°
of frost in the shade of a Rhododendron

The following are known as **Bush Honeysuckles.**

Lonicera chaetocarpa.—A distinct member from W. China with
its branches, leaves and roundish bracts covered with
bristly hairs. The conspicuous flowers in pairs,
are primrose yellow, during June. Height 3—5 ft. ...   **2/6 3/6**

  ,,   **Ferdinandii.**—An uncommon species from N. China,
with slender spreading branches and ovate leaves covered
with bristles. It is a beautiful object during the autumn
when its branches are crowded with bright red fruits, retained long after the leaves drop **2/6 3/6**

E   ,,   **fragrantissima.**—E. China. A branching shrub, 6—12 ft.
high, with ovate leathery greyish leaves and creamy-white
fragrant flowers from December to March. It is best
on a south or west wall, but is perfectly hardy **2/6 3/6**

  ,,   **hispida.**—Central Asia, Siberia. A very hardy shrub,
3—5 ft. high and clothed with bristly hairs. The yellow
funnel-shaped flowers are in pairs, held in greenish round
bracts, in late May **2/6 3/6**

  ,,   **Maackii podocarpa.**—W. & C. China. An open-
branched shrub, 6—10 ft. high, laden with yellow
flowers in May and June, followed by small red fruits.
A superior plant to L. Maackii **2/6 3/6**

  ,,   **pyrenaica.**—A choice, pretty shrub from the Pyrenees,
2 ft. high, with glaucous obovate leaves and rose-white
funnel-shaped flowers, fading to creamy-white. These
are followed by orange-red berries. It is one of our
very best dwarf shrubs and is invaluable for the larger
rock gardens. Unfortunately many inferior Loniceras
have done and do duty for this rarity **3/6**

  ,,   **Standishii.**—A shrub much confused with L. fragrantissima. This one has lanceolate rough green leaves.
The sweetly-scented cream-coloured flowers appear
from November to March, according to the season.
Height about 4—5 ft., but 10 ft. on a sheltered wall   **2/6 3/6**

  ,,   **syringantha.**—N.W. China. An elegant shrub with
2—4 ft. growths. Its pale lilac flowers, borne during
May and June, are hyacinth-scented **1/6 2/6**

  ,,   **tartarica.**—S. Russia & Turkestan. A strong-growing
bushy shrub, 6—8 ft. high with numerous white or pink
flowers in pairs, followed by red fruits **2/6**

Lonicera tartarica lutea (xanthocarpa).—A striking May-flowering shrub of spreading habit, 3—4 ft. high, received here from the Pyrenees. Its slender arching branches are crowded with bright pink flowers, followed by quantities of translucent amber-coloured fruits which ripen in late June **3/6**

    „   „   **sibirica.**—Beautiful form, with larger leaves and handsome rosy-red flowers and fruits **2/6**

CLIMBING SECTION.

E   „   **americana (caprifolium × etrusca) (grata).**—Natural Hybrid. Undoubtedly one of the very best climbers and one of the most neglected. It is attractive from May until autumn with its 2—3 in. tubular fragrant flowers, yellow and bright carmine, cream-coloured within. Previously distributed as L. italica **3/6**

    „   **Brownii (sempervirens × hirsuta).**—Better known as the Scarlet Trumpet Honeysuckle. Planted in semi-shade, it ramps away, bearing conspicuous orange scarlet flowers from June to autumn. A plant for every garden **2/6   3/6**

    „   **ciliosa.**—W. N. America. A lovely twining plant, not generally hardy but well worth a sheltered semi-shady spot. 1½ in. yellow to orange-scarlet flowers are borne   **3/6**

    „   **dioica (glauca).**—N. America. This species has large dark green leaves, those uppermost quite small and all covered beneath with grey down. It bears clusters of 1 in. tubular yellow flowers during June and July   ...   **3/6**

    „   **etrusca.**—Mediterranean Region. A rampant semi-evergreen with clusters of yellow fragrant flowers on the upper parts of the current season's growths, from early July to autumn **2/6   3/6**

    „   „   **superba (gigantea).**—Equally good and with much downier leaves **2/6   3/6**

    „   **Heckrottii (sempervirens × americana).**—A hybrid with oblong leaves, glaucous beneath, and striking 1½ in. orange-yellow and pink fragrant flowers from June to autumn frosts. Not a fast grower and averse to full sun **3/6**

E   „   **Henryi.**—China. Discarded as it is an inferior plant.

    „   **Hildebrandiana.**—Burma, Siam, China. This rampant Honeysuckle requires a cool house but it can be grown outside in Cornwall and the south and west Ireland. The 4—6 in. tubular orange-yellow flowers are attractive against its large leathery oval leaves **5/-**

E   „   **japonica aureo-reticulata.**—A form. A rampant climber for pergolas, etc., with beautiful nettled yellow foliage, changing in autumn to gold and bronze **1/6   2/6**

E   „   „   **flexuosa (brachypoda).**—The stems are reddish purple, also the ovate leaves, whilst it is furnished with many showy fragrant pale red flowers, white within, which age to buff-yellow. A pretty climber in flower from June to late autumn and a better plant than the type L. japonica **2/6   3/6**

E   „   „   **Halliana.**—The white flowers, ageing to a delightful primrose colour, are richly scented and freely borne from May to late autumn **2/6   3/6**

each.

Lonicera Periclymenum.—Europe, N. Africa. The Woodbine or Honeysuckle, the common plant of the hedgerow and one of the most cheerful for its fragrance 1/6   2/6

  ,,   ,, **belgica (Early Dutch Honeysuckle).**—An old favourite bearing clusters of many red tinged tubular fragrant flowers ; strong growing and free-flowering ...   2/6   3/6

  ,,   ,, **serotina (Late Dutch Honeysuckle).**—A relative, with clusters of longer and larger reddish tubular yellow flowers, ageing to pale yellow, from May to autumn ; also strong growing 2/6   3/6

  ,, **sempervirens.**—S.E. United States. The true Trumpet Honeysuckle was introduced in 1656. In the south and west and similar climates, it is best climbing through some shrub, but in colder districts it should be given the protection of a wall. From early June until late September its 1½—2 in. orange-scarlet flowers, white within are a delightful sight, held above the elliptic-ovate, green, glaucous leaves 3/6   5/-

  ,, **Tellmanniana (L. tragophylla × L. sempervirens superba).**—It is a strong grower bearing long-tubed rich yellow flowers tipped with bronzy-red. It received an Award of Merit on June 16th, 1931, and a beautiful coloured plate of this climber appeared in the Gardeners' Chronicle for December 5th, 1931 ... ...   2/6   3/6

  ,, **tragophylla.**—C. China. A strong grower, reaching in one year 10—15 ft. The oval tapering leaves are purplish-red, bluey-white beneath, and the flowers, conspicuous terminal heads of ten to twenty, 4—6 ins. long and orange-yellow, from June to September. It requires semi-shade, is perfectly hardy and one of the most glorious of all China's gifts to western gardens 5/-

Lyonia ligustrina (Andromeda ligustrina).—N.E. United States. Attains a height of 3—6 ft. ; alternate obovate leaves ; 6 in. panicles of lily-of-the-valley-like flowers in July and August ; autumn foliage blood red ...   2/6   3/6

Magnolia acuminata (The Cucumber Tree).—U.S.A. A strong-growing wide-spreading tree with dense wavy 5—10 in. oval leaves, bright green on both sides. The green-yellow flowers are only seen on mature trees   3/6   5/6   7/6

  ,, **Campbellii.**—E. Himalaya. A large tree of pyramidal habit, with handsome greyish leaves. The cup-shaped rosy-pink 9 in. flowers are fragrant but seldom seen on trees under fifteen to twenty years of age. From layers 15/6 21/-

  ,, **cordata (acuminata cordata).**—South U.S.A. A rarity of pyramidal habit, 5—12 ft. high. At the least touch the wood and leaves emit an aromatic fragrance that can be detected about it. The upright canary-yellow, scented flowers are freely borne in May and June, even on small plants 10/6 15/6

  ,, **Dawsoniana.**—Yunnan, China. Of bushy habit probably wider than high, it has 5—8 in. narrow obovate leaves, wedge-shaped at the base. It does not appear to have flowered yet in western gardens 15/6 21/-

Magnolia denudata (conspicua).—Yulan, C. China. This strik-　each.
ing large shrub or small tree grows freely in British
gardens, providing it is given an open position sheltered
by taller plants. The many goblet-shaped, pure white
flowers are borne from March to June, according to
season ... ...　7/6　10/6

E　　　　　**grandiflora.**—South U.S.A. Usually seen on south or
west walls, but in the south it is quite hardy in the open.
The 8 in. creamy-white flowers are conspicuous in late
summer and autumn, nestling among the huge glossy green
leaves ... ...　3/6　5/6　7/6

E　　　　　　　**ferruginea.**—A form reproduced by layering.
Its leaves on the underside are covered with a thick
russet felt ... ...　7/6　10/6

E　　　　　　　**Goliath.**—This stiff-branched ornamental carries
4—8 in. undulated oval-oblong leaves, the undersides
of which are covered thinly with a red-brown tomentum.
Its ivory-white, scented flowers, each consisting of 8—10
broad petals, are like huge tulips and when expanded
measure 12 ins. across ... ...　from 7/6

E　　　　　　　**lanceolata (Exmouth Variety of Gardens).**—
Also from layers. This form has narrower leaves, and
the large white flowers are borne on quite small plants　7/6　10/6

M. grandiflora and its forms grow and flower freely
in the open in sheltered gardens in the south and west.

"　　　**Kobus.**—Japan. An attractive species of pyramidal habit.
The creamy-white flowers, with ligulate petals, open in
May and somewhat resemble M. salicifolia, but much
larger. The stems and leaves are aromatic ...　3/6　5/6　7/6

"　　　　　**borealis.**—Hokkaido, N. Hondo. This rare and
distinct form ultimately makes a fine wide pyramidal
tree possibly 30 ft. high. The slender growths are
clothed with large deep green leaves, broadly obovate, and
the flowers are much larger than those of the type plant　7/6　10/6

"　　　**Lennei (denudata × liliflora) (Soulangeana Lennei of
Rehder).**—A hybrid with broad spreading branches
and flowers 4 ins. across. These are a lovely shade of
rich purple, white inside, and borne freely from early
April to the end of June, even on plants less than 3 ft.
high ... ...　5/6　7/6　10/6

"　　　**liliflora (purpurea) (M. obovata of Willd).**—China.
One of the best of the genus for villa or other small
gardens. It slowly grows to 5 ft. high and as much
wide. The aromatic thin stems are pretty from early
April to June with 3 in. bell-shaped, white-suffused
wine-red flowers nestling among the obovate-ovate
green leaves ... ...　7/6　10/6

"　　　　　**nigra (Soulangeana nigra of gardens).**—It is a
good ornamental for small gardens as it is slow to develop.
Even on quite small plants, the stiff short growths bear
many large deep wine-red coloured flowers (the darkest of
the family), from mid-March to the end of May ...　7/6　10/6

Magnolia macrophylla.—South U.S.A. Introduced as long ago   each.
as 1800, this handsome Magnolia is still rare in British
gardens. It develops into a large or small tree, according to locality and it requires a sheltered position to
prevent its huge leaves being damaged by summer gales.
The creamy-white fragrant flowers, often 12 ins. across,
are only produced on specimens fifteen or more years old
                                                    10/6 15/6 21/-

  ,,   **obovata (hypoleuca of Siebold and Zucc).**—Japan.
This makes a tall tree with a straight trunk two-thirds of
its height. It is a noble ornamental from spring till
autumn with its outward growing branches carrying
handsome, wavy, ovate, dark green leaves, glaucous
beneath and 15 ins. or more in length. The strongly
scented 8 in. creamy-white flowers, each with a boss
of crimson stamens and yellow anthers, are exhibited
during June here, but a little later in the north **5/-** **7/6 10/6**

E ,,   **parviflora (of Blume 1843) (M. fuscata) (Michelia
fuscata).**—China. A charming dwarf shrub, 2—3 ft.
high, with small glossy leaves. Being tender, it requires
a wall, preferably with west or northern aspect. The
small egg-shaped flowers are freely borne and enrich
the air about them with a beautiful perfume, not easily
described **10/6 15/6 21/-**

  ,,   **salicifolia.**—Japan. An upright, pyramidal tree, up to
40 ft. high, with lanceolate pale green leaves, bluey
beneath. The narrow-petalled, sweetly-scented white
flowers are borne on naked branches during April. Both
the wood and the leaves of the best form are aromatic **5/6** **7/6 10/6**

  ,,   **Sargentiana.**—W. China. This flowered in April, 1931,
at Caerhays Castle. A slender, graceful deciduous tree,
about 25 ft. high. The flowers are a long oval, white
tinted violet, and those who were fortunate enough to see
it agreed that it was one of the most beautiful trees they
had ever beheld. Unfortunately the flowers are only
borne on trees 15 or more years old **15/6 21/-**

  ,,   **Sieboldii (parviflora of Sieb. and Zucc. not of Blume)
1843.**—Japan. A wide-branching shrub, 7—15 ft. high,
producing its drooping 4 in. fragrant flowers with rosy-
crimson stamens, on quite small plants, from May to
August. It is a splendid plant and one of the easiest to
grow, especially if given a semi-shady position **3/6** **5/6** **7/6 10/6**

  ,,   **sinensis (Nicholsoniana of gardens).**—W. China.
Worthy of every garden. It grows into a large shrub or
small tree with large obovate leaves, covered beneath with
soft hairs. The elegant 4—6 in. cup-shaped pure white
flowers with glowing crimson stamens are freely borne
in May and June. It is beautifully illustrated in W. J.
Bean's Trees and Shrubs, Vol. III, page 224 ... **5/6** **7/6 10/6**

  ,,   **Soulangeana (denudata × liliflora).**—A noble hybrid,
rapidly developing into a fine tree. The handsome
flowers, purple shaded without, white within, are produced from April to June **5/6** **7/6 10/6**

Magnolia Soulangeana alba (alba superba of gardens).—One   each.
of the very best of the family and an easy grower,
ultimately developing into a large pyramidal shrub or
small tree. The first crop of handsome white perfumed
flowers are borne on leafless stems while the succeeding
ones develop and nestle among the green leaves. It
blooms from early April to mid-June **5/6**   **7/6 10/6**

"   "   **Alexandrina.**—A strong grower with spreading
branches, freely producing during May and June many
showy white flowers, each with a purple-red stain at the
base outside **7/6 10/6**

"   "   **Brozzonii.**—One of the most beautiful Magnolias
but exceedingly rare in British gardens. It soon grows
into a fine specimen 15 ft. or more high by as much wide.
It carries bold green leaves and the white flowers, 8—10
ins. wide and stained with purple at the base, are borne
freely, even on quite small plants from mid-April to
late May ... ... — —

"   "   **rustica.** This also is a vigorous grower and it
bears many discoloured flowers, not so heavily stained
as those of the former **7/6 10/6**

"   **stellata.**—Japan. It forms a wide, rounded head, taking
many years to grow 4 ft. high and 6 ft. across. It is
smothered during March and April with snow-white
flowers like water-lilies, almost hiding the bare
branches **3/6**   **5/6 7/6**

"   **Thompsoniana (virginiana × tripetala).**—1808. This
natural hybrid is of looser habit than M. virginiana and
has much larger, beautiful, fragrant flowers, freely borne
even on small plants, from May to September. The
4—9 in. wavy elliptical-oblong leaves are pale green
above and glaucous grey beneath. It is often seen as
a wide bush **10/6**

"   **tripetala (The Umbrella Magnolia).**—East U.S.A.
This grows into a large tree with a wide head. Its
obovate-oblong pale green leaves, glaucous beneath are
12—20 ins. long and 6—10 ins. wide and are very similar
to those of M. obovata. Its scented flowers are creamy-
white and 9 ins. across, in May and June ... **3/6**   **5/6 7/6**

"   **virginiana (glauca).**—East U.S.A. This choice Magnolia should be given a semi-shady position, in the south
and west, where it will quickly grow into a thin, upright
shrub or small tree, 6—15 ft. high. Its oval-oblong
lanceolate lustrous olive-green leaves are 4—9 ins.
long and blue-white beneath. The 2—3 in. globular
flowers, each with 9—12 petals, are deliciously scented
and borne from June to September **5/6**   **7/6 10/6**

"   **Watsonii.**—A natural hybrid from Japan, attaining to a
small tree. It is of easy culture but should be planted in
a sheltered position as it is susceptible to damage from
late frosts. The leaves are handsome and the upright
fragrant flowers, 5—6 ins. across, are ivory-white with
conspicuous crimson anthers. A specimen in flower
is a great ornament to the garden during May and June **10/6 to 42/-**

Magnolia Wilsonii.—W. China. Of wide-branching habit with long narrow leaves, distinctly glaucous beneath. The erect flowers are cup-shaped, 3—4 ins. across and pure white with showy deep crimson anthers. It flowers from mid-May to the end of June, but unfortunately is not quite hardy here 3/6   5/6   7/6

   each.

All the deciduous **Magnolias** love semi-shade.

FLOWERING AND ORNAMENTAL CRABS.

Malus aldenhamensis.—Hybrid. Splendid from mid-April to mid-May with large wine-red flowers nestling amongst the purplish-red foliage 2/6   3/6

„   **Aldenham Purple.**—Discarded as it cankers badly. M. pumila Wisley Crab has replaced it.

„   **Arnoldiana (floribunda × baccata).**—Discarded as it is such a poor grower.

„   **atrosanguinea (Halliana × Sieboldii) (floribunda atrosanguinea of gardens).**—Its graceful drooping branches, crowded with clusters of rose-red flowers, are a pretty sight every spring. As a standard it makes a fine pendulous head and is suitable for villa gardens   2/6   3/6

„   **baccata.**—Siberian Crab. A small tree with umbels of white flowers during April followed by small round, bright red fruits, retained long after the leaves drop   ...   3/6

„   „   **mandshurica (cerasifera).**—Manchuria. A beautiful crab quickly growing into a small tree, 10—15 ft. high. Its wealth of 1—2 in. sweetly scented white flowers are followed by ½—¾ in. bright red crabs which are retained long after the leaves drop. For many years it was incorrectly known as M. hupehensis (theifera)   3/6   5/6

„   **coronaria (M. fragrans of Rehder).** Ontario to Ohio. This uncommon species was first introduced in 1724. It quickly attains small tree size and is suitable for almost any kind of soil. The 2 in. violet-scented rose-coloured flowers are much admired every May and June. The handsome, wavy, ovate lobed leaves become gloriously tinted every autumn. This plant and the one following are two of the best ornamentals given to us by America 3/6   5/6   7/6

„   „   **Charlottae.**—A beautiful form with large semi-double bright rose-coloured, violet-scented flowers from mid-May to the end of June. Its large lobed leaves are as richly coloured in the autumn as those of the former. It is a free-grower and soon forms a large shrub or small tree, 12—20 ft. high 5/6   7/6   10/6

„   **earlhamensis.**—Hybrid. A good grower with purplish foliage. The flowers are rosy crimson and the fruits apple-like, crimson, and covered with bloom 3/6   5/6

„   **Eleyi (spectabilis × Niedzwetzkyana).**—A strong grower, of upright habit. Its spring foliage is an effective dark crimson. The flowers are rich wine-red, succeeded by masses of attractive round, bright red fruits shading to scarlet. A first-class ornamental tree 2/6   3/6   5/6

Malus florentina (Pyrus crataegifolia).—A rare slender-branched species, 8—12 ft. high, with grey hawthorn-like foliage which becomes brilliantly coloured every autumn. Its clusters of ¾ in. pure white flowers are succeeded by ½ in. red-faced fruits, speckled with brown 2/6   3/6   5/6

" **floribunda.**—Japan. One of the finest of all flowering small trees. The arching branches are covered with pale pink flowers at the end of April and beginning of May 2/6   3/6   5/6

"   " **purpurea.** (See **purpurea**).

" **fusca (rivularis) (diversifolia).**—Alaska to California. An uncommon shrub or small tree, 8—15 ft. high, with dense, slender, brown-red, downy growths. The ovate-oblong-lanceolate reticulated dark green leaves are tri-lobed, each lobe notched and serrated. Numerous clusters of 6—12, ¾—1¼ in. flesh-coloured flowers are borne during May. During the autumn its leaves become as richly coloured as those of Malus florentina   3/6   5/6

" **glaucescens.**—N. Carolina. This very rare and distinct species is worthy of every garden. The short, stiff, glaucous branches bear pretty lobed leaves and 1½ in. pale pink flowers, succeeded by 1½ in. depressed, globose, oily, green-yellow fruits, each with a corrugated eye. It is one of the most vivid autumn-colouring plants with us. M. bracteata is closely related 3/6   5/6   7/6

" **Halliana.**—A poor grower which has been discarded in favour of the beautiful M. Hartwigii

" **Hartwigii (Halliana × baccata).**—An attractive large shrub or small tree of upright habit, with growths covered with glaucous bloom. Its many flowers are bright pink outside, white within and 2 ins. across and look fine in May and June against the dark green leaves 2/6   3/6   5/6

" **hupehensis (theifera).**—C. & W. China. A very ornamental species, of splendid habit, bearing extra large cup-shaped fragrant pink flowers, ageing to pure white, which are succeeded by shining dark red fruits. It is one of the very best May and June flowering ornamentals 2/6   3/6   5/6

" **ioensis.**—Central U.S.A. The Prairie Crab is a small tree very rare in British gardens and is often confused with its double form and M. coronaria. It is quite as vigorous as the latter and has 3—4 in. tomentose grey-green leaves, these slightly lobed and deeply notched. The scented 1½—2 in. flowers are in loose clusters of 4—6, carmine ageing to pale pink in colour. 1938 delivery 3/6   5/6

"   " **plena (angustifolia plena) (Bechtel's Crab).**—One of the most difficult of all plants to establish in British gardens and no one seems to know its requirements. In a few places it grows into a small tree and produces, for a number of years, its lovely 2 in. full-double, bright pink, violet-scented flowers, during June   3/6   5/6

" **kansuensis.**—N.W. China. A rare species with tri-lobed leaves that colour well in autumn. It bears clusters of white hawthorn-like flowers. The fruits are small and dark crimson, covered with brown dots 2/6   3/6

each.

Malus Lemoinei.—This worthy hybrid has well merited its introduction into our gardens. It is strong growing and of good habit. The bronze-red leaves make a good background for the mass of deep crimson flowers and small red fruits 2/6   3/6   5/6

„ **magdeburgensis (spectabilis × pumila).**—It is a first-class ornamental of upright habit and soon grows into a standard. During May its branches are wreathed with conspicuous clusters of semi-double rich-pink flowers. It is a grand substitute where the double Almond and double Peach are not a success 3/6   5/6

„ **micromalus (spectabilis × ? baccata) (Kaido or Riversii of gardens).**—It soon grows into a large shrub or small tree, 8—12 ft. high. The upright growths carry an abundance of 2 in. semi-double flowers, wine-red in bud opening to rose-red 3/6   5/6

„ **orthocarpa (edulis).**—Japan. A large shrub or small tree, 6—10 ft. high, with numerous clusters of flesh-coloured flowers during April. It is one of the most conspicuous of all autumn-fruiting ornamentals with its mass of orange and scarlet-coloured crabs, held long after the leaves drop 2/6   3/6   5/6

„ **Prattii.**—C. & W. China. This distinct strong-growing species has large handsome lime-like leaves which seldom assume their brilliant tints before November. It carries ½ in. white flowers and small red fruits which are not attractive 2/6   3/6   5/6

„ **prunifolia.**—N.E. Asia. Of free and upright growth with clusters of 1½ in. white flowers. The branches even of young specimens, are laden from August to mid-November with brilliant red sub-globose or ovoid fruits. A good ornamental for any garden. This and M.p. fructu coccineo (Cheal's Crimson) appear to be identical 2/6   3/6   5/6

„ „ **rinki (Ringo).**—Unfortunately this large shrub or small tree is seldom seen in British gardens. It produces quantities of flesh-coloured flowers in May, and these are followed by a heavy crop of 1 in. bright yellow crabs, crowned with calyx lobes, which hang until November. It is undoubtedly the most conspicuous yellow-fruiting ornamental we have. This, Cashmere Crab, Cheal's Golden Gem and Gibbs' Golden Gage seem to be identical 3/6   5/6

„ „ **xanthocarpa (luteo).**—Showy throughout autumn with its large golden-yellow fruits. Known in gardens as the Yellow Siberian Crab 3/6   5/6

„ **pumila (Wild Apple).**—Europe and W. Asia ... ... — —

„ „ **Beauty of Montreal.**—One of the most attractive of all the Crabs, either in spring with its wealth of flowers, or in autumn when its branches are roped with 1½—2 in. conical, bright red-streaked fruits 3/6   5/6

„ „ **Dartmouth.**—Excellent in spring with its large white flowers. It bears showy plum-like fruits, covered with a reddish-purple bloom 2/6   3/6   5/6

„ „ **John Downie.**—The branches are laden during spring with large white flowers. A beautiful ornamental in autumn with its finely coloured conical fruits 2/6   3/6   5/6

Malus pumila Lady Northcliffe.—Wreathed in spring with   each.
pretty pink and white flowers, followed by a profusion of
small yellow fruits 2/6   3/6   5/6

„   „   **Veitch's Scarlet.**—Either in bush or standard
form, it makes a beautiful specimen and is worthy of
every garden. It bears large white flowers succeeded by
attractive scarlet fruits 2/6   3/6   5/6

„   „   **Wisley Crab.**—A handsome seedling with flowers
of a brilliant rich rose, nearly 2 ins. across and borne in
great profusion. They are followed by deep red fruits,
very similar to those of M. Aldenham Purple. The
strong growths and large leaves are bronze-red tinted 2/6   3/6   5/6

„   **purpurea (atrosanguinea × Niedzwetzkyana).**—One
of the most picturesque of all small trees and a great
favourite. Its semi-pendulous branches carry purple-
red leaves and are wreathed in spring with deep crimson
flowers. These are succeeded by variable rich crimson
crabs. It will thrive in any part of the British Isles   2/6   3/6   5/6

„   **Sargentii.**—Japan. A small shrub 5—8 ft. high, with
dense short growths. It is wreathed in May with pretty
white flowers succeeded by masses of small bright red
fruits 2/6   3/6   5/6

„   **Scheideckeri (floribunda × prunifolia).**—A splendid
flowering ornamental during May with its profusion of
1½ in. semi-double pale rose flowers ; not a fast grower,
of rather erect habit 3/6   5/6

„   **Sieboldii (Toringo).**—Japan. A fine habited large
shrub or small tree with small rose-pink flowers in May,
followed by a mass of glistening crimson cherry-like
fruits, held on 1½ in. thread-like stalks and retained for
weeks during autumn 2/6   3/6   5/6

„   **spectabilis.**—N. China. A small tree of round form,
15—25 ft. high, beautiful from mid-April to mid-May
with its large rosy-red flowers ageing to pale pink   ...   3/6   5/6

„   **sublobata (Sieboldii × prunifolia).**—This shrub
originated in Japan. It grows about 6 ft. high, of
pyramidal habit. The branches carry elliptic-oblong
leaves, each with one or two lobes, hairy beneath. It is
pretty in spring with clusters of pink-white flowers and
these are followed by ¾ in. globe-shaped, yellow fruits.
1938 delivery 3/6   5/6

„   **toringoides.**—W. China. A free-growing small tree
with wiry, semi-arching growths 2—5 ft. long, clothed
with pretty lobed leaves. It bears hawthorn-like
flowers and masses of decorative fruits the size of White
Heart Cherries 3/6   5/6

„   **trilobata.**—Syria. A worthy species, of pyramidal habit,
10—15 ft. high. The leaves are tri-lobed, leathery and
bright green, becoming seven-parted, buff-felted
beneath. Corymbs of white flowers are succeeded by
globular or pear-shaped fruits. Its foliage for weeks
during autumn changes to blood-red, ageing through
many tints to a vivid crimson 3/6   5/6   7/6

Malus Tschonoskii.—Japan. A unique species and a strong grower, reaching tree size. The young growths are attractively covered with downy felt. As an autumn tree it has few equals. The foliage turns through bronze to blood-red, flushed and streaked with vivid scarlet. The flowers are of little beauty but are followed by ¾ in. globose yellow-green fruits, with crimson cheeks and numerous yellow-brown dots ... ... 3/6   5/6   7/6   each.

   „ **yunnanensis.**—W. China. A fast-growing tree, possibly 25 ft. in height. The large apple leaves are covered on the underside with buff felt. For many weeks during autumn its orange and scarlet foliage is among the most attractive in the nursery 2/6   3/6   5/6

   „   „ **Veitchii.**—C. China. This handsome form has large cordate, lobulate leaves covered on both sides with a dense tomentum. The heads of white flowers are followed by bright red, white-dotted fruits 3/6   5/6

   „ **Zumi.**—Japan. Of shrubby habit, 8—12 ft. high, bearing clusters of pink flowers, ageing to white. The round glistening bright red fruits hang until late autumn ... 3/6   5/-

   „   „ **calocarpa.**—Japan. This charming shrub makes a fine pyramid, 8—12 ft. high, and its branches are densely packed with white flowers during May. The numerous round, polished, bright yellow, cherry-like fruits, held on ½—¾ in. stalks, are very similar to those of Viburnum Opulus xanthocarpa and last long after the leaves drop. A fine plant for any garden 3/6   5/6

See also **Standard Trees.**

E **Margyricarpus setosus.**—Ecuador to Patagonia. A charming prostrate shrub requiring a sloping position ; ideal for the heather garden. The insignificant flowers are followed by a mass of pearl-like fruits 1/6   2/6

E **Maytenus Boaria.**—Chile. A rare thinly-branched evergreen with oblong, dark green, finely serrated leaves, paler beneath 5/-   7/6

E   „ **chilensis.**—Chile. Of more open habit with smaller leaves. These are alternate, oblong, undulated, having the uppermost two-thirds slightly serrated. A specimen 10 ft. high, and in full fruit, may be easily mistaken for our native spindlewood when seen from a distance ... 5/-   7/6

Meliosma myriantha.—China, Japan. A choice shrub, tender in its young state so that it needs careful attention until it becomes hard-wooded ; sweet-chestnut-like leaves and panicles of many small whitish fragrant flowers in June and July 5/-   7/6

Menziesia ciliicalyx.—Japan. This is of stiff upright habit with short growths and tufts of 1—2½ in. obovate green leaves, glaucous grey beneath and edged with bristly hairs. The ends of the previous year's growths bear clusters of ½ in. cylindrical, exquisite pink flowers, with lobes of a deeper pink, during May and June ... 7/6   10/6

   „ **empetriformis.** (See **Phyllodoce empetriformis**).

Menziesia multiflora.—Japan. A bushy shrub, 3—5 ft. high, with its current growths coated with glaucous bloom. Its round or oval-obovate, reticulated leaves are 1—2 ins. long, metallic-green above and light blue beneath and are edged with bristly hairs. From early May to July, it is very pretty with its many drooping clusters of flesh-coloured, contracted bells two-thirds as large as those of M. ciliicalyx   ...   .   10/6   each.

„   **pilosa (globularis).**—N. America. A shrub for semi-shade, 18—30 ins. high. The obovate leaves are pale green, the underside covered with grey down. The amber to white bell-shaped flowers are borne during May and June 2/6   3/6   5/6

„   **polifolia.** (See **Daboecia cantabrica**).

„   **purpurea.**—Japan. A bushy shrub, 3—5 ft. high, with short, stiff, wiry twigs and tufts of oval-obovate green leaves, glaucous blue beneath. The freely borne ½ in. rich wine-red campanulate flowers are in groups and are a grand sight every May, June and July. It is also one of the very best autumn-colouring shrubs 10/6
The genus **Menziesia** contains some of the finest of flowering shrubs. They grow and flower freely if given woodland conditions or semi-shade from distant trees.

E **Mitchella repens.**—N. America. Known as long ago as 1761. It grows quite flat on the ground and has wiry shoots which carry pretty, opposite, ¼—½ in. ovate-round leaves. Large irregular orange-scarlet fruits are held from September to May. It is a charming plant for a semi-shady position in the Ericaceae border and a lovely specimen was much admired at the Alpine Garden Society's Show April 20th, 1937   ...   .   2/6   3/6   5/6

E **Mitraria coccinea.**—Chile. A prostrate shrub or a climber according to position, bearing from June onwards, orange-scarlet flowers, like suspended penstemons. It is not so tender as many suppose, and well worth trying in semi-shade or on a north or west wall 2/6   3/6

Mountain Ash. (See **Sorbus Aucuparia**).

EC **Muehlenbeckia complexa.**—New Zealand. A rampant trailer or climber with wiry interlacing growths and pretty fiddle-shaped leaves. In a garden near here, it has made a splendid hedge and wind-break by working its way through a stretch of wire netting. It is also good for hiding stack-pipes, etc. 2/6   3/6

EC **Mutisia decurrens (Comber's Form).**—A choice climber from Chile. In the south and west it is much happier if planted in the open under some deciduous twiggy shrub and allowed to ramble at will. The flowers are great marigolds of flaming orange, 4—5 ins. across. It dislikes drought or sun on its roots   ...   .   —   —

Myrica asplenifolia. (See **Comptonia asplenifolia**).

E „   **californica.**—California. A conspicuous shrub with serrated aromatic bright green glossy leaves, toothed and slightly recurved. Its small greenish flowers are followed by purple fruits, coated with showy grey-white wax. A very hardy evergreen 5/-   7/6

Myrica caroliniensis.—U.S.A. and Canada. A rare, very hardy, bushy, compact shrub with oval shining green leaves notched towards the apex, the underside resin dotted, which are pleasantly fragrant, and during storms the air is filled with lemon scent. The small fruits are coated with white wax, whilst the autumn foliage is magnificently coloured ... ... **each.** 2/6 3/6

„ **cerifera.**—U.S.A. A very hardy semi-evergreen shrub, 2—5 ft. high. The variable oblanceolate dark green leaves, notched towards the apex, are deliciously fragrant and many assume rich autumnal tints. Small fruits covered with white wax are borne along the previous year's growths 1/6 2/6

E „ **rubra.**—Received from Japan and one of the most distinct of all evergreens. It grows 5 ft. or more high in gardens in the south and west counties and has pleasing 5—10 in. obovate-oblanceolate, aromatic, green leaves, wavy and coarsely toothed 3/6 5/6

The Myricas will grow in almost any soil free from lime. In the south they love the shade of distant trees.

E **Myrsine africana.**—China, Himalayas, Azores. A dense, twiggy, compact shrub, 3—5 ft. high, clothed with box-like leaves. The tiny green flowers are succeeded by numerous small orange-shaped red fruits. It loves semi-shade 2/6 3/6

E „ „ **retusa.**—An interesting and rare slow-growing shrub of compact habit, suitable for a pan in the alpine house, or for a position on the rock garden. A specimen 10 years old may only be 6 ins. × 9 ins. Its twigs bear dense, obovate or orbicular tiny green leaves, crowned with small teeth 10/6

E „ **Urvillei.**—New Zealand. In mild parts this is a handsome bush. The undulated leaves are similar to Pittosporum Buchananii and assume a bronze colour. It bears small white flowers and black fruits 7/6

E **Myrtus Bidwillii.**—New Zealand. An erect-growing small shrub. The minute box-like leaves are brightly coloured. It is a tender plant and only suitable for the south-west 2/6 3/6

E „ **bullata.**—New Zealand. A hardy shrub around the sea coast of the south and west of Ireland. The conspicuous corrugated leaves are remarkable and in many shades of red, distinctly attractive 5/-

E „ **communis (Common Myrtle).**—Mediterranean. Quite hardy in many parts of the south and west and is well known for its fragrant creamy flowers during July and August 2/6 3/6

E „ „ **tarentina (Tarentum Myrtle).**—Of dense bushy habit with small narrow dark green leaves, rather small white flowers and white fruits. As hardy as the common myrtle 2/6 3/6

E „ **Luma** (See **Eugenia apiculata**).

E „ **nummularia.**—A prostrate alpine shrub from the Falkland Islands with trailing growths, never exceeding 1 in. in height, starred with white flowers. These are followed by attractive pink fruits. In the south, it loves semi-shade 1/6 2/6

E **Myrtus obcordata.**—New Zealand. A graceful shrub with thin   each.
erect branches and tiny grey leaves. The small white
flowers are followed by dark red fruits, ageing to dark
violet. It is perfectly hardy in the south and west
seaside gardens 2/6   3/6

E „ **Ugni.**—Chile. A treasure for a hot corner or wall. Its
flowers are waxy pink bells, richly scented, and are followed by edible fruits, mahogany-red in colour, borne
in great profusion 2/6   3/6

E **Nandina domestica.**—C. China to Japan. An erect shrub of
graceful appearance. The much divided leaves are 1½ ft.
or more long, highly coloured during spring and autumn.
It bears 8—12 in. panicles of white flowers during June
and July. In the south of Europe this plant fruits freely
in gardens sheltered from the north winds. The fruits
are brilliant coral-red 2/6   3/6   5/6

Neillia longiracemosa.—One of the prettiest of May and June
flowering shrubs. It grows 5—8 ft. high, and its
elegant growths bear many pendulous racemes of rose-
pink flowers 2/6   3/6

„ **ribesioides.**—Yunnan, China. This rare and pretty
species produces slender arching brown-red shoots,
4—6 ft. high, which carry numerous 1—3 in. racemes
packed with bright pink flowers during May and June.
It is happy in almost any soil and situation ...   3/6   5/6

Nothofagus antarctica.—Terra del Fuego to Chile. The thin
elegant branches are densely clothed with ½—1 in. cordate or ovate-truncate, crumpled, bright green leaves   7/6   10/6

E „ **cliffortioides.**—New Zealand. Its black-brown stems
carry tiny, closely packed, polished green, net-veined
leaves, very similar to those of Myrtus Bidwillii   ...   7/6   10/6

E „ **Cunninghamii.**—A graceful small glossy-leaved evergreen Beech from Tasmania, attaining 8—20 ft. in the
milder parts. The young foliage is coppery coloured 5/6   7/6   10/6

E „ **Dombeyi.**—Chile, Argentine. An extremely rare species
with very slender growths. The ovate glossy green
leaves are 1 in. long by ½—¾ in. wide, irregularly toothed 10/6   15/6

E „ **fusca.**—New Zealand. It is one of the fastest-
growing evergreen Nothofagus. Its thin zig-zag growths
are furnished with widely spaced ¾—1½ in. ovate or ovate-
orbicular, undulated, glistening, bronze-green leaves   7/6   10/6

E „ **Menziesii.**—New Zealand. This is one of the prettiest of
the southern Nothofagus. Its small, broad, ovate, grey-
green leaves are doubly toothed and many of them are
wedge-shaped at the base. They are evenly distributed
along the downy, brown twigs 5/6   7/6   10/6

E „ **Moorei.**—New South Wales. The most attractive of the
evergreen Nothofagus, but only suitable for gardens in
the west, Ireland and west of Scotland. Its 1—3 in.
ovate-lanceolate, serrated leaves are brilliantly tinted
when young and age to olive green ... ...   —   —

„ **obliqua.**—Chile. In a sheltered position, it quickly
grows to 30 ft. or more high by half as wide and a tree
here withstands 20 degrees of frost. It makes a beautiful pyramidal head and its thin growths are a pleasing
sight throughout the growing season when they are
densely furnished with 1½—3 in. ovate or oblong bright
green leaves. During September and October these
turn brilliant yellow ... ...   —   —

each.

Nothofagus procera.—Chile. A handsome fast-growing species which withstood twenty-six degrees of frost. The oval tapering leaves are conspicuously corrugated, turning in autumn a ripe yellow 10/6

E   „   **Solandri.**—New Zealand. Its slender and slightly zig-zag wiry branches are decorated with small ovate burnished bronze-green leaves which age to pale green. They are much smaller and are held more loosely than those of M. cliffortioides 7/6   10/6

The evergreen **Nothofagus** are fast-growing and soon reach a height of 10—30 ft. They are happiest in thin woodlands, or where they get the semi-shade from distant trees, around the south and west coast, Ireland or the west of Scotland.

Notospartium Carmichaeliae.—A beautiful shrub from New Zealand, of elegant habit 6—12 ft. high. The almost leafless branches are crowded with short racemes of twelve to twenty pink pea-like flowers in June and July. The best specimens in the south and west are in semi-shade 3/6   5/6

Nuttallia cerasiformis (male and female).—California. A very hardy shrub, 6—12 ft. high which will grow in almost any soil. The short racemes of white, deliciously almond-scented flowers are borne from January to March on leafless twigs and are followed by showy purple plum fruits, coated with bluey bloom 1/6   2/6   3/6

Nyssa aquatica (tomentosa).—N. America. The true plant is very rare in British gardens. It can be easily distinguished from N. sylvatica by its upright habit, dull red annual growths, and 3—6 in. ovate-oblong-acuminate, wavy, bright green leaves, glaucous-grey beneath. These assume bright yellow and orange-red tints during the autumn. It is quite easy to grow if given woodland conditions 7/6   10/6

„   **sylvatica (multiflora).**—N. America. In 10 years, in a loose soil, this tree should attain 15 ft. or more. It has outward-growing branches which become more or less pendulous with age. They are densely furnished with obovate-elliptical acuminate, metallic-green leaves, pale green beneath and often wedge-shaped at the base. It is one of the most beautiful autumn-colouring trees. In a famous Sussex garden there are many hundreds, 10—25 ft. high and in autumn they are one of the finest sights to be seen in these Islands 5/-   7/6   10/6

Both species love woodland conditions, where the scorching sun does not get at their roots. If planted in the open, it is advisable to have dwarf heathers about them to keep the soil cool during summer.

E   **Olea chrysantha.**—In the south and west it forms a shapely bush 6—10 ft. high. The opposite twisted leaves are pale green beneath 3/6   5/6

E   „   **europaea.**—S. Europe, Asia Minor. The fruiting Olive. It has 2—3 in. oblong smooth leaves of deep glossy green. It is hardy along the south and west coast, where it grows to a height of 6—10 ft. 3/6   5/6

			each.
E	**Olea excelsa.**—This beautiful evergreen, 8—10 ft. high, is quite hardy in the south and west. The dark green undulated leaves, pale beneath, are 3—6 ins. long and 1½—3 ins. wide with shallow teeth towards the apex	5/-	7/6
E	„ **rotundifolia.**—An uncommon elegant shrub for a south or west wall in the south, but quite hardy in the south and west of Ireland and in Cornwall. Its variable leaves are dark green and polished	3/6	5/6
E	**Olearia albida (oleifolia of gardens).**—It is one of the most attractive of July and August flowering shrubs with its mass of white flowers nestling among its 1—4 in. ovate shining green leaves, these being white beneath. It grows into a compact bush 4—7 ft. high and as much wide and is invaluable as a wind break in the southern and western counties	2/6	3/6
E	„ **arborescens (nitida).**—In the south and west this attains tree size. The large ovate deep green leaves are silvery beneath. It is conspicuous from July to September with large trusses of white, daisy-like sweetly-scented flowers	2/6	3/6
E	„ **argophylla.**—A tender species, only suitable for mild parts, but a strong grower. The musk-scented leaves are silvery white beneath. Its flowers are white, from July to September	2/6	3/6
E	„ **avicenniaefolia.**—A handsome shrub with deep green leaves narrowed at each end and silvery and buff beneath. The flowers are white, in July. It grows freely in the south and west	2/6	3/6
E	„ **chathamica.**—Chatham Islands. A grand species for mild and coastal districts, with similar leaves to O. semidentata, but larger, and white flowers	3/6	5/6
E	„ **Colensoi.**—A noble-looking shrub for the south-west. The large grey leaves are covered beneath with thick white tomentum	—	—
E	„ **erubescens.**—Australia. A loose scandent shrub suitable for a wall. It has 1 in. oblong leaves, with the margins unevenly toothed, and small white flowers in May and June. Previously distributed as O. myrsinoides	2/6	3/6
E	„ **Forsteri (paniculata).**—An upright shrub growing 6—20 ft. high. The leaves are pale green with distinct wavy margins, silvery beneath. One of the last to flower and the least conspicuous, but deliciously scented	2/6	3/6
E	„ **furfuracea (ferruginea).**—A conspicuous shrub 5—10 ft. high, of rounded form. The ovate-oblong leaves are grey with dark chocolate mid-rib, tawny coloured beneath. The panicles of white flowers are produced at midsummer	2/6	3/6
E	„ **Gunniana (stellulata of gardens).**—Tasmania. A hardy shrub throughout the south and west counties, of compact habit and 3—5 ft. high, with 1 in. oblong, grey aromatic leaves. The whole plant during May is smothered with white daisy-like flowers. A pleasing and very useful shrub	1/6	2/6
E	„ „ **Comber's varieties.**—In shades of purple, red, mauve and blue. These new forms from Tasmania are more open in habit, but not so hardy here as the type. They grow in many seaside gardens in the south and west and flower every spring ... ... To colour	2/6	3/6

			each.
E	**Olearia ilicifolia (Maori Holly).**—A distinct branching shrub 3—7 ft. high, with lanceolate glaucous fragrant leaves, the margins set with uneven, coarse, spinose teeth, which are silvery-grey beneath. It bears corymbs of musk-scented white flowers during summer and is reasonably hardy		2/6 3/6
E	„ **insignis (Pachystegia insignis).**—An aristocratic-looking dwarf shrub for the south and west, with few straggling tomentose branches. The ovate leaves are 3—4 ins. long, covered beneath with a thick white tomentum. Its 3 in. white marguerite-like flowers are borne on 6—12 in. stalks. It requires a sloping position with stones around its roots		— —
E	„ **lacunosa.**—An exceedingly rare and most distinct shrub, slowly growing to 4 ft. or more. Its short, stiff, erect growths are decorated with linear-lanceolate, glazed, green leaves, 3—7 ins. long and $\frac{1}{4}$—$\frac{1}{2}$ in. wide. They are buff-felted beneath and have conspicuous midribs, pearl-white on both sides		21/-
E	„ „ This form is free-growing, of upright habit, 4—8 ft. high. The stiff branches are closely packed with long narrow leaves, very similar to those of Ilex verticillata, buff-felted beneath and with midribs duller than those of the former...		3/6 5/6
E	„ **lineata.**—Attains 6—12 ft. high, of narrow habit, with effective, slender, drooping branches and opposite tufts of five grass-like recurved leaves. It bears numerous clusters of white flowers during June		2/6 3/6
E	„ **macrodonta.**—A splendid shrub for the south and west counties, 8—15 ft. high, which makes a good seaside hedge. The handsome grey holly-like leaves are silvery beneath. It is covered during June with 3—8 in. heads of many white honey-scented flowers ... 1/6	2/6 3/6
E	„ **moschata.**—A compact shrub, $1\frac{1}{2}$—$2\frac{1}{2}$ ft. high, of short branches furnished with small greyish-green leaves. The small white flowers develop from July to September	1/6 2/6
E	„ **myrsinoides.**—Australia & Tasmania. Similar to O. argophylla in the scent of the leaves, which are smaller. It is of more open habit and bears many white flowers during late summer and autumn. Previously distributed as O. erubescens		2/6 3/6
E	„ **nummularifolia.**—A short, twiggy shrub of dense habit, 2—4 ft. high and almost as wide. It is pretty during June and July with masses of small white flowers held above the recurved leaves		1/6 2/6
E	„ **Rossii.**—A natural hybrid between O. macrodonta and O. argophylla, with the habit of the latter but hardier. The greyish leaves are silvery beneath		2/6 3/6
E	„ **semidentata.**—Chatham Isles. A magnificent shrub for milder districts, attaining 3—8 ft. The lustrous green lanceolate leaves are thickly white felted beneath. Its heads of beautiful $1\frac{1}{2}$ in. mauve daisies with violet discs are borne during summer and autumn. It requires well-drained soil 1/6	2/6 3/6
E	„ **Solandri.**—An erect, dense-branched shrub, 3—5 ft. high, clothed with tiny leaves having a golden-yellow appearance		2/6

E **Olearia speciosa.**—Australia. An attractive shrub for mild parts,   each.
2—4 ft. high, although at Killarney, Cork, Bantry, etc.
it grows to a height of 5—8 ft. and quite as much in
width. The ovate-oblong, irregularly-toothed leaves
are 1—2½ ins. long and thickly covered beneath with
tawny felt. The loose heads of 1 in. white flowers are
produced from June to September 3/6

     All the **Olearias** are native to New Zealand except
where otherwise stated. They are indispensable for
seaside gardens ; some make splendid wind breaks and
will grow in practically any soil.

E **Osmanthus Aquifolium.**—Japan. A handsome shrub of
rounded habit, attaining 4—8 ft., with dark green,
polished, holly-like leaves. Its numerous small white
scented flowers are borne from September to October.
In the southern and western counties and especially near
the sea, it makes a beautiful ornamental hedge and is
easily kept in shape 2/6   3/6   5/6

E   „   **armatus.**—W. Hupeh, China. A stiff-branched shrub
of rounded form with 3—6 in. oblong-lanceolate leaves,
the margins furnished with uneven teeth. It bears
small creamy-white flowers during autumn and is a free-
growing shrub in semi-shade 3/6   5/6

E   „   **Delavayi.**—Yunnan, China. A dense, twiggy-branched
shrub of compact habit with small, round, glossy green
leaves. During April it is a mass of tubular, scented
snow-white flowers in bunches of five to nine. It is
free-growing in semi-shade and one of the best of hardy
shrubs 1/6   2/6   3/6   5/6

E   „   **Forrestii.**—N.W. Yunnan, China. A fast-growing species
of erect habit, 5—12 ft. high. In the south, it loves a
semi-shady position. The attractive, leathery, 3—8 in.
ovate-lanceolate leaves are wavy and furrowed and are
graced with a conspicuous pale yellow midrib. They
are edged with spines similar to those of the holly   ...   3/6   5/6

E   „   **serrulatus.**—W. Szechuan, China. A compact slow-
growing species a few feet high. It bears polished green
lanceolate leaves, tapering to sharp points, the margins
set with saw-like teeth. The clusters of sweetly-scented
white flowers are borne from February to April, according to the weather 2/6   3/6   5/6

E   „   **suavis (Siphonosmanthus suavis).** — Himalaya. This
rare evergreen will grow to 6 ft. or more, if given a semi-
shady position. Its verrucose stems carry pairs of 1—3 in.
glossy, deep green, oval-lanceolate leaves, the margins
finely serrated. The small white sweetly-scented
flowers occur in groups, in the axils of the leaves,
from mid-winter until late March 5/6   7/6

E **Osmarea Burkwoodii.**—A bigeneric hybrid, the result of a
cross between Osmanthus Delavayi and Phillyrea decora,
the seed parent being the former species. It bears
clusters of seven to nine ½ in. tubular white flowers,
distinctly fragrant, during May 3/6   5/6

E **Osteomeles Schwerinae.**—W. China. A very useful hardy each.
shrub for south or west walls, with slender arching
branches. It is furnished with pinnate leaves of eleven
to fourteen pairs of small greyish leaflets. The clusters of
fragrant hawthorn-like flowers in June are followed by
egg-shaped dark red fruits. It is often confused with
O. anthyllidifolia (Lindley), a distinct and much tenderer
plant from the Bonin Islands 3/6   5/6

E   „   „   **subrotunda.**—E. China. A distinct small shrub
with short growths. The leaves, 1 in. long and pinnate,
consist of seven to nine pairs of tiny leaflets. Small
corymbs of ½ in. white flowers in June 3/6   5/6

Oxydendrum arboreum (Andromeda arborea).—N. America.
It soon grows to a height of 10—20 ft. and its branches
often sweep the ground. It loves semi-shade and a lime-
free soil. From early July to September, the many
terminal panicles, composed of 6—10 in. drooping racemes
of white bell-shaped flowers are a beautiful sight. The
3—6 in. red-tinged, oblong-lanceolate, furrowed leaves
assume gorgeous colourings in autumn   3/6   5/6   7/6 10/6

Ozothamnus rosmarinifolius. (See **Helichrysum**).

E **Pachysandra terminalis.**—Japan. An invaluable dwarf plant
for a shady position and under trees. It grows 4—8 ins.
high, ultimately forming a mass of leafy twigs 1/6   2/6

E **Pachystima Canbyi.**—Virginia to N. Carolina. A rare compact
shrub, 6—12 ins. high, of interest to collectors of the
uncommon. The thin growths carry numerous tiny
opposite linear-oblong green leaves with decurved
margins. It is suitable for a position on the rock garden in lime-free soil 2/6   3/6

Pampas Grass (See **Cortaderia**).

Parrotia persica.—Persia. Once established, this soon forms a
small tree 10—20 ft. high, with spreading branches.
The young foliage is tinged pink, whilst in autumn   3/6   5/6
it turns crimson, gold and orange. It resents drought   7/6 10/6

Parrotiopsis Jacquemontiana (Parrotia Jacquemontiana).—
W. Himalayas. An uncommon bushy shrub, 4—6 ft.
high. The 1½ in. flowers (bracts) are borne on the
ends of the short twigs from April to the end of August.
During autumn the roundish leaves assume various
shades of yellow 3/6   5/6   7/6 10/6

C **Passiflora coerulea.**—S. Brazil, Peru. The well-known blue
Passion Flower. It produces its 3—4 in. flowers from
June to September 2/6   3/6

C   „   „   **Constance Elliott.**—Ivory-white flowers ...   2/6   3/6

Paulownia tomentosa (imperialis).—Japan. It is tender in
its youth, but with age develops into a round headed
tree, 15—30 ft. high, according to locality. It is worth
a place in the garden for its handsome leaves. Unfortunately the violet-blue, campanulate or foxglove-like
flowers are seldom seen except after hot summers.
It blooms in May 3/6   5/6   7/6

Pavia. (See **Aesculus**).

Peraphyllum ramosissimum.—Oregon to Colorado. An
extremely rare shrub with spreading branches, rarely
more than 3 ft. high. It bears greyish narrow oblanceolate leaves and white hawthorn-like flowers in April and
May 3/6   5/6

each.

E **Pernettya furiens (ciliaris) (Gaultheria furiens) (Arbutus furiens).**—Chile. It has been named and renamed many times but it is undoubtedly a true Pernettya, for its fruits are held in a fleshy calyx. It is an interesting shrub for the Ericaceae border and in a shady position, it will attain 2—4 ft. The many clusters of white lily-of-the-valley-like flowers are borne among the 1—1½ in. leathery, ovate-lanceolate green leaves during May and June and are followed by plum-coloured dented fruits. This is illustrated under the name of Gaultheria furiens in A. T. Johnson's "Woodland Garden," page 92   2/6   **3/6   5/6**

E   „ **leucocarpa (Gayana).**—Chile, Argentine. An upright-growing shrub, 6—12 ins. high but much wider. The short wiry growths are densely clothed with ½ in. linear-oblong green leaves. It is one of the most free flowering of the genus, and has pink or white berries 2/6   **3/6**

E   „   „ **linearis.**—S. America. A delightful form, 6—9 ins. high, with a mass of interlacing short twiggy growths crowded with linear leaves ½—¾ in. long by one-tenth of an inch wide 2/6   **3/6**

E   „ **macrostigma.**—Previously distributed as Gaultheria perplexa. A wiry intricate branching shrub, 6—12 ins. high, but much wider, having narrow linear leaves, ¼—½ in. long and tiny white flowers. It is one of the joys of all dwarf flowering shrubs with its mass of corrugated rose-red fruits, held well into the new year   ...   2/6   **3/6**

E   „ **mucronata.**—Chile, Patagonia. An admirable shrub where rhododendrons and heathers grow, forming dense bushes 2 ft. or more high. From autumn to spring the twiggy branches are laden with round crimson fruits   1/6   **2/6**

E   „   „ **Bell's Seedling.**—The handsomest of all the shrubby Pernettyas. Its slender branches are loaded from September till March with crimson-red fruits, like tiny crabs, each ½ in. or more in diameter 2/6   **3/6**

E   „   „ **Davis's Hybrids.**—In the following coloured fruits : white, several distinct shades of red, cream, pink, lilac, crimson and almost black. These hybrids and Bell's Seedling carry heavy crops of fruits every autumn, without the aid of a recognised male form, but they are visited by many bees during the flowering season. The colours vary in tint, according to the soil   ...   1/6   **2/6   3/6**

E   „   „ **rupicola.**—Chile, Argentine. A slender shrub 2 ft. high, with twiggy growths carrying ovate-lanceolate leaves about ½ in. long and with usually five shallow teeth on each side. The many ½ in. cream-coloured fruits are held until the new year...   ...   .   **3/6**

E   „ **prostrata Pentlandii.**—Venezuela, Patagonia. This is reputed to be tender but here, in a shady border, it is quite happy although the soil often gets frozen to a depth of 6 ins. It is a semi-prostrate shrub, 6—12 ins. high, with overlapping branches carrying many slightly corrugated blue-purple fruits, from July to autumn frosts   2/6   **3/6**

E   „ **pumila (empetrifolia).**—Falkland Islands & Patagonia. Its compact flat habit and bright green appearance make it one of the most cherished of all dwarf plants. It bears quantities of small white lily-of-the-valley-like flowers. Height 3—4 ins. Previously distributed as P. magellanica 2/6   **3/6**

E **Pernettya rigida (Bridgesii).**—Juan Fernandez Islands. Shaded by taller shrubs, in an exposed New Forest garden, it is 2 ft. high and 5 ft. across. Its rigid semi-pendulous, branches carry numerous closely set ½—¾ in. broadly ovate leaves edged with shallow teeth. The numerous small white flowers are followed by many fruits which however, do not colour in this part of the country ... **each.** **3/6**

E „ **tasmanica.**—Tasmania. A shade-loving, spreading dwarf shrub, less than 3 ins. high, clothed with tiny green leaves. The small white flowers in April and May are followed by ½ in. grooved bright red fruits, retained well into the new year **2/6** **3/6** **5/6**

The genus **Pernettya** has been revised by H. Sleumer in " Notizblatt des Bot. Gart. und Museums zu Berlin—Dahlem." No. 115, Vol. XII, 626-655 (December, 1935).

Perowskia atriplicifolia.—Afghanistan, Himalayas, Tibet. A charming sub-shrub, 2—3 ft. high, with scented small grey leaves and 6—15 in. spikes of violet-blue flowers from August to October. It delights in heat and sunshine in almost any kind of soil, including chalk ... **1/6** **2/6**

Pertya sinensis.—C. China. An interesting botanical shrub, 3—5 ft. high, related to Artemisia Abrotanum, better known as Boy's Love. The brown twiggy branches are clothed with 2—3 in. ovate or oblong-lanceolate, pointed leaves some of which have 1—3 teeth. It produces many ½ in. heads, each containing 10—12 purple-pink flowers during June and July **3/6**

Petteria ramentacea.—E. Europe. An erect-growing shrub, 6—10 ft. high, related to the Laburnums, with trifoliate leaves and 3 in. upright showy racemes of yellow, scented flowers during May and June **2/6** **3/6**

Philadelphus (Mock Orange). Incorrectly known as **Syringa.**

„ **brachybotrys.**—China. It is one of the showiest of June-flowering shrubs and has 5—8 ft. slender branches wreathed from end to end with racemes of 1 in. fragrant white flowers **1/6** **2/6**

„ **Coulteri.**—N. Mexico. This admirable shrub is of erect habit, 4—6 ft. high, and is hardy in many gardens, within reach of the salt air in the south and west. Inland it requires a south or west wall, where it quickly attains 7—12 ft. The beautiful 1 in. cupped flowers are like carved ivory, a tinge of purple at the base. These scent the air about them from July onwards **2/6** **3/6**

„ **Delavayi.**—The Chinese form of P. tomentosus. The large roundish leaves are grey-felted beneath. 4—6 in. racemes of 1 in. white fragrant flowers are borne during May and early June. A very pretty flowering species **2/6** **3/6**

„ **grandiflorus.**—S. United States. Large bushes, 10—12 ft. high, often seen in old cottage gardens, are beautiful in June and July when their swaying branches are white with 2 in. saucer-shaped, scentless flowers ... **1/6** **2/6**

„ **hybridus Albâtre.** — Free-flowering ; large panicles of double white, fragrant flowers **2/6**

„ „ **Argentine.** — 2 in. pure white flowers of perfect form **2/6**

	each.	
Philadelphus hybridus Avalanche.—Arching branches wreathed with 1 in. single, white, scented flowers. One of the very best	1/6	2/6
„ „ **Belle Etoile.**—The most beautiful of the purple-blotched Philadelphus ; 3—5 ft. flexible branches, laden with numerous 2 in. saucer-shaped, very fragrant white flowers during July		2/6
„ „ **Boule d'Argent.**—Quantities of showy fragrant white double flowers	1/6	2/6
„ „ **Bouquet Blanc.**—Very effective masses of snow-white double flowers	1/6	2/6
„ „ **Dame Blanche.**—Sweetly-scented fimbriated semi-double creamy-white flowers		2/6
„ „ **Fantaisie.**—1 in. pure white fimbriated flat flowers with distinct rosy-purple base, sweetly scented ...	1/6	2/6
„ „ **Favorite.**—It is the third best hybrid Mock Orange and an ornament to any garden. It grows 5—8 ft. high and its stiff erect growths are decorated with 3 in. cup-shaped pure white flowers, their petals serrated, during June and early July		2/6
„ „ **Girandole.**—Double milk-white imbricated flowers of perfect form		2/6
„ „ **Glacier.**—Milk-white double flowers in clusters		2/6
„ „ **Mont Blanc.**—Erect-growing branches wreathed with very sweetly-scented single white flowers	1/6	2/6
„ „ **Norma.**—Large, single, white		2/6
„ „ **Nuée Blanche.**—Large, round, snow-white flowers		2/6
„ „ **Pyramidal.**—Tall-growing, with panicles of large double white flowers		2/6
„ „ **Virginal.**—The most conspicuous of the double Philadelphus as yet. Extra large panicles of snow-white double flowers during June, and one of the loveliest of summer shrubs	1/6	2/6
„ „ **Voie Lactée.**—2 in. round, flattish, snow-white flowers with showy yellow stamens		2/6
The above hybrids flower during June.		
„ **insignis (Billiardii) (pubescens × californicus).**—This beautiful hardy Mock Orange attains 5—10 ft., according to soil and position. It carries many attractive 5—9 in. leafy panicles of 15—30, 1—1½ in. cup-shaped white flowers, during July	1/6	2/6
„ **mexicanus.**—Mexico. Requires similar culture to P. Coulteri. It is tall and of spreading habit with pure white flowers, during June and July, beautifully scented	2/6	3/6
„ **microphyllus.**—Colorado. A dense graceful specimen, 5 ft. × 5 ft., was the finest sight seen in an open border, in a Gloucestershire garden, in June, 1935. The numerous wiry growths were laden with 1 in. white, stained purple, flowers nestling among the small ovate leaves. They were strongly pineapple-scented like Magnolia Watsonii	2/6	3/6
„ **satsumanus (acuminatus).**—Japan. A strong grower, with open branches, freely producing in July numerous erect racemes of five to eleven large pure white flowers. A distinct and beautiful shrub	1/6	2/6
„ **Wilsonii.**—China. Pretty in June, with seven to eleven white campanulate flowers on thin wiry stalks		2/6

E **Philesia buxifolia.**—Chile. This treasure requires a sheltered, each. shady spot, in lime-free soil. Once established, it throws up strong suckers which form flat branches. The striking rose-red, tubular flowers are borne freely from June to October 3/6 5/6 **7/6 10/6**

E   „   „   **rosea.**—This is taller-growing with denser branches, slightly narrower leaves and numerous rose-pink flowers 3/6 5/6 **7/6 10/6**
    Specimens of each of the above, 10 ft. across, were seen growing in semi-shade and carrying several thousands of flowers. The fallen petals of earlier blooms almost hid the soil. It was a sight not easily forgotten.

E **Phillyrea angustifolia.**—Mediterranean. A neat and densely-branched shrub 5—10 ft. high, with linear leaves up to 2½ ins. long and dark green. The axillary clusters of cream-coloured flowers are as fragrant as those of Osmanthus Aquifolium **2/6 3/6**

E   „   **decora (Vilmoriniana).**—Lazistan, Black Sea. A very hardy free-growing shrub in semi-shade, with dark green glossy oblong leaves and numerous small white deliciously scented flowers during April. It is very striking in autumn with its mass of oval purple fruits, covered with blue bloom. On own roots ... 1/6 **2/6 3/6**

E **Phormium Colensoi (Cookianum).**—New Zealand. Dwarf growing, but a pretty plant during summer with its 3 ft. spikes of yellow flowers **2/6 3/6**

E   „   **tenax.**—Common New Zealand Flax. Sword-like leaves and 3—6 ft. spikes of reddish-yellow flowers 1/6 **2/6 3/6**

E   „   „   **purpureum.**—Leaves of a beautiful purple suffused with a reddish tinge **5/– 7/6**

Photinia Beauverdiana.—Szechuan, China. An attractive addition to the autumn garden. It is a fast grower possibly reaching 20 ft. or more in height. The large oblong leaves, scarlet tinted in autumn, and retained for weeks, notably extend the autumn display. Fruits globose, bright red **5/– 7/6**

E   „   **Davidsoniae.**—W. Hupeh, China. A new species with glossy, leathery, oblanceolate leaves finely toothed, which are effectively coloured in spring. It carries 3 in. corymbs of many small white flowers in May and June **3/6 5/6**

E   „   **glabra.**—China. An uncommon shrub, 4—5 ft. high, for a sheltered garden. The variable evergreen leaves are brightly coloured for weeks during spring and summer. The white pink tinted flowers in June are hawthorn-like and scented. Previously sent out as P. Benthamiana, a deciduous species apparently not in cultivation 2/6 **3/6 5/6**

E   „   **serrulata.**—China. A large shrub, striking at any time of the year, but especially in spring when the young leaves are a conspicuous crimson. It bears large panicles of many white flowers during April and May **3/6 5/6**

   „   **villosa (P. variabilis of gardens).**—N. China, Japan, Korea. A small tree, 8—15 ft. high, with thin spreading branches and hawthorn-like flowers in May followed by bright red fruits. It has magnificently coloured leaves from early October to mid-November and is one of the star ornamentals at Sheffield Park ... **2/6 3/6**

E **Phygelius capensis.**—S. Africa. The best coloured form grows   each.
into a shrubby bush 2 ft. high along the south and west
coast ; when grown on a wall it will often reach a height
of 20 ft. It is beautiful from June to late autumn with
12—18 in. panicles of scarlet tubular flowers 2/6   3/6

E **Phyllodoce aleutica (Bryanthus).**—N. Asia, N.W. America.
This desirable species has developed into a dense shrub
9 ins. high and 3 ft. across. The numerous heads of
globose flowers, contracted at the tip, are cream-coloured
and a pleasing sight during May and June 3/6   5/6

E   „   **Breweri.**—California. The Heath of Sierra Nevada.
A charming shrub with spreading branches 6—12 ins.
high. The terminal leafy racemes, 3—6 ins. long, are
richly decorated with saucer-shaped wine-red, sweet-
scented flowers during May and June 5/-   7/6

E   „   **coerulea (Menziesia) (Bryanthus).**—N. Europe, N.W.
America, Scotland. The rarest of our native heaths.
A twiggy dense shrub, 6 ins. high, with linear leaves.
The many umbels of egg-shaped, blue-mauve blossoms,
one-third of an inch long, are borne on erect 1½ in.
stalks, during May and June and often again during the
autumn. A true specimen is well illustrated in A. T.
Johnson's "Woodland Garden," page 223   ...   ...   10/6

E   „   **empetriformis (Menziesia empetriformis).**—B.
Columbia. A charming dwarf shrub, the heath of
Vancouver. It rarely attains 1 ft., and is bright in
spring with rosy urn-shaped flowers on 1 in. stems.
It sometimes flowers again in late summer. A beautiful illustration of this plant appeared in the New Flora
and Silva, January, 1933, page 88   ...   .   2/6   3/6

E   „   **glanduliflora.**—B. Columbia, Alaska. A precious,
rigid-branched shrub, 4—8 ins. high. Leaves numerous
and crowded. It bears during June and July loose heads
of six to ten ¼ in. ovoid, contracted, glandular flowers,
sulphur-yellow ageing to white. There is a coloured
plate of this rarity in the "Alpine Flora of the Rocky
Mountains" by Stewardson Brown (1907), page 216   7/6   10/6

E   „   **hybrida (P. empetriformis × P. Breweri).**—Natural
Hybrid. Mt. Garibaldi, Vancouver. One of the
original plants has developed into a shrub 1 ft. high and 3 ft
ft. across. During the spring and again in the autumn,
it is a beautiful sight with its numerous heads of hand-
bell-shaped, rose-red, wrinkly, scented flowers, with
reflexed lobes 2/6   3/6

E   „   **intermedia (P. glanduliflora × P. empetriformis).**—
Natural Hybrid. Vancouver, British Columbia. An
extremely rare and much branched shrub, from a more
or less decumbent base. The dense ¼—½ in. linear
leaves are leathery, obtuse and revolute. The pale pink
or flesh-coloured crinkly, fragrant flowers, held on ½—1
in. stalks, are urn-shaped and slightly contracted 3/6   5/6   7/6

E   „   **nipponica.**—Japan. A pleasing and one of the most
contented of all treasures if planted on the north side of a
shady border. One eagerly awaits the opening of its
lovely white, pink tinted bells in May. It slowly grows
to a height of 6—9 ins. and its dense linear reflexed leaves
are woodruff-scented. A beautiful plate of a plant in
flower appeared in the R.H.S. Journal, Vol. LX, Part II,
(November, 1935), page 480   ...   ...   3/6   5/6   7/6   10/6

each.

E   Phyllodoce nipponica alpina.—Japan.   A miniature mountain
form of dense habit, 1—3 ins. high but 6—12 ins. wide.
The numerous white suffused pink bells are compar-
atively large for the size of the plant 5/-   7/6

E   „   „   tseugaefolia.—Japan.   An extremely rare form
of similar habit but with slightly larger leaves.   Almost
every shoot bears a group of 3—5 white, pink-tinted,
bell-shaped flowers, the domes much narrower than
those of the type 5/-   7/6   10/6

**E   Phyllothamnus erectus (Phyllodoce empetriformis ×
Rhodothamnus Chamaecistus).**—Although it was
raised as long ago as 1845, it is still one of our most
treasured dwarf shrubs.   During April and May the
tips of the twigs are bright with four to ten delicate rose
funnel-shaped flowers, each having five triangular lobes.
Height 9—18 ins.   This rarity and the Phyllodoces
resent limy soils, full sunshine or coddling.   Given
woodland treatment they are free-growing   ...   5/-   7/6   10/6

Picrasma ailanthoides.—N. China, Korea, Japan.   This thinly
branched small tree is rare in British gardens.   The red-
brown new growths have prominent yellow-white lenticels.   It is attractive during the autumn when its pinnate leaves, composed of 9—13 leaflets, assume rich
varied tints 3/6   5/6

E   Pieris floribunda (Andromeda).—Virginia to Georgia.   A
charming evergreen shrub about 5 ft. high.   Panicles of
pure white pitcher-shaped flowers are carried well above
the foliage in March and April.   A particularly good
strain is offered 2/6   3/6

E   „   formosa.—This handsome species from the Himalayas
is only suitable for mild parts, where it attains 6—10 ft.
The spring foliage is bright pink shading to brilliant
crimson.   Panicles of white pitcher-shaped flowers
are borne in May 3/6   5/6

E   „   Forrestii.—S.W. China.   Allied to P. formosa, but
eclipsing it.   Equally vigorous, its distinction lies
chiefly in the brilliance of its young growth.   This easily
surpasses anything of its kind in the spring garden, its
scarlet suggesting a Poinsettia.   As in P. formosa, the
inflorescence is a massive panicle of white urn-shaped
flowers.   Secondary growth, not unusual, is as brilliant
as the earlier   ...   . 7/6 to 21/-

E   „   japonica. — Japan.   An attractive evergreen seldom more
than 5 ft. high, with brilliantly coloured young foliage.
The 3—6 in. pendulous racemes of flowers are white,
during March and April 2/6   3/6

E   „   lucida (nitida) (Xolisma lucida).—S.E. United States.
Introduced in 1765.   A rare and slender branching shrub
3—5 ft. high, with leathery, glossy, oval leaves and
numerous clusters of small pink cylindrical flowers in
June and July.   It grows and flowers freely in the south
and west counties and it was one of the prettiest flowering shrubs seen when at the last Lily Group outing 5/-   7/6   10/6

„   Mariana (Xolisma Mariana).—One of the most beautiful of all N. American small shrubs, bearing large white,
tinted red, cylindrical flowers, and having gorgeous
autumn foliage 2/6   3/6   5/6

E **Pieris Species F. 8945.**—China.   A choice shrub of erect   each.
habit, 10 ft. high.   The medium-sized ovate leaves
are magnificently coloured when unfolding in spring,
and remain so until early summer.   Terminal panicles
of white pitcher-shaped flowers in May **3/6   5/6**

E „ **taiwanensis.**—Formosa.   A   really   beautiful   plant,
developing into a bush 3—8 ft. high, according to position.   It is brilliant every spring with its gloriously
coloured unfolding leaves, with age becoming glossy
green.   From March to June, it is decorated with 4—8
in. erect-spreading racemes of large pure white lily-of-the-
valley-like flowers **2/6   3/6   5/6**

The **Pieris** and allied genera love semi-shade and will
grow in almost any soil free of lime.
See also **Andromeda, Cassandra, Cassiope,
Enkianthus, Leucothoe, Lyonia, Oxydendrum** and
Zenobia.

EC **Pileostegia viburnoides (Schizophragma viburnoides).**—
Khasia Hills, India, Japan, China.   A handsome shrub
with large glossy laurel-like leaves, for a semi-shady
position.   It has pretty 6—9 in. flat umbels of creamy-
white fragrant flowers during August and September.   It
clings like Ivy to shady walls.   This beautiful flowering
plant is illustrated in Gardening Illustrated, September
28th, 1935, page 594   ...   .   **2/6   3/6**

E **Pittosporum bicolor.**—Tasmania.   A handsome fast-growing
tree of pyramidal habit, with narrow greyish leaves and
small yellow flowers.   It is quite hardy and useful as a
wind-break in the south and west counties **2/6   3/6**

E „ **Buchananii.**—New Zealand.   An erect-grower with
attractive glossy pale green leaves.   It makes an excellent
ornamental hedge along the south and west coast   ...   **2/6   3/6**

E „ **cornifolium.**—New Zealand.   This little-known   and
distinct stiff-branched shrub grows 5—10 ft. high.   The
brown-green leaves are in whorls, elliptic-obovate and
1—3 ins. long **10/6**

E „ **crassifolium.**—New Zealand.   This forms a large bush
in mild parts, up to 15 ft. high, with obovate leathery
dark green leaves with dull white tomentum beneath 2/6   **3/6   5/6**

E „ **Dallii.**—New Zealand.   An   attractive-looking   shrub,
5—10 ft. high, with large dull green, elliptical, toothed
leaves, pale beneath.   It bears clusters of 1 in. white,
sweetly scented flowers and is much hardier than is
generally supposed **2/6   3/6   5/6**

E „ **daphniphylloides.**—W. China.   Previously distributed
as P. daphnoides (grandiflorum).   A small tree with
open wide-spreading branches.   The leaves are oblanceolate, deep green, tawny beneath and 6—9 ins. long.
In its best form, it is smothered from April to July with
1—2 in. tubular milk-white and deliciously-scented
flowers, but it is only suitable for the south and west,
Ireland and the west of Scotland **7/6   10/6**

E „ **divaricatum.**—New Zealand.   A rare and interesting
rigid shrub with dense interlacing branches.   During
youth its leaves are obovate, becoming with age lanceolate and deeply lobed **5/-   7/6**

					each.	

E **Pittosporum eugenioides.**—New Zealand. It makes a noble evergreen, 6—20 ft. high, according to locality, and it is decorated with 3—4 in. oblong pale green wavy leaves ... 2/6 3/6

E   "   **heterophyllum.**—A very rare species from China, with variable leaves and open branching growths, possibly not more than 6 ft. high. The flowers are yellow and scented 3/6 5/6

E   "   **patulum**—New Zealand. One of the most distinct and interesting of all the Pittosporums. It is a fast grower, of erect habit, 5—10 ft. high. The stiff spreading branches are clothed with 1—2½ in. narrow leathery pinnatifid leaves 7/6 10/6

E   "   **Ralphii.**—New Zealand. An open-branched shrub, 6—15 ft. high, with leathery oblong greyish leaves. It is one of the hardiest of the genus 3/6 5/6

E   "   **tenuifolium (Mayi).**—New Zealand. The hardiest of all the Pittosporums. Near the sea in the south and west, it makes a charming ornamental hedge. It is effective with its small green wavy leaves and black stems. The dark chocolate flowers in May are honey-scented   **1/6** 2/6 3/6

E   "   **Tobira.**—Japan, China. One of the best seaside shrubs though quite hardy in sheltered corners in inland gardens. It grows 6—8 ft. high, but in the west and in Ireland, 10—20 ft. It has handsome dark green obovate leaves and clusters of 1 in. fragrant creamy-white flowers from April to August 2/6 3/6

E   "   **Turneri.**—New Zealand. A spreading shrub or small tree, 8—15 ft. high. The divaricating zig-zag branches are furnished with spathulate deeply-lobed leaves   ...   5/- 7/6

E   "   **umbellatum.**—New Zealand. An attractive shrub, 6—12 ft. high, for the south and west and similar climates. The olive-green obovate or elliptical, 2—4 in. polished leaves have uneven margins and are reticulate ... 10/6

   Plagianthus betulinus.—New Zealand. A fast-growing small tree, with slender branches of elegant appearance   ... 5/-

   "   **divaricatus.**—Chatham Is. A slender, twiggy shrub, 3—6 ft. high, with 1 in. narrow linear-oblong leaves and minute, yellow, scented flowers in June 2/6 3/6

   "   **Lyallii.**—(See **Hoheria Lyallii**).

E **Polygala Chamaebuxus.**—Alps of C. Europe. A dwarf, creeping shrub, 6—12 ins. high, soon forming a dense mat with numerous showy bright yellow pea-shaped flowers from March to the end of May 1/6 2/6

E   "   "   **grandiflora (purpurea).**—A delightful carpeting plant, 4—6 ins. high, of coarser habit than P.C. rhodoptera, and with much larger leaves. Its rich purple winged flowers are borne freely, more or less, from early April to October 1/6 2/6

E   "   "   **rhodoptera.**—Alps of C. Europe. It is unfortunate that P. Chamaebuxus grandiflora (purpurea) is often made to do justice for this treasure. The true plant seldom grows 3 ins. high and forms a mat 2 ft. or more across. It likes semi-shade. From March to June it is lit up with thousands of glowing carmine-red pea-shaped flowers, almost hiding the tiny leaves   ... 3/6

each.

E Polygala Vayredae.—Pyrenees. A creeping shrub with wiry
branches smothered with showy deep purple pea-
shaped flowers in March and April 1/6   2/6
> The **Polygalas** need a semi-shady position, and as a
> rule lime-free soil.

C Polygonum baldschuanicum.—Bokhara. A rampant climber
suitable for covering rough trees where it can be allowed
its own way. Pretty with its festoons of white or rosy
flowers during summer and autumn 2/6

„   **vaccinifolium.**—Himalayas. A creeping shrub forming
a dense mat yards wide, splendid in the heather garden.
It will grow in any soils free from lime. It is pretty
from early August to late autumn with numerous 3—6 in.
spikes of bright rose-coloured flowers 1/6

Populus lasiocarpa.—C. China. A beautiful species, of tree
size, upright in habit. Owing to the great size of the
leaves it requires shelter from gales 2/6   3/6   5/6

Potentilla davurica (glabra).—N. China and Siberia. Introduced in 1822. This rare and compact shrub grows
1—1½ ft. high and is easily distinguished by its erect
stems and drooping twigs. It carries numerous leaves
composed of five tiny stalkless leaflets and the ¾—1 in.
strawberry-like white flowers are borne from May to
September 2/6

„   **Fredrichsenii (davurica × fruticosa).**—Of spreading
habit, 3—5 ft. high, with pale yellow flowers 1/6   2/6

„   **fruticosa.**—N. England, Ireland. Erect and compact in
habit, 2—5 ft. high, with 1 in. bright yellow flowers   ...   1/6   2/6

„   „   **arbuscula.**—Manchuria. An uncommon shrub
seldom more than 1 ft. high. Its semi-prostrate growths
are coated with red-brown tomentum and the bold golden
yellow flowers are borne from June to late autumn   ...   2/6

„   „   **Beesii.**—A compact grower, 1 ft. high, with grey
leaves and deep yellow flowers from early June to mid-
September 1/6   2/6

„   „   **mandshurica.**—Manchuria. A choice dwarf-
growing shrub having dense silvery leaves covered with
silky hairs. It produces white flowers from June to
autumn 2/6

„   „   **ochroleuca.**—The erect stems with spreading
branches are gay from early June till late September with
sulphur-yellow flowers 1/6   2/6

„   „   **parvifolia (Farreri) (humilus).**—C. Asia. A
choice shrub 12—18 ins. high with twiggy branches.
Its conspicuous flat flowers are buttercup-yellow   ...   1/6   2/6

„   „   **Purdomii.**—N. China. This has thin erect
growths, 18—24 ins. high and is one of the best of the
genus. The golden-yellow flowers are produced from
June till autumn frosts. 1/6   2/6

„   „   **pyrenaica (prostrata).**—One of the most charming of the family with almost prostrate growths decorated
from early summer to autumn frosts, with numerous
1 in. conspicuous, buttercup-yellow flowers 2/6   3/6

„   „   **Veitchii.**—Hupeh, China. Dwarf in habit, with
pure white flowers 1/6   2/6

		each.

Potentilla fruticosa Vilmoriniana.—W. China. This is the most distinct of the shrubby Potentillas, 3—5 ft. high, with upright branches carrying silvery-grey leaves. Quantities of creamy-white or sulphur-coloured flowers are borne throughout the summer and autumn 1/6   2/6

The **Potentillas** are very hardy shrubs and will grow in almost any soil and situation.

Prinsepia sinensis (Plagiospermum sinense).—Manchuria. A rare member of the order Rosaceae, of spreading habit, 3—10 ft. high and stiffly branched. It bears 3 in. oblong-lanceolate leaves. The bright yellow plum-like flowers are borne in the leaf axils on ½ in. stalks during March ...   3/6   5/6

E **Prostranthera rotundifolia.**—Australia. A tender but beautiful shrub well worthy of a south or west wall. The small crenulated leaves are aromatic. From May to late June the whole plant is a mass of small purple flowers ...   2/6   3/6

ALMOND SECTION.

Those marked "X" should be grown to provide cut sprays for indoor decoration from February to April.

X **Prunus communis (Amygdalus communis) (Almond).**—One of the most popular ornamentals carrying its wealth of single pink flowers, on leafless branches, from mid-March to the end of April 3/6   5/6

X   ,,   ,,   **macrocarpa.**—2 in. pale pink flowers starting to open in early April 3/6   5/6

X   ,,   ,,   **Pollardii (Almond × Peach).**—This originated with Mr. Pollard of Ballarat, Victoria, Australia. It is one of the most beautiful of spring-flowering ornamentals, quickly developing into a small tree. The spreading branches are attractive from mid-February to mid-April with substantial 2 in. bright pink flowers. These are followed by a heavy crop of fruits 5/6   7/6

X   ,,   ,,   **roseo plena.**—It grows into a large bush or small tree with a compact head and is suitable for small gardens. The double, daisy-like, bright pink flowers are much admired every March and April 3/6   5/6

X   ,,   **Davidiana alba.**—China. This and its variety are not satisfactory in the south and west, but in colder districts they grow and flower freely every year. During February and March, according to weather conditions, its branches are conspicuous with numerous 1 in. white flowers ...   5/-   7/6

X   ,,   ,,   **rubra.**—This form has rather spreading branches and during mild spells in February and March, they are crowded with rose-red flowers 5/-   7/6

  ,,   **glandulosa (japonica) albo plena.**—China, Japan. A shrub, 3—4 ft. high, and as much wide. Beautiful during spring with its branches laden with pure white double flowers. 2/6   3/6

  ,,   ,,   **sinensis (roseo plena of gardens).**—Similar in habit and height to the former, but with bright pink double flowers 2/6   3/6

X   ,,   **kansuensis.**—N.W. China. A delightful companion for early flowering trees and shrubs and is related to the Peach. It grows 6 ft. or more high and is of twiggy habit. During February and March it is decorated with pale pink flowers ... ...Delivery 1938   —   —

Prunus mira.—A rarity from W. China, developing into a large bush or small tree, according to soil and climate. The thin branches carry evenly placed, 2—5 in., narrow, lanceolate and reticulate green leaves, with shallow teeth and uneven margins. The leafless branches are gay with 1 in. white flowers during March and April. It is one of the most distinct members of the genus 5/-   7/6

    „   **nana (Amygdalus nana).**—S. Russia. A charming small shrub 3—4 ft. high, with a profusion of rosy-pink flowers the whole length of its branches during late March and April. On own roots. 2/6   3/6

X   „   **Persica var. duplex (roseo-plena of gardens).**—The double-flowering Peach is one of the most conspicuous of all early flowering trees and shrubs. During April the branches are wreathed with full double rose-pink blossoms 5/-   7/6

    „   „   **magnifica.**—This is a great addition to the spring garden, with its show of fiery-red, double, Peach blossoms. Shelter of any kind, from a hedge or trees, is an advantage and it does exceedingly well around London. P. persica Cambridge Carmine and Russell's Red are closely related to this plant 3/6   5/6

X   „   **triloba plena.**—China. With delicate rose-coloured double flowers but unfortunately not hardy enough for general planting in the open. On a sheltered wall it is quite satisfactory and flowers profusely yearly. On own roots. 5/-

APRICOT SECTION.

Prunus Mume.—Japan. It is generally of a shrubby character and its green and brown branches are decorated during March with deliciously scented white or pale pink flowers. Unfortunately it is often damaged by early and late frosts 3/6   5/6

X   „   **tomentosa.**—N. and W. China, Japan. A shrub with arching growths, 4—6 ft. high and as much wide. It needs a sheltered spot, free from east winds. Pretty at the end of March with white, rose-tinted flowers ...   3/6

X   „   „   **endotricha.**—C. and W. China. One of the choicest shrubs from China, quickly growing 5—8 ft. high and of upright habit. The twiggy branches are wreathed during April and May with white blossoms, succeeded by attractive bright red cherry-like fruits ripe in July ...   2/6   3/6

    „   „   „   **rosea.**—A delightful form from China. Its 5—8 ft. twiggy growths are crowded with rose-pink flowers and polished red cherry-like fruits 7/6

PLUM SECTION.

X **Prunus cerasifera (Cherry Plum).**—W. Asia, Caucasus. Few shrubs or small trees are more beautiful than this when its branches are laden with white flowers from mid-February to late March. It is worth a place in the garden to provide cut sprays when flowers are scarce. It also blooms profusely in Scotland 1/6   2/6

X **Prunus cerasifera Blireiana.**—A shrub 6—10 ft. high, with purple foliage and lovely bright rose double flowers, borne from mid-February to the end of March, according to climate and position. It has unfortunately proved to be shy-flowering and is a poor grower in many soils ... | each. 2/6 | 3/6

X „ „ **Pissartii (Pissardii) (atropurpurea).** The well-known purple-leaved plum, effective during March with its flowers, pale pink in bud, opening to white. Once established, it should be pollarded yearly after flowering to encourage larger and better coloured foliage and a greater display of flowers for the following year 1/6 | 2/6 | 3/6

X „ „ „ **Woodii.**—This is more attractive than the previous one, the leaves are larger and the deeper red colouring is constant throughout the growing season. It also has deep rose-coloured flowers. The effect of a few plants on the outskirts of the woodland is surprising 1/6 | 2/6 | 3/6

„ **spinosa plena.**—The double white-flowering form of the common sloe, a most beautiful object when in flower. On own roots ... ... | 3/6

„ „ **purpurea.**—The purple-leaved form of the common sloe is quite a pretty shrub or small tree. The spines are not so formidable as those of the type and the flowers are pink ... ... 2/6 | 3/6 | 5/6

CHERRY SECTION.

Prunus acida semperflorens (All Saints' Cherry). This has been discarded as it was so shy-flowering ... ... | — | —

„ **avium (Gean).**—Europe and W. Asia. Plants in a wood-land garden near here are lit up every spring with masses of single white flowers and again in autumn when the leaves assume magnificent tints ... ... | 2/6 | 3/6

„ „ **plena (Double flowered Gean).**—A beautiful tree in early spring with its mass of drooping pure white double flowers, each 1½ ins. across, in April and May 2/6 | 3/6 | 5/6

„ **Besseyi.**—W. N. America. A slender erect-branched shrub 3—4 ft. high, wreathed in early spring with small white flowers. Its foliage during autumn is vividly coloured ... ... | 2/6 | 3/6

„ **campanulata (The Taiwan Cherry).**—Japan, Formosa. Known since 1899, but has been exceedingly rare in cultivation. This very beautiful cherry has large bright green ovate leaves, often doubly toothed. The flowers are campanulate and bright rose, on leafless stalks, and in a well-known garden near Lymington, a plant is a beautiful sight every year. It is possibly the brightest coloured flowering cherry yet known. Here it is often cut to the ground by 15—24° of frost ... ... 5/6 | 7/6

„ **Cerasus Rhexii (ranunculiflora).**—The double-flower-ing Morello Cherry makes a fine shapely bush with a profusion of double pure white flowers in May and June | 3/6 | 5/6

X „ **Conradinae.**—W. Hupeh, China. In its best form it attains small tree size and is of spreading habit with large, lustrous, metallic-green leaves. Its campanulate flesh-pink flowers are beautiful from early February to April, according to weather conditions ... ... 3/6 | 5/6

X **Prunus Conradinae semi-plena.**—This worthy form is not quite so robust as the type. During February and March, its slender branches are attractive with ¾—1 in. carmine-pink flowers, each with an inner row of petaloid stamens which gives them a semi-double appearance ... each. 3/6 5/6

X „ **hupehensis (thibetica).**—This valuable species is very similar in habit to a Williams' Pear. It has polished bright coppery young foliage and the upright branches are smothered with pink flowers, rather smaller than those of P. Sargentii. It is invaluable for the autumn garden with its brightly tinted leaves 5/- 7/6

X „ **incisa (The Fuji or Mame Cherry).**—China, Japan. Of twiggy-branched, pyramidal habit, 6—10 ft. high. It bears abundance of pink campanulate flowers in March and April. A splendid shrub for villa gardens where space is limited 3/6 5/6

X „ „ **serrata.**—Known as the pygmy prunus of Japan, but here, by pruning and training to a leader, it has reached 10—15 ft. in five years. The slender branches are wreathed with bell-shaped pink flowers, before the leaves appear. In a Gloucestershire garden it is one of the most valued of spring-flowering ornamentals... 2/6 3/6 5/6

„ **Jacquemontii.**—Afghanistan. The Afghan Cherry is a handsome shrub 6—12 ft. high. During April and May the branches are pretty with many ½ in. funnel-shaped, rose-pink flowers, succeeded by globose red fruits, ripe in July 5/- 7/6

„ **Lannesiana.**—Japan. This quickly grows into a fine specimen and in habit resembles P. avium, our native Gean. The 1½ in. slightly fragrant flowers are a delicate pink ageing to pure white and are borne in quantity during April and May 3/6 5/6

X „ **litigiosa (pilosiuscula media).**—China. It grows into a pyramid of perfect shape, 8—20 ft. high, according to soil. The branches are almost hidden by the multitude of drooping clusters of pure white flowers, with yellow anthers, borne just as the leaves unfold. A choice shrub where space is limited 3/6 5/6

„ **Maximowiczii.**—Japan. This rare Cherry develops into a fine-headed tree, 12—20 ft. high, but it is of little value as a flowering or fruiting plant. It is, however, one of the best for the autumn garden, its obovate-elliptic, pointed, green leaves assuming a riot of magnificent tints 2/6 3/6 5/6

„ **Miqueliana** (See Prunus subhirtella autumnalis).

X „ **Sargentii (serrulata sachalinensis) (Yama-zakura).**—Japan, Korea. A tree of great beauty, strong growing, possibly 30 ft. or more high and of spreading habit. The many large, single, soft-pink flowers, borne during March and April are effective amongst the bronzy-red foliage, which becomes richly coloured in autumn. It has quickly become a great favourite in this country and in America. It is one of the first twelve trees to plant for its flowers and autumn foliage 3/6 5/6

Prunus serrula tibetica.—One of China's treasures, it forms a round-headed tree 15—20 ft. in height. During autumn the golden-brown bark peeling reveals a mahogany-red and polished bark beneath. Its handsome stem and branches are attractive at any time of the year, but it is of little value as a flowering plant. The specimen at Kew is well worth a visit ... ... **3/6**   each. **5/6 7/6**

  ,, **serrulata pubescens.**—Japan, Korea, China. Previously distributed as P. tenuiflora. This tree grows 12—20 ft. high and is most distinct with its pubescent stems and bold, hairy, bright green and deeply notched, oval-elliptical, pointed leaves. Each leaf is guarded by two laciniate carpels. It is one of the prettiest of the section during April and May with its clusters of semi-drooping rose-pink single flowers **5/- 7/6**

  ,, **Sieboldii (Takasago Cherry) (Naden) (Watereri).**—Introduced in 1804. Good specimens, 20 ft. × 30 ft. may be seen in older gardens. It has upright branches though in youth is apt to grow one-sided and should be pruned to shape. Starting to flower in mid-April the profuse compact clusters of semi-double, fragrant, pink blossoms look attractive among the ovate-elliptic, bronze-red, young leaves **3/6** **5/6 7/6**

X ,, **subhirtella (Higan or Rosebud Cherry).**—A good ornamental from the eastern part of Asia, quickly growing 10—20 ft. high, and the twiggy branches are absolutely crowded with flesh-pink flowers, giving unique spring effect **2/6** **3/6 5/6**

X ,, ,, **ascendens (Shiro-higan).**—Japan. This Cherry is quite distinct with its upright pyramidal habit. It is 8—12 ft. high and starts to flower in April, being smothered in campanulate bright rose-pink blossoms ... **3/6** **5/6 7/6**

X ,, ,, **autumnalis (Jugatsu-zakura) (microlepis) (Miqueliana of gardens).**—A beautiful form, producing its lovely semi-double, almond-scented, pale pink flowers yearly from about mid-October to April. It is a much better tree on its own roots ; worked plants do not give a true character. It grows freely, ultimately reaching a height of 20—30 ft. **3/6** **5/6 7/6**

  ,, ,, **Fukubana (Makino)** (Bot: Mag: Tokyo, Vol. xxii, p.118).—Japan. It is strong-growing and ultimately forms a head 10—20 ft. wide, according to soil. The thin weeping branches are a lovely sight during March and April with clusters of flowers, like tiny double roses, vivid crimson in bud and opening to deep carmine red. **5/- 7/6**

X ,, ,, **pendula (Shidare-higan).**—The weeping Rosebud Cherry of Japan. If planted at the back of a large stone or on a steep bank so that its pendulous branches fall over it, it is very effective, wreathed in spring with pale pink flowers. If worked on a high standard, it forms a picturesque tree with weeping branches **3/6 5/6**

  ,, ,, ,, **rubra.**—Japan. This has the same graceful pendulous habit as the latter. The branches are pretty in March and April with numerous rose-red flowers **5/- 7/6**

X **Prunus Vilmorinii.**—A beautiful unrecorded species, possibly   each. attaining tree size. Its spreading branches are clothed with handsome metallic-green leaves and are decorated from mid-March to May with white flowers, suffused rose 3/6   5/6   7/6

X ,, **yedoensis (Yoshino).**—The flowering Cherry of Tokyo quickly grows 20—30 ft. high and with a spreading head almost as wide. The numerous large fragrant blush flowers, ageing to white, are borne just before the leaves expand 3/6   5/6

 ,,   ,, **perpendens, of Wilson (Shidare-yoshino) (pendula).**—Japan. This is a rare weeping form of the well-known Tokyo Cherry and is a choice companion for Prunus Kiku-shidare, P. subhirtella pendula, Betula verrucosa Youngii and Salix vitellina pendula. It is a vigorous grower and the single pink or blush-coloured flowers are as freely produced as those of the type   ...   3/6   5/6 See also under Standards.

JAPANESE FLOWERING CHERRIES.
HYBRIDS.

Prunus Amanogawa (Milky Way) (erecta).—A splendid variety of perfectly upright habit, like a Lombardy Poplar. The flowers are single, sometimes semi-double, pale pink, fragrant and in dense clusters. Its habit of growth makes it a very useful plant for small gardens   ...   3/6   5/6   7/6

 ,, **Ariake (Dawn).**—It grows 10 ft. or more high and has upright branches which become spreading with age. The single or semi-double flowers, pink in the bud and ageing to flesh-colour, open quite flat and are 2 ins. across. It is scarcely distinguishable from P. Ojochin 5/-   7/6

 ,, **Daikoku (Japanese God of Prosperity).**—The red-brown branches carry pale green leaves and long-stalked drooping clusters of full double deep pink flowers, each 2—2½ ins. across 5/-   7/6

 ,, **Fugenzo (Goddess on a White Elephant) (J. H. Veitch) (Kofugen).**—This appears to love the cooler conditions of the north and it makes a dense tree, of medium size, quite as wide as it is high. It can easily be distinguished by its interlacing branches, roped with deep rose-pink flowers. P. Benifugen (Wilson) is very similar in habit and flower 3/6   5/6

 ,, **Hokusai (Famous Japanese Artist) (roseo-pleno of nurseries).**—This forms a tall shapely tree and has brown branches and bronze-tinted leaves. It is very free-flowering, carrying in April, loose clusters of 2 in. semi-double pale pink flowers, held on long threads. P. Udzu-zakura (spiralis) is very similar in flower   ...   5/-   7/6

 ,, **Horinji (Ancient Temple in Kyoto).**—An upright grower with thick branches, attaining a height of about 12 ft. It freely produces clusters of up to six drooping flowers, semi- or full double, 1½—2 ins. across and rather flat. The outer petals are deep pink, those in the centre much paler 5/-   7/6

	each.	
Prunus Ichiyo (unifolia) (One or more leafy carpels in the centre of each flower).—This is the true P. Hi-zakura. It has spreading branches and grows 10 ft. or more high and quite as much wide. The pretty 1½ in. full double, soft pink flowers are in leafy clusters of 2 or 3 and age to pure white before falling	5/-	7/6
„ **Jo-nioi (Supreme Fragrance) (affinis).**—It is aptly named for it is deliciously fragrant, and is perhaps one of the three best white-flowering Cherries. It is often referred to as Snow on the Mountain. As a bush it is of upright habit, 10 ft. or more in height, but when worked as a standard, it makes a compact head as much across as it is high. P. Taki-nioi is very similar in habit and flower	3/6	5/6
„ **Kiku-shidare (Weeping Chrysanthemum) (rosea) (Shidare-zakura) (Lidera Nova) (Cheal's Weeping).** —This is of weeping habit and is far more effective grown as a tall standard. The long drooping branches, carrying dense compact bunches of 1—1¼ in full-double deep rose-pink flowers, are very attractive. See also under standards	3/6	5/6
„ **Kirin.**—This is very near Kwanzan, but is a little earlier in opening its flowers, which are shorter stemmed and in more compact corymbs. It forms a shorter and broader tree than Kwanzan. The large pointed leaves are well coloured during November	5/-	7/6
„ **Kwanzan (Named for a Japanese Mountain) (Incorrectly Kanzan and Hi-zakura) (Also Seki-yama, Sekizan, New Red, purpurascens and rubra nova).** —The favourite among the coloured Japanese Cherries and a vigorous grower, of upright habit, 25 ft. or more high. The drooping clusters of large full-double flowers, deep pink in bud and ageing to rose-red, are a magnificent sight from mid-April to mid-May. This tree also gives most lovely autumn colouring	3/6	5/6
„ **Mikuruma-gaeshi (The Royal Carriage Returns).**— Uncommon in western gardens and about 18 ft. high, of upright bushy habit. During April and May it has a magnificent show of very long stemmed clusters of 2 in. single pink flowers ; the petals overlap and each has a small notch at the top		7/6
„ **Ojochin (Large Lantern).**—In a garden near here, this handsome Cherry has developed into a tree 25 ft. × 35 ft. The wrinkled flowers are large, pink in the bud, changing to palest pink or white when fully open, and are almost always single. It is closely related to P. Ariake	5/-	7/6
„ **Senriko (japonica alba of nurseries).**—Discarded as it is so shy-flowering	—	—
„ **serrulata albo-plena (Schneider).**—This is said to be of Chinese origin, and has been grown in British gardens for many years. It is often twice as wide as it is high, with some of its branches horizontal. From mid-April to mid-May, it is very pretty with clusters of 1—1¼ in. white double flowers	3/6	5/6

X **Prunus serrulata semperflorens (Fudan-zakura)(Continuous**   each.
Cherry)—Miyoshi, in "Tokyo Bot. Mag. XXXVI No.
421, 12," Collingwood Ingram in "R.H.S. Journal
LIV, 175 (1929)." It is very similar in habit to the common Hazel and 8—15 ft. in height. It is aptly named for
the charming pink flowers, 1—1¼ ins. wide and with red
sepals, are freely produced in pairs from late November
to mid-April, according to locality. A splendid addition
to hardy plants and suitable for any garden in the British
Isles 5/–   7/6

„   **Shiro-fugen (White Goddess) (albo-rosea).**—It is one
of the most free-growing of the Japanese Cherries and like
P. Kwanzan, it is useful either as a single tree or in an
avenue. It comes into flower when the bronzed-toned
young foliage has opened ; the flowers are pink in the
bud, passing to white when fully open but changing
again to pale pink before falling. They are large, double
and hang on long stalks 3/6   5/6   7/6

„   **Shirotae (Snow White) (Kojima) (Mount Fuji) (Snow-
flake) (Sirotae).**—This is one of the best white-flowering Cherries and grows 25 ft. or more across, with stiff
horizontal branches. The large pale green leaves show
up the clusters of 2 or 3 drooping, 2 in. single or semi-
double flowers. These are incised, snow-white and
fragrant and are held on very long stalks. The flowers
often appear in March and remain until the end of April
    3/6   5/6   7/6

„   **Shogetsu (Moon Hanging Low by a Pine) (Oku-
miyako) (Longipes).**—It is one of the best and most
distinct, forming a rather flat-headed tree. The flowers
are borne on long stalks, are pink in the bud, opening
to pure white, and are very double. The foliage is light
green 5/–   7/6

„   **Shujaku (A Southern Constellation) (campanuloides
of trade and gardens).**—It has been on trial here for
seven years and has proved to be a valuable ornamental.
It is 12 ft. or more high and has long upright branches
with lateral spreading growths. The decorative clusters
of 1½ in. pale rose-coloured flowers, each with three rows
of petals, are held for several weeks and keep their colour
until just before they drop 5/–   7/6

„   **Sumizome.**—This may be a form of P. Washino-o. An
uncommon ornamental in British gardens but one of the
most beautiful. It is of medium size with branches
tightly packed with handsome, large, apple blossom-pink,
fragrant flowers. These may have one or two rows of
petals and they change to blush-pink before they drop   ...   5/–   7/6

„   **Tai-haku (Great White Cherry).**—A strong grower, of
upright habit and forming a good head. The abundance
of single white flowers, 2½ in. across and with the tips of
their petals notched, look fine nestling among the rich
copper-red leaves 5/–   7/6

„   **Taizan-fukun (God of Taizan Mountain. China)
(Hoki-zakura) (serrulata ambigua ?).**—This is best
described as the fragrant double form of the well-known
P. Amanogawa. It has rather more branches, giving
it a fuller appearance. A magnificent ornamental   ...   5/–   7/6

Prunus Temari (Ball).—An active grower at first but much less   each.
vigorous as it develops. When young, it produces
many clusters of 2 in. upright, apple blossom-like, rose-
pink flowers which do not fade before they fall. Adult
plants produce single and double flowers. This exquisite
Cherry was in flower for a month last spring and was
much admired 5/-   7/6

   ,,   **Torano-o (Tiger's Tail) (caudata).**—A large bush or small
tree having many upright slender branches and ultimately
developing a flattened head. It bears many clusters,
each of 3 or 4 single white flowers, 1½ ins. across. The
petals are often pink-tinted at the base 5/-   7/6

   ,,   **Ukon (Yellowish) (grandiflora).**—In a good holding
loam, it will develop into a specimen 20 ft. × 30 ft. and
with stiff, wide-placed branches, but it is much smaller on
poorer soils. In a Gloucestershire garden, five specimen
trees planted against a holly and laurel background are
garlanded with semi-double, primrose-yellow flowers
every spring. A sight not easily forgotten. P. Asagi
(luteoides) is closely related to this Cherry ... **3/6**   5/6   7/6

   ,,   **Washino-o (Eagle's Tail) (Wasinowo).**—A rampant
grower with stiff outward-pointing branches, usually
seen with an open head. The clusters each contain
2 to 5 fragrant, single, blush-coloured flowers ageing to
white. These are mainly single but sometimes have one
or two extra petals and are held on stiff stalks 5/-   7/6

   ,,   **Yedo-zakura (Yedo Cherry) (nobilis).**—The Yedo
Cherry is not so vigorous as many of the others but will
become 10—18 ft. high and as much wide. It is worth
growing for its many clusters of 3 to 5 semi- or full-
double 3 in. flowers, the centre petals of which are pale
pink and the outer deep pink. P. Akebono, P. Beni-
torano-o and P. Oshokun are very similar to this cherry ...   5/-   7/6

The foliage of many of the Prunus is gorgeously tinted
from October to the end of November.

See also under Standard Trees.

BIRD CHERRIES.

Prunus demissa.—West U.S.A. A large shrub or small tree,
9—18 ft. high, with pyramidal branches and broad ovate
leaves. During May the 6 in. cylindrical racemes are
crowded with small white flowers 3/6   5/-

   ,,   **Maackii.**—Manchuria, Korea, C. China. This handsome
and uncommon tree will probably grow 20 ft. or more in
height. The stems and branches are covered with
brown lenticels, but it peels like the Silver Birch. The
bark, brown and yellow, shed, discloses a new, bright,
polished one below it. It is a beautiful companion for
P. serrula tibetica **3/6**   5/6   7/6

   ,,   **Padus (Bird Cherry).**—Europe, W. Asia. This makes a
fine specimen with spreading branches and 3—6 in.
drooping racemes of many white flowers in April and
May **2/6**   3/6   5/6

   ,,   ,,   **Albertii.**—A dense, twiggy, small tree of pyramidal habit, quite pretty during May and June with 4—6 in.
narrow racemes of flowers larger than those of the type ...   3/6   5/6

   ,,   ,,   **plena.**—The double-flowering form 5/6   7/6

Prunus Padus Watereri (grandiflora).—A large shrub or small   each.
tree, 10—20 ft. high and as much wide. Its numerous
elegant, 6—8 in. racemes of white flowers, borne during
May and early June, make it one of our best flowering
ornamentals 3/6   5/6

LAUROCERASUS (CHERRY LAUREL) SECTION.

E   **Prunus caroliniana.**—S. United States. The young tips of this
rare evergreen are magnificently coloured throughout
the growing season. It is a fine plant along the south
and west coast and in the south of Ireland. Its oblong-
lanceolate leaves are 3—4½ ins. in length 3/6   5/6

E   „   **ilicifolia.**—W. United States. A shrub 3—5 ft. high, but
not generally hardy. It has small round glossy green
leaves and 3 in. racemes of white flowers from March to
May 3/6   5/6

Many gardens on chalk (limy) soils can be enhanced
by planting a selection from the beautiful Prunus, Pyrus,
Cotoneaster and Viburnum families. Even some of the
Heathers will thrive and flower freely.

Ptelea trifoliata.—East U.S.A. A very hardy small-growing
tree with trifoliate green leaves and aromatic wood. It is
worth a place in the shrubbery for its clusters of deliciously scented yellow-green flowers borne during June and
July 2/6   3/6

Pterostyrax hispida.—This guest from China is usually seen as
a small tree of spreading habit 12—20 ft. in height. It
is particularly graceful during June and July with its
4—9 in. pendulous panicles of creamy-white and fragrant
flowers 2/6   3/6   5/6

E   **Pyracantha angustifolia (Cotoneaster angustifolia).**—W.
China. It is quite hardy in many gardens in the south
and west, etc., but inland should be given a wall. The
numerous attractive clusters of orange-yellow fruits
start to colour in August and are retained till early spring 2/6   3/6

E   „   **atalantioides (1880) Gibbsii (1907).**—C. & W. China.
The most beautiful of all the Pyracanthas and thriving on
walls where many other plants are not a success. It is
free-growing and two plants on a cottage wall in the New
Forest were so packed with brilliant red fruits from mid-
September till February, that they were admired by all
who saw them 2/6   3/6

E   „   „   **forma aurea.**—Quite as free-growing as the type
and with yellow-tinted branches which are crowded
with golden-yellow berries from September until February 2/6   3/6

E   „   **coccinea Lalandii.**—S. Europe. This well-known and
very hardy evergreen decorates the walls of numerous
dwellings in and around London. It has closely packed
clusters of large brilliant orange-red berries from mid-
September to Xmas. 2/6   3/6

E   „   **crenulata.**—Himalayas. Discarded as it is an inferior
plant. ... ... —   —

E   „   **Gibbsii.**—(See **atalantioides**).

			each.	

E **Pyracantha Rogersiana.**—Yunnan, China. It is the hardiest and perhaps the best Pyracantha for forming a hedge 4—6 ft. high. The mass of loose corymbs of orange-coloured fruits nestling among the small green leaves look charming 2/6   3/6

E „ „ **aurantiaca.**—A charming Chinese form with loose corymbs of orange-red fruits 2/6   3/6

E „ „ **fructu luteo (flava).**—This is one of the most delightful of all yellow fruiting plants either as a specimen against a wall, bush or ornamental hedge 2/6   3/6

E „ **yunnanensis.**—This valuable plant bears abundantly loose corymbs of very showy fruits, at first orange-red, ageing to brilliant crimson, on long stalks and retained until the new year 2/6   3/6

Pyrus arbutifolia (See **Aronia arbutifolia**).

„ **Malus (Flowering and Ornamental Crabs).** See **Malus.**

„ **salicifolia.**—The Willow-leaved Pear. S.E. Europe, W. Asia, 1780. A small tree easily distinguished by its rugged stem, pendulous growths and silvery willow-like leaves. It is attractive from spring to autumn. 5/6   7/6

Quercus coccinea. (N. American Scarlet Oak).—A fast-growing tree with large lustrous green leaves changing in autumn to brilliant red. In this neighbourhood many have been established in front of a plantation of Scots firs, making a splendid picture every autumn 1/6   2/6   3/6   5/6   7/6

„ „ **splendens (Knaphill Scarlet Oak).**—The best form, but slower growing than the former. The handsome leaves for at least six weeks during the autumn are magnificently coloured. These are retained until late November. One of the first six autumnals to plant 5/6   7/6   10/6

E „ **Ilex.** Mediterranean Region.—The Common Evergreen Oak. It thrives around the south and west coasts and few plants are better suited for wind breaks. It also forms a beautiful hedge if carefully trimmed ... 1/6   2/6   3/6

Quince.—(See **Cydonia**).

E **Raphiolepis Delacourii (umbellata × indica).**—Garden Hybrid. A splendid shrub but not generally hardy, 3—5 ft. high. Its leaves are leathery and dark green, and it bears 4—6 in. terminal racemes of ¾ in. pink flowers during May 2/6   3/6   5/6

E „ **indica.**—China. Only hardy in the south-west, but a beautiful wall shrub in colder districts. The leaves are lanceolate, and short terminal racemes of white flowers, tinged pink, are borne from March to June. Also incorrectly known as R. salicifolia 3/6   5/6

E „ **umbellata (japonica of gardens)**—Japan. A choice hardy shrub for the southern counties, of round compact form, slowly growing 4—6 ft. high. Its leaves are leathery and dark green. Numerous 3—4 in. racemes of ¾ in. hawthorn-like fragrant flowers are borne during June. The fruits are blue-black 2/6   3/6   5/6

The **Raphiolepises** make splendid seaside shrubs.

E **Restio subverticillata.**—S. Africa. A tender but elegant evergreen shrub with graceful 4—6 ft. arching growths, known as Mare's Tail 10/6

E **Rhaphithamnus spinosus (cyanocarpus).**—Chile. A dense   each.
small-leaved shrub with pale blue flowers during April
and May followed by ½ in. round violet fruits, suitable
for the south-west. Inland it requires a south or west
wall 2/6   3/6

Rhododendron.—(See end of Catalogue).

**Rhodora canadensis (Rhododendron canadense) (The
Rhodora).**—N.E.N. America. A twiggy shrub 2—4 ft.
high, delightful during April with its 1—1½ in. wide,
bright rosy-purple flowers on leafless branches 2/6   3/6

E **Rhodothamnus Chamaecistus.**—Austrian Alps. Introduced in
1786. It is a slow grower but perfectly happy in semi-
shade in the Ericaceae border. At the Alpine Society's
Show on September 13th, 1935, a superb pot-grown
specimen full of Kalmia-like pale pink flowers, was much
admired and an excellent photograph of it appears in the
Society's Quarterly Bulletin, Vol. 3, No. 3, No. 21,
page 216   ...   .   10/6

Rhodotypos kerrioides.—China. Japan, An erect-branched
shrub, 4—6 ft. high. The large white four-petalled
flowers at the end of short twigs are very showy from
early May to August 1/6   2/6

Rhus canadensis.—N. America. A twiggy spreading shrub
3—4 ft. high. The trifoliate aromatic green leaves
become orange-yellow and red tinted in autumn. It
was one of the most beautifully coloured shrubs at
Wisley last autumn 2/6   3/6

„   **copallina.**—East U.S.A. A rare species, slowly growing
to a few feet high, with pinnate leaves composed of nine
to fifteen leaflets, changing in autumn to vivid scarlet.
The panicles of yellowish flowers are succeeded by hairy
bright red fruits 3/6   5/6

„   **cotinoides (Cotinus americanus).**—South U.S.A.
Chittam Wood. An extremely scarce species even in
nature. The large leaves are glaucous blue on both
sides, while the leaf stalk and current growths are tinged
orange red. Towards autumn the foliage becomes a
riot of scarlet and orange 7/6   10/6

„   **Cotinus.**—Europe, N. India, C. China. An attractive
shrub 10—15 ft. high, of easy culture. It bears loosely-
branched panicles of silky reddish hairs with small, pale
flesh-coloured flowers. The glaucous foliage fades
during autumn to various shades of yellow. It is commonly called the " Smoke Plant " 1/6   2/6

„   „   **foliis purpureis (rubrifolius).**—A particularly
beautiful shrub with constant wine-coloured foliage
from spring to autumn. It should be pruned hard every
March to encourage young growths and larger coloured
leaves. Cut sprays placed in water last a long time   ...   2/6   3/6

„   **glabra laciniata.**—U.S.A. A much more beautiful shrub
than the type R. glabra (Smooth Sumach) although it
has a rather awkward habit. The leaves, 12—18 ins.
long, are divided into small leaflets. It is very striking
in autumn with hues of orange-yellow, red and gold   ...   2/6   3/6

		each.	
Rhus javanica.—Previously distributed as R. Osbeckii.—China, Japan. A notable species, attaining a height of 8—15 ft., with wide-spreading branches. Its leaves are 8—20 in. long, composed of seven to thirteen large leaflets, the leaf stalk widely winged. The autumn foliage is conspicuously coloured		3/6	5/6
„ **Potaninii.**—C. & W. China. A noble small tree with stiff, spreading branches. Its leaves are pinnate, 10—16 ins. long, turning to exceptionally brilliant tints in autumn		2/6	3/6
„ **succedanea.**—Japan, China. The Wax Tree of Japan is not hardy at Kew, but in this district it gets only its tips damaged by early frosts. Given an open, well-drained position, it will grow to 10 ft. or more in height. During the autumn its handsome pinnate leaves are as brilliantly coloured as a huntsman's coat. Nicholson was mistaken in describing it as evergreen		3/6	5/6
„ **sylvestris.**—China, Japan. A distinct species with pinnate leaves that become brilliantly coloured in autumn		3/6	5/6
„ **trichocarpa.**—Japan, Korea. A very uncommon shrub or small tree with handsome pinnate leaves 12—20 ins. long, each containing 13—17 furrowed, oblong-ovate-acuminate leaflets. It is quite hardy in the south and west counties. A plant at Kew is well worth a visit because of its exceptionally beautiful tints from mid-September to autumn frosts		3/6	5/6
„ **typhina** (Female).—U.S.A. Though a very old species, it is still an attractive small tree worth planting. The 12—30 in. pinnate leaves are brilliantly coloured for weeks during late autumn. Commonly called the Stag's Horn Sumach.		1/6	2/6
„ „ **laciniata.**—A handsome form with finely-cut fringed leaves, beautifully coloured during autumn ...		2/6	3/6
„ „ **viridiflora (coronaria).**—New Hampshire, U.S.A. This is the male form and it makes a wide bush or small tree. It has large pinnate leaves, which colour as well as those of the female form, and conspicuous panicles of fruits covered with red hairs **1/6**	2/6	3/6
„ **verniciflua.**—China, Japan. If pruned back every March, it will develop a good head and reach 15—25 ft., though much higher if allowed to grow wild. The handsome leaves are usually 1½—2 ft. long and consist of 7—13 ovate-oblong, pointed leaflets, each 5—7 ins. in length but with the terminal one much larger. They assume beautiful buttercup-yellow tints before falling ...		3/6	5/6
A **Rhus** will grow in any ordinary soil. The best autumn colours are seen on plants growing in sandy ones.			
Rhyncospermum.—(See **Trachelospermum**).			
Ribes americanum (floridum).—N. America. Similar in growth, foliage and height to the garden black currant. For one month during autumn the leaves are dark red, ageing to vivid crimson. It should be pruned back every year to obtain the largest leaves		1/6	2/6
„ **aureum (fragrans).**—W.N. America. The Buffalo Currant. A free-growing shrub with whip-like branches and flowers golden-yellow, sweetly-scented, in April. The tri-lobed leaves are richly coloured in late summer ...		1/6	2/6

Ribes fasciculatum.—Japan, Korea. A slender branching   each.
shrub 3—6 ft. high, with five-lobed leaves which become
magnificently coloured before falling. It bears clusters
of yellow fragrant flowers during April and red currants
in autumn 3/6

" **Gordonianum (sanguineum × aureum).**—Similar in
growth to R. aureum. Its flowers are attractive bronzy-
red, yellow within. The deeply-incised leaves are
bright coppery-red during early autumn 1/6 2/6

" **lacustre.**—N. America. A small shrub about 3 ft. high.
Its branches are covered with small bristles, and it
bears distinct lobed leaves and drooping racemes of many
flowers with white petals and chocolate-coloured sepals   1/6 2/6

E " **laurifolium.**—W. Szechuan, China. A slow-growing
shrub seldom more than 3 ft. high and with few branches,
these clothed with 3—5 in. coriaceous, ovate-oval, coarsely toothed and pointed leaves. It is a welcome addition
to hardy shrubs for its attractive racemes of green-yellow
flowers borne during February and March. Male and
Female 3/6

" **Lobbii.**—California. A twiggy-branching shrub of dense
habit, slowly growing to about 3 ft. It has small fuchsia-
like flowers with reddish calyx and white petals 3/6

" **luridum.**—An attractive unarmed species from W. China,
bearing large gooseberry-like leaves. The bark of the
erect growths is strikingly-polished brilliant red, ageing
to brown. During August the bark splits and hangs in
fringes 2/6 3/6

" **Menziesii.**—N. America. A thickly-branched shrub,
8—10 ft. high. In autumn its distinct lobed leaves are
beautifully coloured. The flowers are bell-shaped,
calyx reddish, petals white, rose tinted 1/6 2/6

" **Roezlii.**—California. A rare and pretty species, slowly
growing 3—4 ft. high. Its branches are wreathed during
May with attractive cylindrical flowers, calyx bright
crimson, petals rosy-white ... ...   — —

" " **cruentum.**—California. An attractive form,
quickly forming a bush 4—6 ft. high, with numerous
bell-shaped crimson and white flowers during May ...   1/6 2/6

" **sanguineum (Flowering Currant).**—California.—One
of the most pleasing of all flowering shrubs, having deep
rosy-red flowers during April 1/6 2/6

" " **albidum.**—Quite a pretty flowering shrub during
April with its white suffused-pink flowers. It is free-
growing and 4—6 ft. high 1/6 2/6

" " **atrorubens.**—It is a much better flowering shrub
than R. s. atrosanguineum. The strong growths, 4—10
ft. high, are decorated with narrow 3—4 in. racemes of
rich crimson-red flowers during March 1/6 2/6

" " **King Edward VII.**—Closely resembles the following form, but of more compact habit, not so strong growing, with shorter racemes, and is two weeks later in
flowering. The flowers are of a similar colour 2/6 3/6

" " **splendens.**—A beautiful form, 6—10 ft. high,
worthy of every garden and covered during April with
racemes of blood-red flowers, ageing to bright crimson 1/6 2/6 3/6

Ribes speciosum (Fuchsia Gooseberry).—California. A splendid large shrub, attaining 10 ft. and as much wide. The arching branches are wreathed from end to end during April and May with crimson-red pendent flowers. In the south and west a semi-shady position suits it best and under these conditions it will become much wider ... **2/6 3/6**   each.

Robinia hispida (Rose Acacia).—South U.S.A. An open growing shrub 4—6 ft. high and as much wide, with short racemes of deep pink flowers during May and June. A beautiful shrub but unfortunately very brittle. On own roots **3/6 5/6**

„ **Kelseyi.**—East U.S.A. This forms a large spreading shrub, 10—15 ft. high, but is very brittle. The slender branches are laden with drooping racemes of bright rose-coloured flowers, and the young bronzy leaves are a beautiful sight during June **2/6 3/6**

„ **Pseudo-Acacia (False Acacia).**—U.S.A. A beautiful ornamental tree in June, when it is smothered with pendulous racemes of slightly fragrant white flowers. This and the Silver-leaved Poplar unfortunately become pests as their roots send up shoots over a wide area **1/6 2/6 3/6**

Owing to their brittleness the Robinias need shelter from rough winds.

Romneya Coulteri. (The Californian Tree Poppy).—A sub-shrub at home, it is better in this country if cut to the ground each spring. It delights in a sunny position, and so planted, it bears its great white fragrant poppies from July to late autumn **2/6 3/6**

„ **trichocalyx.**—California. Similar flowers to those of the former but the buds are covered with hairs. The foliage is also similar. It is not so tall and is generally a hardier plant and easier to handle **2/6 3/6**

Rosa acicularis (Sayi).—N.E. Asia, N. America. A choice shrub, 4—6 ft. high, with grey leaves, glaucous beneath. The 2½ in. clear rose-pink flowers in May are followed by quantities of singly borne pear-shaped or round fruits, orange-red ageing to deep crimson **2/6**

„ **alba.**—Europe. A natural hybrid 4—8 ft. high, with grey leaves and clusters of sweetly-scented flowers, 3 in. across, in June and July. The oblong bright red fruits are very showy **2/6**

„ **altaica.**—(See **spinosissima altaica**).

„ **amblyotis.**—Kamtschatka. This rare species grows 4—6 ft. high by as much wide and has pinnate leaves. The 1¼—1½ in. pink, suffused red flowers are followed by depressed, globose or pear-shaped hips. It has attractive crimson-red stems but these should be cut back every March so as to get brighter coloured growths for next season. **3/6**

„ **Andersonii.**—A glorious Dog Rose 4 or 5 ft. high but of spreading habit, bearing along the branches, in June and July, upright clusters of large cerise-pink flowers, faintly scented. These, most vivid when opening, retain their colour to the last **3/6**

C Rosa anemoneflora (multiflora × laevigata) (sinica each.
anemone).—E. China. This needs a south or west wall
and its branches should be trained in zig-zag fashion to
encourage more clusters of 3—4 in. rose-pink flowers.
These look pretty nestling among the attractive leaves
from April onwards. 2/6   3/6

C „ Banksiae.—China. The Banksian Rose. Of two colours,
white and yellow, this beautiful climber is only suited
to S. or W. walls in the southern and western counties.
The exceptionally sweet double flowers are freely borne
on quite small plants if the soil is not too rich   ...   **1/6**   2/6   3/6

„ Beggeriana.—N.W. Asia. An elegant species, 5—8 ft.
high, with glaucous growths and leaves composed of seven
to nine grey-green leaflets, having a sweet briar scent.
The clusters of seven to twelve pure white flowers open
singly from May to September 2/6

„ blanda.—N. America. It has upright stems, 4 ft. or more
high and almost devoid of prickles, and ultimately
makes a bushy head. Its clusters of handsome 2½—3 in.
rose-pink flowers are borne singly or in groups of three or
more and they are followed by globose or pear-shaped
red hips 2/6   3/6

„ bracteata.—China. A wall shrub for the south and west.
From June to autumn frosts the 2—3 in. snow-white
flowers nestling amongst the rich foliage are a magnificent
sight 2/6   3/6

„ carolina Nuttalliana.—N. America. An erect-growing
shrub 6—10 ft. high. The mass of 2—2½ in. pale pink
flowers during June and July are deliciously scented.
The branches are laden until late winter with bright
crimson, orange-shaped fruits 2/6   3/6

„ cinnamomea.—Europe, Siberia, N. China. This very old
and widely distributed species is illustrated in Sowerby's
English Botany, 2nd Edition, Vol. IV. It makes a
shapely bush 5—9 ft. in height and during May and
June its many 2—3 in. glowing rose-pink fragrant
flowers are a lovely sight. They are followed by globose
or elongated bright red hips 2/6   3/6

„ Davidii.—W. Szechuan, China. An elegant species 6 ft.
or more high and quite as wide. Its spreading growths
carry 1½—2 in. rose-pink flowers, followed by ¾ in.
glistening, orange-yellow and crimson, bottle-shaped,
bristly fruits. In a well-known Perthshire garden, there
is a specimen 8 ft. × 15 ft. which is a beautiful sight
every autumn. 2/6   3/6

„ „ elongata.—China. This distinct form sends up
strong erect shoots with lateral spreading growths
8—12 ft. high. They carry large pinnate leaves, grey
beneath, and loose clusters of 3—7 paler pink flowers
which are succeeded by longer, hairy, bottle-shaped,
orange-yellow and crimson fruits 2/6   3/6

„ Dupontii.—An old hybrid between the Musk and Gallica
roses, of arching habit and growing 6—8 ft. high. The
corymbs of white flowers, blush in the bud, open in
June and July. Each flower is 2½ in. wide and is adorned
by a bunch of golden stamens 3/6

Rosa Farreri persetosa (Threepenny-bit Rose).—C. Kansu, China. This dense spreading shrub is about 5 ft. high and elegantly clothed with 1—2½ in. pinnate, metallic-green leaves, each composed of seven to nine tiny leaflets. The short wiry twigs carry pretty ¾—1 in. pale pink flowers succeeded by small delicately coloured oval fruits ... ...   each.   3/6

„ **filipes.**—W. China. Of semi-scandent habit with enormous trusses of fifty to eighty white fragrant flowers, scenting the air around it during June and July. A beautiful ornamental if planted at the base of, and allowed to grow through the heads of, thin-growing trees such as Holly, Thorn, Crabs, Laburnum, Oak, etc. 2/6   3/6

„ **Giraldii.**—C. China. A graceful shrub 5—8 ft. high with erect spreading branches clothed with slender spines and pinnate leaves composed of seven small hairy leaflets. The bright pink flowers, 1—2 ins. across, are followed by brilliant scarlet ovoid fruits 3/6

„ **gymnocarpa.**—West N. America. A pretty shrub of slender growth, attaining a height of 4—6 ft. The branches are decorated with 1—1½ in. rosy flowers, succeeded by globular or pear-shaped bright red fruits which hang long after the leaves have dropped 2/6   3/6

„ **Harrisonii.**—A semi-double rose of American origin, more than a century old and said to be a hybrid between the Austrian Briar and the Burnet Rose. It develops into a bush 3—4 ft. high. The flowers are soft pale yellow, opening successively, on short branches in June ...   2/6   3/6

„ **Helenae.**—C. China. First rate for the wild garden. It bears clusters of fragrant white flowers, followed by a mass of oval yellow fruits flushed with red 2/6

„ **highdownensis.**—A hybrid of R. Moyesii and a vigorous free-flowering rose with flowers of a beautiful clear carmine, large, with a very expressive eye. The stems are well thorned and the fruits, large, flagon-shaped, and deep scarlet, become darker with age. These are evidently disagreeable to birds 2/6

„ **Hillieri (Moyesii × Wilmottiae).**—A lovely addition and a vigorous grower. From mid-May to mid-June, the branches are lit up by flowers, deeper in colour than those of R. Moyesii. These are followed by showy fruits which hang long after the leaves have fallen ...   3/6

„ **hispida.**—Country of origin unknown. It is a charming rose for associating with R. spinosissima altaica but it is a little later in exhibiting its 2—3 in. yellow flowers which age to creamy white. It is of upright habit, 4 ft. or more high 3/6

„ **holodonta (R. Moyesii rosea of Rehder and Wilson).** W. China.—The bold leaves are glaucous beneath and the large refined bright rose-pink flowers are displayed in May and June. The many 1¾ in. orange peel-coloured and crimson fruits are narrow, with long thin necks and closed sepals. In a garden near Salisbury, several large specimens were quite weighed down with their handsome fruits last autumn 2/6   3/6

each.

Rosa Hugonis.—China.   A graceful shrub 5—8 ft. high, with slender branches clothed with pretty leaves. It is charming during May and June with its numerous 2 in. bright yellow, sweetly-scented flowers 2/6   3/6

" **longicuspis.**—W. China.   An attractive species from spring to autumn but requiring a south or west wall in the midland counties.   Both the branches and the underside of the handsome polished leaves are bright red.   During June, it bears clusters of 2 in. creamy-white flowers, often pink tinted 2/6   3/6

" **lutea (foetida).**—Austrian Briar.   W. Asia.   It is conspicuous from mid-May to early July with its glowing deep yellow flowers 1/6   2/6

"   " **punicea (bicolor).**—Austrian Copper Rose. The petals of this attractive rose are copper-red inside, hence its name 1/6   2/6

"   " **persiana.**—Persian Yellow Rose.   It is not quite as strong-growing as the two former but freely produces its full double bright yellow flowers 2/6   3/6

" **macrantha (gallica × canina).**—W. Europe.   Of spreading habit, forming a bush 4—6 ft. high.   From May onwards the branches are laden with 3—4 in. white, rose-tinted flowers with yellow anthers, deliciously scented.   A worthy ornamental to decorate any garden.   2/6

" **macrophylla.**—China, Himalaya.   A strong grower, throwing its branches 6—9 ft. high, clothed with handsome pinnate foliage and many 2—3 in. rosy-red flowers during June.   These are followed by attractive bottle-shaped bright red fruits.   A splendid shrub 2/6   3/6

" **Mermaid.**—On a south or west wall it soon forms a large plant.   The huge single sulphur-yellow flowers, with amber-coloured stamens, are freely produced from June till autumn frosts 2/6

" **microphylla.**—(See **Roxburghii**).

" **Moyesii.**—W. China.   Strong growing 6—12 ft. high, and a notable sight during June and July.   The numerous attractive flowers are blood-red.   The branches are weighed until autumn frosts with large pitcher-shaped crimson fruits.   A species to be included in the first twenty-five hardy shrubs 2/6   3/6

"   " **Fargesii.**—China.   A handsome shrub 4—8 ft. high, pretty during May and June with its numerous 2—2½ in. rich rose flowers.   It is equally attractive from September onwards with long bottle-shaped orange-red fruits, ageing to crimson 2/6   3/6

"   " **Geranium.**—This first class seedling form of R. Moyesii is quite as robust as its parent and was raised at Wisley.   It has Robinia-like leaves, covered with bloom above and glaucous beneath.   The outstanding 2 in. single flowers are geranium-red. 3/6   5/6

"   " **Maroon.**—This is a selected seedling from R. Moyesii.   Its sturdy branches are attractive during May with 2—2½ in. maroon-red flowers and again from August to November with bulging, crimson-red fruits   ...   2/6   3/6

Rosa multibracteata.—W. Szechuan, China. This plant throws up strong erect growths 6—10 ft. high and ultimately develops a semi-pendulous head. From early June to September, the sub-lateral growths are decorated with numerous leafy clusters of 20—50, 1—1½ in. bright pink flowers ... ...
each.
2/6 3/6

C „ **multiflora.**—N. China, Korea, Japan. A good companion for R. filipes. It is happy rambling through the heads of thin trees and over fences or will make a semi-scandent large bush. It is one of the most beautiful of wild roses and carries the numerous panicles, each containing many single, pale pink or flesh-coloured, deliciously fragrant flowers, above its elegant pinnate, pink-tinted green leaves ... ...
1/6 2/6

„ **Murielae.**—W. China. The slender spreading branches are covered with light brown prickles and bristles. Its pinnate leaves are composed of 9—15 elliptical leaflets and the corymbs of 3—7 white flowers, each 1½ ins. across, are followed by small bright red elliptical fruits
2/6 3/6

„ **nitida.**—N. America. A delightful shrub, 1—2 ft. high, with bright rosy-red flowers, 2—2½ ins. across, during June. The polished green pinnate leaves assume in autumn vivid tints, making a contrast with the red bristly stems and round scarlet fruits ... ...
1/6 2/6

„ **nutkana.**—West N. America. A handsome species, attaining 8—10 ft. The numerous 2—2½ in. bright red flowers are borne during June. The fruits are bright red and orange-shaped ... ...
2/6 3/6

„ **pendulina (alpina),**—Mts. of S. and C. Europe. A compact shrub, 5—8 ft. high. The young growths towards autumn become bright red and the 1½ in. deep pink flowers are followed by narrow pear-shaped red fruits ... ...
1/6 2/6

„ „ **plena.**—Mts. of N. Italy and Austria. This uncommon shrub is 3—5 ft. high and worth a place in the autumn garden for its deep red dogwood-like growths and coloured pinnate leaves, these hanging for many weeks. It should be pruned back hard every spring to encourage brighter coloured stems. Its double magenta-red flowers may not be so attractive in every garden ...
2/6

„ „ **pyrenaica.**—Pyrenees. A variety growing about 1 ft. high, of spreading habit, with glaucous leaves and 2 in. rose-red flowers. It bears very pretty long orange-yellow fruits. Ideal for rockeries or front of sloping borders ... ...
3/6

„ **pisocarpa.**—W. N. America. This dense almost spineless shrub grows 4—6 ft. high. It should be in every garden for its display of brilliantly coloured fruits, firmly held from September to February. These elliptical hips are almost ¾ in. long, with short necks, and have five sepals. They are not always pea-shaped as the name implies ...
1/6 2/6

each.

C **Rosa polyantha grandiflora.** (Of Willmott's Genus Rosa, 34). Probably R. moschata × multiflora and raised by Bernaix from seed of R. moschata (R. Wilsoniana of some gardens). One of the attractions of the garden during June and July when it presents its huge clusters of 2—2½ in. saucer-shaped, paper-white flowers, these set off by a magnificent bunch of bright yellow stamens. The air is filled with their delicious fragrance. It is of semi-scandent habit, 6 ft. or more high and is clothed with noble pinnate leaves **2/6   3/6**

„ **pomifera (villosa pomifera).**—C. Europe. A deserving shrub, 4—6 ft. high, of greyish appearance. The flowers are deep rosy-pink, up to 2 in. across. It is striking in early autumn with many large, bristly, red fruits **2/6**

„ **Prattii.**—W. China. Of long, slender growth, this is one of the most effective of pinnate-foliaged shrubs. The flowers are deep rose-coloured **2/6**

„ **Roxburghii.**—China, Japan. Previously distributed as R. microphylla. The Burr Rose is a rare species with short growths, ultimately reaching 4 ft., well clothed with pretty leaves. The flowers, pale rose, 2—2½ in. across, are very fragrant and are followed by 1½ in. flattish yellow spiny fruits **2/6   3/6**

„ **rubrifolia.**—Mts. of C. Europe. A beautiful ornamental shrub, 4—6 ft. high. The stems and leaves are glaucous red throughout the growing season. The flowers and globose fruits are deep red **1/6   2/6**

„ **rugosa × rubiginosa.**—Natural Hybrid. A beautiful ornamental shrub, 3—6 ft. high, of spreading habit, with pink flowers 2—3 ins. across. From early August the branches are weighed with globose orange-scarlet fruits, ageing in autumn to deep crimson. One of the best of all fruiting ornamentals. **2/6**

„ **Sayi.**—(See **acicularis**).

„ **sericea (Of Lindley) (R. omeiensis of Rolfe).**—India, Mt. Omi, W. China. A dense shrub 5—8 ft. high and as much through, with elegant arching branches densely clothed with pinnate leaves. It is wreathed in May and June with 1½—2 in. creamy-white flowers and these are followed by ½—¾ in. pear-shaped, yellow-red fruits which, in Scottish gardens, are held until mid-October ...   **2/6**

„ „ **atrosanguinea.**—W. China. In a Perthshire garden there is a specimen 7 ft. × 7 ft. and it is a magnificent sight from August to mid-October when its spreading branches are laden with brilliant crimson, humming-top-like fruits **2/6   3/6**

„ „ **polyphylla.**—W. China. The distinctive character of this variety is its rich crimson-red fruits, perhaps not quite so large as the yellow and red ones of the type. They are very freely produced and in August the bushes look most attractive...   ...   .   **2/6   3/6**

„ „ **pteracantha.**—W. China. Of open habit, 5—8 ft. high. The growing stems, covered with blood-red translucent spines up to 1½ in. across, are attractive at any time of the year. The second year's growths should be cut out to encourage young growths **2/6**

		each.	

Rosa sericea pteracantha lutea.—W. China. This form is similar in habit to R. s. pteracantha. It produces numerous soft yellow flowers and the branches are illuminated with broad, richly-coloured spines throughout the year ... **3/6 5/6**

„ **setipoda.**—W. China. A strong grower, of open habit, 6—10 ft. high, with large loose clusters of many showy pink flowers, followed by handsome brilliant red bottle-shaped fruits which are a joy to any autumn garden ... **2/6 3/6**

„ **Soulieana.**—W. China. This species grows 10 ft. high and has grey leaves and branches. It bears corymbs of many 1½ in. yellowish-white flowers followed by small bright red egg-shaped fruits **2/6 3/6**

„ **spinosissima altaica. (R. grandiflora of Lindley).**— Siberia. This delightful shrub grows 3—6 ft. high, according to soil. Its wands of 3 in. creamy-white flowers are quite as bold as those of Rubus deliciosus **1/6 2/6**

„ „ **lutea.**—Origin unknown. It soon grows, by underground suckers into a thick bush 3 ft. high. From mid-May to July, numerous very beautiful rich buttercup-yellow 2 in. flowers are borne **2/6 3/6**

„ „ **myriacantha.**—S. France. One of the treasures of the genus. It has compact wiry shoots 12—24 ins. high and increases by underground suckers. From mid-May to late July, it is a lovely sight with its numerous 2 in. fragrant, pearl-white suffused rose blossoms. It has small pinnate leaves and is lit up with conspicuous ½—1 in. ovoid red hips from mid-August until late autumn. There is a plate of this beautiful shrub in Willmott's Genus Rosa, but it is described as having globose brown fruits. See also Bean's Vol. II, page 446 **2/6 3/6**

„ „ **William III.**—A rare Scotch rose, 1—2 ft. high, but through throwing up suckers it is much wider. It produces in May and June a profusion of double wine-red flowers **2/6**

„ **Sweginzowii (of Koehne) (R. Moyesii in part of Stapf).**—N.W. China. A distinct shrub developing thin whip-like growths, 6 ft. or more high and furnished with pinnate leaves and ¾ in. brown-red flat spines. The flowers are bright pink and are followed by narrow bottle-like bright crimson fruits **2/6 3/6**

„ **virginiana.**—East U.S.A. An erect-growing shrub 4 ft. high. The rose-red 2½ in. flowers are followed by round bright red fruits, and the glossy green foliage turns brilliant crimson in autumn. Also known as R. lucida ... **1/6 2/6**

„ **Webbiana.**—Himalayas. An uncommon species, 4—6 ft. high, furnished with pinnate grey-green leaves. The flowers are pale pink and are succeeded by pretty pitcher-shaped bright red fruits **3/6**

„ **Willmottiae.**—N. China. The glaucous dark red branches have small outward-pointing spines and elegant pinnate leaves. The 1—1½ in. rose-purple flowers, singly borne during July and August, are followed by small, round, orange-red fruits. It is closely related to R. multi-bracteata **2/6 3/6**

Rosa **Wilsonii.**—Received here under this name. It is a   each. twiggy, branching shrub 3—4 ft. in height, with rugose-like leaves. The magnificent erect saucer-shaped flowers are silver-pink with four to five petals and are 3—5 ins. across. Their presence can be detected by their delicious perfume 2/6   3/6

"   **xanthina spontanea.**—N. China, Korea. Previously distributed as R. xanthina. This is the wild form and is one of the best of the family. It has upright mahogany-red branches, 4 ft. or more high. One is quickly arrested by the magnificence of the many 1½ in. deliciously-scented, buttercup-like, rich yellow flowers borne during May and June. It is a much better ornamental than the feeble and over-rated R. Ecae 2/6   3/6

The various species of roses will grow in almost any soil and are some of the most interesting of all hardy shrubs, especially when loaded with their beautifully-coloured hips, which are highly ornamental from September to February. Many are a great success as dot plants in the heather garden.

EC Rubus bambusarum.—(See **R. Henryi bambusarum**).

"   **biflorus.**—Himalayas. This species, with its white-washed growths, up to 8 ft. or more high, is very effective among other plants during the winter. The flowers are white and the fruits yellow 2/6   3/6

E   "   **cissoides pauperatus.**—Previously distributed as R. australis. New Zealand. The Tataramoa is a pretty rambling shrub with intricate branches covered with small spines. In the south-west it will climb thin-growing trees 2/6   3/6

"   **deliciosus.**—Rocky Mountains. A splendid shrub 5—8 ft. high, with arching branches and currant-like leaves. It is beautiful during May and June with 2 in. pure white flowers 2/6   3/6

EC   "   **flagelliflorus.**—C. China. An elegant climbing species with attractive dark green marbled leaves. It should be planted in a semi-shady position 2/6   3/6

"   **Giraldianus.**—N. & C. China. A beautiful shrub for winter effect, with arching white stems 6—10 ft. long. The leaves are pinnate and grey-green 2/6   3/6

EC   "   **Henryi.**—C. & W. China. A slender, branching shrub with distinct three-lobed leaves 3/6

EC   "   "   **bambusarum.**—C. China. A climbing shrub with growths 3—6 ft. long. The divided leaves are very distinct 2/6   3/6

E   "   **irenaeus.**—C. China. A distinct species with trailing growths. The roundish green leaves have a metallic surface, are 6 ins. wide and very like those of Coltsfoot. It grows freely in semi-shade. 2/6   3/6

"   **lasiostylus.**—C. China. A striking shrub with arching white-stemmed growths covered with fine bristles ...   2/6   3/6

E   "   **Moorei.**—Australia. A rarity of prostrate or climbing habit with slender growths furnished with pretty three-parted leaves. Each leaflet is ovate, long-pointed and glossy green and is edged with neat, brown-red, spiny teeth ; the stalks and midribs are armed with small dark spines 5/-

			each.	
E	**Rubus Parkeri.**—C. China. An elegant shrub, 3—5 ft. high, with distinct lanceolate leaves		2/6	3/6

E   **" parvus.**—New Zealand. A choice dwarf shrub with creeping growths, only a few inches high. The lanceolate serrated leaves lie flat ; the flowers are white and erect ; the fruits oblong. Unfortunately, not generally hardy 1/6   2/6

     " thyrsoideus plenus. (Double White Bramble).—This beautiful shrub will thrive almost anywhere including a place in semi-shade. The attractive panicles of double, daisy-like, white flowers are produced from mid-July to October, a time when flowering shrubs are not too plentiful 2/6

     " ulmifolius bellidiflorus (plenus).—The well-known double pink-flowering bramble. A specimen here with more than one hundred 9—15 in. panicles of double, rose-pink, daisy-like flowers was much admired from early July to September of last year 1/6   2/6

E   **Ruscus aculeatus. (Male and Female forms).**—Better known as the Butcher's Broom. In a small copse near us it is growing 3 ft. high, and is a picture every autumn with its many large round bright red berries. Cut sprays are very useful during winter 1/6   2/6

E   **" hermaphroditus.**—A splendid plant with a thicket of erect growths, about 18 ins. in height and as much through. It bears flowers of both sexes, followed by countless ¾ in. bright crimson fruits, retained until the new year 2/6   3/6

     " racemosus.—(See **Danaë racemosa**).

Salix alba argentea (regalis).—The Silver-leaved Willow is one of the most conspicuous of all small trees, especially if allowed to develop into a standard. It is not often seen in good condition in our hot heathland soil 1/6   2/6

     " daphnoides.—Europe to C. Asia. Grown as a standard, the Violet Willow forms a handsome head quite as wide as it is high. It is invaluable during the winter for its attractive purple-violet-coloured branches and silvery white catkins. It should be pollarded every March to encourage brighter coloured growths 1/6   2/6   3/6

     " Fargesii.—Previously distributed as S. hypoleuca. W. China. Of bushy spreading habit, possibly 5—8 ft. high, and suitable for a moist position. Its 6—9 in. narrow furrowed dark green leaves are crimson veined and glaucous beneath, whilst the varnished deep crimson growths with their lighter protruding buds are attractive the year round. Not hardy in the midland counties ...   3/6   5/6

     " magnifica.—W. China. A very beautiful Willow of upright habit 8—14 ft. high, with purple young growths. The large, broad and elliptical leaves are covered with a glaucous bloom. The staminate catkins are 4—7 ins. long, the pistillate 7—12 ins. 2/6   3/6   5/6

     " vitellina britzensis.—This is probably the best landscape Willow we have. It will grow into a shapely tree 20—30 ft. high, with a straight stem. The naked orange-scarlet branches are a pleasing sight from September to April. The yellow catkins in May are attractive 1/6   2/6   3/6

Salix vitellina pendula (ramulis aureis of gardens).—Weeping   each. Golden-barked Willow. This delightful Willow with its long pendulous branches covered with golden bark is probably the most admired of all weeping trees. In the southern counties, it hates being planted alone in the open **1/6 2/6 3/6**

Salvia Grahamii.—Mexico. In the open around the south and west coast it forms a shrub 2 ft. high, but it will attain 8 ft. or more on a south or west wall, even as far north as the Salisbury Downs. It bears quantities of scarlet flowers from June till autumn frosts. The hardiest of the Salvias. **1/6 2/6**

     „   **Greggii.**—Discarded as it has proved much too tender even when planted against a wall. ... ... **— —**

     „   **neurepia.**—Mexico. A beautiful shrub 3—4 ft. high, with large, sage-scented leaves suitable for gardens in the south and west and similar climates. It bears plenty of brilliant scarlet flowers throughout the summer and autumn. In good soils it grows quickly but is apt to get broken down by summer and autumn winds **2/6**

Sambucus racemosa.—N. Hemisphere. Given the situation and soil it loves, it can be a striking ornamental bush 10—15 ft. high. It bears tightly-packed panicles of brilliant scarlet fruits. These ripen in June and July. Unfortunately the species does not fruit in this district whereas the common Elder fruits freely **1/6 2/6**

E   **Santolina Chamaecyparissus (incana).**—S. Europe. The Lavender Cotton, a very old favourite, is invaluable for providing a patch of grey-blue in the heather garden which is especially appreciated during the dull days of winter **1/- 1/6**

E   **Sarcococca Hookeriana.**—Afghanistan, W. Himalayas. An erect-growing shrub of open habit, slowly attaining to three feet in height. The erect branches are pretty from January to March with fragrant whitish flowers, followed by shining egg-shaped blue-black fruits **3/6**

E   „   „   **digyna.**—W. China. This beautiful form has more slender branches and narrower lanceolate leaves. The flesh-coloured flowers and larger egg-shaped fruits are abundantly produced. The latter are retained throughout the winter and the plant is worth a place for its delightful perfume **2/6 3/6**

E   „   **humilis.**—W. China. A much smaller shrub, of erect compact habit, densely clothed with narrow oval leaves. During late February and March, its branches are crowded with white sweetly scented flowers. The black fruits are not freely produced with us **2/6**

E   „   **ruscifolia.**—C. China. This neat-habited shrub grows to 3 ft. high with Ruscus-like leaves. The very fragrant, narrow-petalled, white flowers are borne on the upper half of its wiry stems. From October to March it is decorated with numerous deep scarlet fruits **2/6 3/6**

each.

E **Sarcococca saligna angustifolia (Of Baillon).**—N. W. Himalaya. This narrow-leaved form makes an upright bush 2—3 ft. high but is not so hardy as the Chinese species. The leaves, usually three-veined, are drawn out into long-tailed points. The fruits are purple and of the size of a wild cherry. It is rare in British gardens   3/6
    In the south the **Sarcococcas** love a semi-shady position.

Sassafras officinale.—E.N. America. The Sassafras is a handsome, slow-growing tree requiring a sheltered well-drained position in lime-free soil. Its dark green leaves, of unusual outline, change to orange and scarlet in autumn **3/6**   5/6   7/6

E **Schima argentea.**—(Forrest, 1917-19). W. China. A most attractive evergreen of great character. The shining, long-pointed leaves are glaucous beneath and the many terminal trusses of ivory-white, Eucryphia-like flowers open in October. It should be given a sheltered and sunny position in the garden and will grow 6 ft. or more high and as much wide. A fine article, accompanied by a beautiful illustration of this shrub, appears in New Flora and Silva for April, 1936, Pages 205-7   ...   ...   21/-

C **Schizandra chinensis.**—China, Japan. A vigorous grower. Its rose-coloured flowers in April and May are followed by berry-like scarlet fruits, retained until late autumn   **2/6**   3/6   5/6

EC   „   **propinqua.**—C. & W. China. A distinct plant with lanceolate leaves, growing 6 ft. high. The round orange-yellow flowers are freely borne during July 3/6   5/6

C   „   **rubriflora.**—Mt. Omi, Szechuan, China. Fast growing and interesting during April and May with its ¾ in. red flowers. Its fruits are bright red 5/-

C   „   **sphenanthera.**—C. & W. China. Also vigorous growing and attractive during April and May with numerous coppery-yellow flowers. Fruits red 3/6   5/6
    The **Schizandras** are related to the Magnolias, but dislike scorching sun. In the south and west they grow freely on sheltered north and east walls.

E **Schizocodon macrophylla.**—Japan. An attractive species with polished net-veined, cordate, olive-green leaves, unevenly serrated and 2½—3½ in. long by as much wide. The many 3—8 in. scapes of large, campanulate, frilled, bright pink flowers are borne from March to June   **2/6**   3/6   5/6

E   „   **soldanelloides.**—Japan. With age it forms a tuft 12 ins. or more across but seldom more than 3 ins. high. The dense, leathery, rugose, heart-shaped, bronze-green leaves, have uneven shallow teeth and are 1—1½ ins. long by as much wide. Every spring it sends up 4—6 in. scapes of four to six fringed deep rose flowers, shading to blush **2/6**   3/6   5/6

E   „   „   **alpina.**—Japan. The tiny one of the family, having ⅓—¾ in. leaves on 1—1½ in. stalks which lie more or less on the ground. It produces bright pink, frilled flowers, comparatively large for the size of the plant   **3/6**   5/6   7/6

E   „   „   **ilicifolia.**—Japan. A rarity with rosettes of 1½—2½ in. cordate leaves, edged with spiny teeth. From mid-March to July it produces 4—6 in. scapes of beautiful ¾ in. campanulate, fringed, pink flowers   ...   **3/6**   5/6   7/6

E **Schizocodon soldanelloides ilicifolia albus.**—Japan. This each. gem is gaily decorated from mid-March to July and often again in autumn, with 3—6 in. scapes of delightful pure white, frilled flowers. It is well illustrated in the Alpine Society's Bulletin, Vol. III, No. 3 (Sept. 1935) page 221 ... ... 2/6   3/6   5/6   7/6

  The **Schizocodons** and **Shortias** flourish and flower freely if given a lime-free, sandy loam to which a sprinkling of leafmould has been added. They love woodland conditions or can be planted on the north side of a Rhododendron hedge. If they are happy, they will give a good show of flowers during the autumn.

C **Schizophragma hydrangeoides.**—Japan. It is much confused with the following species. Its cord-like growths are furnished with broad, cordate, metallic-green, hairy leaves with coarse deep teeth and red stalks ; they are net-veined and glossy, pale green or glaucous beneath. From mid-July to October, it has wide inflorescences, attractive with conspicuous heart-shaped, pale yellow bracts, each 1—1½ in. long. It climbs like ivy on walls, trees and fences but hates full sun in the south ... 2/6   3/6   5/6

C   „   **integrifolium.**—C. & W. China. One of the handsomest of wall climbers, attaching itself as the Ivy, but hating full sun in the southern counties. It has thick, stiff growths and 3—7 in. soft, ovate-acuminate, green, hairy leaves, edged with wide shallow teeth, grey-green beneath. It has numerous conspicuous 1 ft. inflorescences, surrounded by white bracts 3½ ins. × 1¾ ins. wide, from mid-July to September 3/6   5/6

    „   **petiolaris.**—(See **Hydrangea petiolaris**).

    „   **viburnoides.**—(See **Pileostegia viburnoides**).

E **Senecio Bidwillii.**—North Island, New Zealand. A compact shrub, 15—18 ins. high, making not more than 1—2 ins. of growth yearly. The small ovate leaves, shining and leathery, are white to pale buff beneath 7/6

E   „   **compactus.**—New Zealand. Forms a spreading shrub 2 ft. high, with small silvery-green serrated leaves and heads of yellow daisy-like flowers during late summer ... 2/6   3/6

E   „   **Greyi.**—New Zealand. An attractive shrub at any time of the year, 3 ft. high and 8 ft. or more across and having compact semi-prostrate growths. The grey-green leaves are 1½—3 ins. long and silvery beneath and they make a good background for the mass of broad flat corymbs of bright yellow daisy-like flowers borne from June to September. It should be pruned hard back every second year 1/6   2/6

E   „   **Hectori.**—South Island, New Zealand. A rather loose-growing shrub 6 ft. high but only suitable for the warmer districts. Its handsome leaves are broadly lanceolate or ovate-lanceolate and pinnate or pinnatifid at the base and are borne in groups. It is a beautiful shrub during summer and autumn with its 12—18 in. corymbs of 1½—2 in. orange-yellow flowers. The other form has white flowers 7/6

each.

E **Senecio Monroi.**—New Zealand. Of compact habit, seldom more than 2½ ft. high and with pleasing ½—1½ in. oblong-oval or obovate crinkly leaves, grey-green above and silvery white beneath. During late summer and early autumn, it is lit up with many heads of bright yellow flowers. A good companion for S. compactus 2/6   3/6

E   „   **rotundifolius.**—South Island, New Zealand. One of the most attractive of New Zealand evergreens and large specimens are often seen in gardens within reach of the salt sea air. The large leathery round leaves are silvery-white beneath 3/6   5/6
The **Senecios** are beautiful shrubs for seaside gardens on the south and west coasts.

E **Shortia galacifolia.**—N. Carolina. An evergreen herb, forming compact tufts of glossy green leaves which often become brightly tinted during the winter. The pretty 1 in. white flowers on slender scapes are freely produced in early spring **1/6**   2/6   3/6

E   „   **uniflora.**—Japan. The smallest of the family and having a charm of its own. It forms a tuft 2—3 ins. high and has ½—1 in. circular polished leaves with conspicuous veins. The many pretty ¾ in. pink, scented flowers are exhibited during March and April 3/6   5/6

E   „   **grandiflora.**—Japan. Much larger in all its parts than the type. The dense tufts of glossy leaves are almost hidden during March and April by 1½—2 in. pink deliciously scented flowers **2/6**   3/6   5/6

E   „   „   **rosea.**—Japan. This beautiful form produces its 1½—2 in. deep rose-pink flowers quite as freely as S. u. grandiflora though one month earlier. It is usually in full bloom by mid-February 3/6   5/6
The leaves of the **Shortias, Galax and Schizocodons** become gorgeously coloured with the approach of winter and remain attractive until late spring. These plants love a mixture of lime-free soil, leafmould and sand and like semi-shade, such as a position in woodland walks, the north side of an Ericaceae border or on the north side of Rhododendrons ; in the south and west, they hate full sun. For some reason, all Ericaceae plants, including the common Rhododendron, dislike being planted near the roots of Beech trees.

Sinowilsonia Henryi.—C. & W. China. A rare member of the Hamamelids, of botanical interest. It is perfectly hardy in an open border. The young leaves are bronze-tinted and the 6 in. racemes of yellow flowers are inconspicuous 5/-   7/6

E **Skimmia Foremanii (Fortunei × japonica) (Rogersii. Hort.).** —A handsome hybrid with larger leaves and bearing freely, round scarlet fruits 2/6   3/6

E   „   **Fortunei.**—China. A low evergreen with spreading branches, narrow dark green leaves and terminal panicles of fragrant white flowers during April. It carries many large deep crimson fruits throughout the winter, is hermaphrodite, and perhaps the most free fruiting of the family **1/6**   2/6   3/6

E **Skimmia japonica (oblata).**—Japan. An erect-growing, bushy   each.
  shrub, 3—4 ft. high but much wider. The leaves are
  aromatic, speckled beneath, and it bears terminal panicles
  of small white fragrant flowers in April. Its fruits are
  bright red 2/6 3/6

E „ „ **Veitchii.**—A hermaphrodite hybrid. The leaves
  are oval and glossy dark green. It bears spike-like
  racemes of globe-shaped coral red fruits 2/6 3/6

E „ **Laureola (aromatica).**—Himalayas. In the south and
  west in semi-shade it reaches 3 ft., of spreading habit.
  The long deep green leaves are very aromatic when bruised 2/6 3/6

Solanum crispum.—Chile. This beautiful flowering shrub
  stands most winters in open borders around the south
  and west coasts. Inland it should have wall protection.
  It is smothered with 6 in. corymbs of delicate bluish-
  purple flowers from early June to late August, and
  grows 10—15 ft. high 2/6 3/6

 „ „ **autumnalis (Glasnevin Form).**—This distinct
  form has more slender growths and is not quite so hardy
  here as the type. The deeper-coloured flowers are
  produced up to the end of September 2/6 3/6

C „ **jasminoides (Paxton).**—Brazil. A beautiful climbing
  plant for south and west walls, with slender growths.
  The original plant with grey-blue flowers from July
  to early autumn is offered 2/6 3/6

C „ „ **album.**—The white-flowering form, producing
  quantities of flowers from late June to early winter.
  Both are suitable for the south and west ... 1/6 2/6 3/6

C **Sollya heterophylla.**—Australia. A pretty climbing shrub with
  slender wiry growths, hung with light blue nodding
  flowers from early June to late August. Known as the
  Australian Bluebell creeper, but only suitable for warm
  walls in the south and west 2/6 3/6

E **Sophora tetraptera (Edwardsia grandiflora).**—New Zealand,
  Chile. In the south it forms a small tree 10—15 ft. high
  in the open, growing much higher against a wall. The
  leaves are pinnate, and conspicuous pendulous clusters of
  tubular golden-yellow flowers are borne in May and June 2/6 3/6

E „ „ **microphylla (Edwardsia Macnabiana).**—New
  Zealand. On a south or west wall in the southern counties
  it grows 10—15 ft. high, with interlacing branches
  decorated with pinnate leaves composed of many leaflets.
  The golden yellow flowers are a little smaller than those
  of the former 2/6 3/6

 „ **viciifolia.**—N. & W. China. A twiggy-branched shrub,
  4—8 ft. high, clothed with small pinnate leaves. It
  bears short terminal racemes of blue and white pea-
  shaped flowers during June. This beautiful shrub is
  much freer flowering if grown on a south or west wall
  but is perfectly hardy in the open 2/6 3/6 5/6

AUCUPARIA (MOUNTAIN ASH) SECTION.

Sorbus americana.—E.N. America. The American Mountain
  Ash has stiff upright branches, becoming spreading, and
  forms a small tree with a neat head. The large, coarse,
  ash-grey, pinnate leaves open from gummed buds and
  make a good background for the huge corymbs of
  brilliantly coloured fruits 3/6 5/6

each.

Sorbus Aucuparia (Common Mountain Ash).—Siberia, W. Asia, Europe. A well-known native 1/6 2/6 3/6

„ „ **xanthocarpa (fructu luteo) (Fifeana).**—Its branches are much more erect than those of the Common Mountain Ash, and it ultimately makes a fine pyramidal head. It is conspicuous during August and September with its heavy load of bright yellow fruits ... 2/6 3/6 5/6

„ **commixta.**—Japan, Korea.—As erect as the Lombardy Poplar and 15—25 ft. high. The brown-red stems are speckled with light dots. Its young foliage is brightly copper-coloured ageing to lustrous dark green and colouring well in autumn. The many wide corymbs of sealing wax-red fruits are striking during September and October 3/6 5/6 7/6

„ **Conradinae.**—W. China. It is of open habit and stiffer appearance than its relative S. Esserteauiana. The bolder olive-green, flat, pinnate leaves have stipules and usually contain 13 oblong-ovate 1—2 in. leaflets, serrated except at the base ; they have white felt beneath which more or less disappears with age. A first rate ornamental with numerous wide corymbs of ¼ in. orange-scarlet fruits from August to October and gorgeously tinted autumn foliage 3/6 5/6

„ **decurrens (Aria × Aucuparia).**—Natural hybrid. C. Europe. A densely branched tree 12—25 ft. high, of beautiful pyramidal habit and handsomely clothed with partly-pinnate grey-felted leaves which colour well every autumn. It is perhaps the first member of the family one would select on account of its grand display of upright clusters of large vivid red fruits, borne from early August to autumn frosts ; they are seldom attacked by blackbirds 2/6 3/6 5/6

„ **discolor.**—N. China. This forms a handsome-headed upright tree, 15—25 ft. or more high. It has become very popular on account of its deep green glossy pinnate leaves which become magnificently coloured for at least six weeks during the autumn, changing in tint from day to day. Various authorities quote it as having white fruits, but on the many specimens seen in gardens they are ¼ in. round, brilliant orange-red, borne in 4—6 in. corymbs, each containing up to 100. It rightly claims a place among the first twelve trees for the autumn garden 2/6 3/6 5/6

„ **domestica.**—S. & E. Europe & N. Africa.—Service Tree. Previously distributed as Pyrus (Aucuparia) Sorbus. This is worth a place where space can be given for it to develop. Admittedly it is inferior to many of the newer Chinese species, but its pinnate, soft green, downy foliage colours well in the autumn. It bears brown fruits tinged with red on the exposed side 3/6 5/6

„ **Esserteauiana.**—W. China. A charming landscape tree of open habit attaining 20—30 ft. in height. The light brown stems are furnished with deep green pinnate leaves, each containing 13 oblong-lanceolate leaflets, drawn out to a long point, and guarded by 2 laciniate stipules ; they are deeply serrated and covered on the underside with a persistent woolly felt. The branches, laden with large corymbs of bright red fruits nestling among the richly coloured leaves, are a fine sight from September to Christmas 3/6 5/6

Sorbus gracilis.—Japan. A worthy species, of compact habit   each. and slowly growing 8—12 ft. high. The dense leaves are pinnate, composed of 9—11 oval leaflets and have two serrated stipules ; they are brilliantly coloured when young, ageing to bright green and grey beneath. It is one of the best autumn-colouring plants Japan has given us and, grown in standard form, makes a beautiful avenue tree. The fruits are pear-shaped and orange-peel coloured **2/6**   3/6   5/6

   „   **Harrowiana.**—Yunnan, China. The most distinct of this section, growing 6 ft. or more high, but unfortunately only suitable for gardens along the south and west coasts and similar climates. Its attractive, leathery, deep green leaves, composed of 3 or 5 leaflets, remind one of the foliage of Ceratonia siliqua. It is evergreen in gardens in the southwest of Ireland 5/-   7/6

   „   **hupehensis.**—C. & W. China. Of upright habit with brown-red speckled branches, it reaches 20 ft. or more in height. The leaves, composed of 13—17 leaflets, are bronze to blue-green above, grey beneath, and gloriously tinted in autumn. It is distinguished from Sorbus Wilsoniana by having wide corymbs of bright pink fruits 3/6   5/6

   „   **hybrida (intermedia × Aucuparia).**—N. Europe. Previously distributed as Pyrus (Aucuparia) pinnatifida. Of upright habit, forming a head of even outline. The leaves are partly pinnated and dark grey-green. It bears corymbs of many large brilliant red fruits. During autumn it is one of the most striking trees   ...   **2/6**   3/6   5/6

   „   „   **Gibbsii.**—Previously distributed as Pyrus pinnatifida Gibbsii. Horticulture is indebted to the well-known Aldenham House Gardens for this striking fruiting tree. The corymbs of dark crimson fruits, each ¾ in. in diameter are probably the largest in the section 3/6   5/6

   „   **intermedia (scandica).**—N. Europe. The Swedish Mountain Ash is illustrated in Bean's Hardy Trees and Shrubs, Vol. II, page 225. It is a tall-growing and wide tree, densely furnished with grey-green elliptic-ovate leaves which are partly pinnated, lobed and notched. Its 5 in. corymbs of dull white flowers are succeeded by pretty ½ in. oval, orange-red fruits **2/6**   3/6   5/6

   „   **Koehneana.**—Hupeh & Shensi, China. This new species grows into a small tree and has chocolate-red branches dotted with light brown lenticels. The dense and graceful leaves, each 4—8 ins. long, have winged stalks and contain 17—33 oblong-lanceolate, deep green leaflets. It bears a heavy crop of small white fruits which look very attractive among the coloured foliage in autumn   ...   5/-   7/6

   „   **Matsumurana.**—The Japanese Mountain Ash is one of the noblest of this section and is of upright habit 20 ft. or more in height. The bright green pinnate leaves with conspicuous red stalks colour quite as well as those of S. discolor. Its small corymbs of orange-red fruits are ripe in September 3/6   5/6

each.

Sorbus Mougeotii.—S. & E. Europe. This short, stiff-branching small tree is very rare in cultivation. The large obovate-acuminate dark grey leaves are distinctly lobed and are covered beneath with a thick grey-white felt. The round red fruits, about 1 in. in diameter and edible, are borne in small corymbs. An attractive ornamental and ideal for small gardens 3/6   5/6

  „ **pohuashanensis.**—N. China. A striking ornamental, 20—30 ft. high, of upright habit and with pinnate leaves of deep grey-green. It bears corymbs of 200 or more glazed orange-yellow fruits, ageing during August to orange-scarlet, catching the eye from afar... ... ...   3/6   5/6

  „ **Prattii (munda subarachnoidea).**—Szechuan, China. A graceful bushy large shrub or small tree, 10—15 ft. high and with thin growths densely furnished with 3—5 in. pinnate leaves composed of many tiny leaflets. The beauty of its round white fruits can be judged from the illustration in Bean's Trees & Shrubs, Vol. III, page 326   3/6   5/6

  „ **randaiensis (Koidzumi 1913 and Hayata. In Jour Coll. Sci Tokyo XXXIV. Art 2. 52).**—Korea. An exceedingly rare and distinct Mountain Ash, new to cultivation. The glabrous pinnate leaves are bright green on both sides and obovate in outline and are composed of eleven oblong-lanceolate leaflets, deeply notched and finely serrated. It will prove a valuable addition to autumn colouring trees 3/6   5/6   7/6

  „ **rufo-ferruginea.**—A handsome and striking small tree with upright-growing branches with brown lenticels and deep red glutinous buds. Its 4—7 in. pinnate leaves are oval in outline and consist of 13—15 deep green leaflets ; they are grey on the under-side and the midribs are covered with rusty tomentum. Its glorious autumn colourings and glazed sealing wax-red fruits make it equal to S. discolor and S. Matsumurana   ...   3/6   5/6

  „ **Sargentiana.**—W. China. Sargent's Mountain Ash is a notable ornamental tree of rather spreading habit, possibly attaining 20 ft. in height. It is distinct in having resinous crimson buds. The elegant pinnated leaves, composed of eight to thirteen oblong, furrowed leaflets, are densely villous beneath. It also bears 6—9 in. corymbs of vivid scarlet fruits. A fine specimen in a Gloucestershire garden was one of the best twelve coloured trees seen last autumn 7/6   10/6

  „ **scalaris.**—W. China. This is a very distinct Mountain Ash. The slender branches are densely clothed with grey pinnate leaves consisting of twenty-three to twenty-nine narrow, long and leathery, reflexed leaflets. Its corymbs of bright red fruits and the magnificently-coloured leaves are a charming sight every autumn   ...   3/6   5/6

  „ **serotina. (Koehne).**—Japan, Korea. This rare species attains 12—20 ft. and is a distant relative of S. commixta. The leaves consist of 15—17 smooth leaflets which are sharply toothed. It is attractive with its upright corymbs of small chestnut-red fruits, held above the rich red autumn foliage 5/-   7/6

162   *W. J. MARCHANT, KEEPER'S HILL NURSERY,*

Sorbus species. K.W. 7746. (19 : 12 : 27).—This is one of the   each.
most distinct plants Captain Kingdon Ward collected.
He found it at 7,500 ft. on the Japoo Range, Naga Hills,
Assam. Its attractive deep green leathery leaves consist of 9—15 polished leaflets, held on red-tinted stalks,
glaucous beneath and with the midribs covered with
rusty tomentum.   The many large bunches of small red
berries are attractive.   Its leaves, growths and stipules
suggest a relationship with S. Harrowiana but it is
much hardier 7/6

„   **tianshanica.**—Turkestan. A dense-growing species, of
round habit, 8—12 ft. high, with polished brown
branches and handsome deep green pinnate leaves
which colour well in autumn. Its wide corymbs of
attractive pure white flowers are possibly the largest in
the genus, and are followed by bright red fruits   ...   3/6   5/6

„   **Vilmorinii.**—W. China. A decidedly beautiful small
tree of spreading habit. Its slender growths, 3—5 ft.
long, are clothed with elegant pinnate leaves. The
fruits during summer are rosy-red, changing towards
autumn through pale pink to rosy-white and are very
pretty nestling among the richly-coloured leaves   2/6   3/6   5/6

„   **Wilsoniana (forma glaberrima).**—W. Hupeh, China.
A white-fruiting Mountain Ash introduced by the late
Dr. Ernest Wilson. It is a strong grower with 9—12 in.
pinnate leaves glaucous-blue above, grey-white beneath.
For weeks in autumn they are a riot of orange-red and
scarlet tints. The 9 in. conspicuous corymbs of white
fruits are retained till the new year. This form was
given an Award of Merit at the Autumn Tree and Shrub
Show on October 1, 1930   ...   .   2/6   3/6   5/6
See also **Standard Trees.**

ARIA SECTION.

Sorbus alnifolia.—Korea, C. China, Japan. An uncommon small
tree, 15—25 ft. high, and worthy of wider cultivation
for its bright green alder-like leaves which become
beautifully coloured in autumn even in the mild climate
of N. Ireland. After the leaves have fallen, the branches
are still conspicuous with numerous clusters of small oval
bright red fruits which are retained until Xmas   ...   2/6   3/6   5/6

„   **Aria.**—The native Whitebeam is a very hardy tree and
many fine specimens may be seen growing on the wind-
swept chalk downs about Salisbury. The handsome
bright green serrated leaves are grey-white on the reverse
and they change to russet brown and yellow during the
autumn. It bears corymbs of white scented flowers in
May, succeeded by a mass of large bright red fruits   ...   2/6   3/6

„   „   **majestica (Decaisneana).**—Origin unknown.
A beautiful and picturesque tree from spring to autumn,
especially if planted against a dark background. Its
conspicuous 4—7 in. elliptic-ovate, shining, deep green
leaves, with silvery white reverse, are very effective and
turn brilliant yellow before falling 3/6   5/6

„   **cuspidata (vestita).**—Himalayan Whitebeam. A choice
tree for a sheltered position, with large bright green
leaves, silvery-white beneath 3/6   5/6

Sorbus epidendron.—This rarity was introduced from China by the late Mr. Geo. Forrest. Its brown-green speckled shoots are slightly glaucous and the dark green rugose leaves taper to a long point ; they are covered on the underside with a persistent rusty tomentum and are edged with fine teeth. 5/–   7/6

   „   **Folgneri.**—C. China. A rare slender-branched species, possibly 15 ft. or more high. The growing lanceolate leaves are bright copper coloured, ageing to dark green, white beneath, making in autumn a glorious display of varied tints. 3—4 in. corymbs of ½ in. bright red fruits are borne 3/6   5/6

   „   **lanata.**—Also known as Pyrus kumaonensis. Himalaya. Its 6—9 in. elliptic-obovate, olive-green leaves, silvery white beneath and covered with persistent white ' cotton wool ', make it the most conspicuous of this group. It is only suitable for gardens along the south and west coast, Ireland and the west of Scotland 7/6

   „   **magnifica (Aria × auricularis).**—Hybrid. It is one of the most attractive trees and has large lustrous green leaves, silvery-white beneath, measuring 7 in. × 5 in. and very similar to those of S. Aria majestica. During autumn they become rich buttercup-yellow tinted and remain so for several weeks 3/6   5/6

   „   **meliosmifolia.**—W. China. A very rare species in nature and under cultivation. It is a medium grower, possibly 10—15 ft. high, with stiff brown branches. The large ovate leaves in their bronze-green are attractive, being doubly serrated, with many prominent veins 7/6   10/6

   „   **Torminalis. (Wild Service Tree).**—Europe, Asia Minor, N. Africa. It is interesting to consider why this plant has been neglected ; possibly because it is a native and, like P. Sorbus, is rare in the nurseries. A woodland garden near us is lit up every autumn by the brilliancy of its persisting 5 in. thorn-like leaves 3/6   5/6

   „   **umbellata.** (Previously distributed as **Pyrus Aria flabelliformis**).—S.E. Europe, W. Asia. A very distinct large shrub or small tree with fan-shaped leaves varying in size, and white beneath, incised and toothed at the apex 3/6   5/6

   „   **Zahlbruckneri.**—C. China. This handsome species will probably grow to 15—20 ft. in height. It has slender brown branches covered with light dots. The attractive green leaves, prominently veined, are covered beneath with a grey tomentum and they become yellow tinted in autumn. It is one of the prettiest of the genus with its numerous clusters of glistening red Malus hupehensis-like fruits 7/6

      See also **Standards** at end of catalogue.

      The **Sorbus** will grow quite freely in almost any kind of soil, including that containing chalk, and the effect created by planting one or more silver-leaved kinds is surprising.

each.

Spartium junceum.—Europe.   The Spanish Broom.   A very attractive shrub 5—10 ft. high, displaying its numerous
erect racemes of large fragrant yellow flowers from June
to the end of September.   It is a really good seaside
shrub and is also quite happy on the cold chalk downs
about Salisbury 1/6   2/6

Spartocytisus nubigenus (See Cytisus supranubius).

Spiraea Aitchisonii (Sorbaria Aitchisonii).—Afghanistan.
An elegant shrub of round form with pinnate leaves,
up to 15 ins. long.   It also bears large panicles of white
flowers during July and August 1/6   2/6

" **arborea (Sorbaria arborea).**—W. China.   Of open
habit, 6—10 ft. high, with yearly growths 5—8 ft. long.
It is clothed with handsome 12—15 in. pinnate leaves
and bears conspicuous panicles of cream-coloured
flowers from July to September 2/6

" **arguta (Thunbergii × multiflora).**—Hybrid.   A graceful
branching shrub 3—5 ft. high, very effective in April and
May with its mass of small white flowers 1/6   2/6

" **canescens.**—Himalayas.   A graceful arching-branched
shrub of greyish appearance, 6—10 ft. high.   It is very
pretty during June with numerous 2 in. corymbs of
creamy-white flowers 1/6   2/6

" **discolor (ariaefolia).**—N.W. America.   Long known as
S. ariaefolia.   Of erect growth with arching branched
heads, 6—12 ft. high and as much wide.   Its wealth of
drooping plumes of creamy-white flowers is displayed
during June and July.   Its foliage becomes beautifully
coloured during autumn 1/6   2/6

" **grandiflora (See Exochorda racemosa).**

" **japonica Bumalda "Anthony Waterer."**—Hybrid.
An old favourite and one of the most attractive of all
dwarf shrubs.   Its flat corymbs of brilliant crimson
flowers are freely produced from early June to late
September 1/6

" **Margaritae (japonica × superba).**—Hybrid.   The
3—4 ft. current growths produce from July to October
corymbs 9 ins. across of numerous bright pink flowers.
The foliage is brightly tinted during autumn 1/6   2/6

" **Menziesii triumphans.**—This form 5—8 ft. high, with
erect growths, bears terminal broad panicles 8 ins. long,
of showy bright purple-rose flowers from June to the end
of September 1/6

" **nipponica (bracteata).**—Japan.   This forms a large bush
5—8 ft. high.   During June the previous year's growths
are wreathed from end to end with clusters of white
flowers 2/6

" **prunifolia plena.**—Japan.   A slender-branched shrub,
5—10 ft. high.   The small double white flowers are
profusely borne during April and May.   The foliage in
autumn assumes rich tints 1/6   2/6

" **sorbifolia stellipila (Sorbaria).**—E. Asia.   The best
form.   This sends up yearly stout shoots 3—4 ft. high,
with attractive pinnate leaves covered on the underside
with stellate hairs.   It bears conspicuous 15 in. branching panicles of pure white flowers during July and early
August 1/6   2/6

Spiraea syringiflora.—Hybrid. Raised by Lemoine before 1885, and now very seldom seen. It is an attractive shrub 3—4 ft. high, of spreading habit. From June to autumn frosts it is clothed with lanceolate leaves and terminal 6—9 in. branching panicles of rose-pink flowers 1/6 2/6

„ **tomentosa.**—This has been discarded as its seeds blew all over the nursery and the seedlings became a pest ...   — —

„ **trichocarpa.**—A treasure from Korea, attaining 5—7 ft. in height, with arching branches packed during June with pure white flowers. Its second charm is in autumn when these are clothed with 1—2 in. oblong scarlet leaves 1/6 2/6

„ **trilobata.**—N. China, Siberia, etc.—This rare Spiraea has thin interlacing twigs and grows 3—4 ft. high. It is very pretty during June with its numerous clusters of white flowers mingling with the 3—5 lobed gooseberry-like leaves 2/6 3/6

„ **Vanhouttei (cantoniensis × trilobata).**—Although a very old plant, it is still one of our best ornamentals in June. The 4—6 ft. arching branches are crowded with umbel-like clusters of pure white flowers 1/6 2/6

„ **Veitchii.**—C. & W. China. Of graceful habit with growths 6—10 ft. high, producing in the following June and July wreaths of numerous corymbs of white flowers   2/6

Stachyurus praecox.—Japan. A choice shrub of branching habit. The drooping racemes of many small yellowish flowers during February and March are subject to winter conditions unless in a sheltered corner 5/-

Staphylea colchica. Caucasus.—An upright-habited shrub, 5—8 ft. high, with leaves composed of three to five leaflets, and erect panicles of white flowers during May. It is also a useful shrub for early forcing 2/6 3/6

Stauntonia hexaphylla and latifolia (See Holboellia).

Stephanandra incisa (flexuosa).—Japan, Korea. A pleasing shrub during the winter with its naked brown zig-zag branches and graceful during the growing season when clothed with its incised leaves. Sometimes in autumn these become beautifully tinted 1/6 2/6

„ **Tanakae.**—Japan. This elegant shrub, 5—8 ft. high, has more vigorous, brown, and branching stems and the large triangular bronze-green leaves are handsome in autumn. These turn bright orange-scarlet or yellow even in the mild climate of Cornwall 1/6 2/6

Stewartia koreana.—Korea. Introduced by the late Dr. Ernest Wilson to the Arnold Arboretum in 1918. It flowered there in 1930. It is a deciduous tree 15 ft. or more high and is proving to be an easy grower in semi-shade, in a position similar to that which suits Eucryphias, Styrax, Cornus Kousa, etc. It is one of the best of the family for its 2½ in. white blooms borne during June and July and beautifully coloured leaves in autumn. There is an illustration in W. J. Bean's Trees & Shrubs, Vol. III, page 466 ... ...   10/6 15/6 21/-

Stewartia Malachodendron(virginica).—South U.S.A. A very each.
rare and beautiful bushy shrub 5—10 ft. in height. The
ovate or obovate leaves are 2—4 ins. long and toothed,
with the underside more or less hairy. The white,
silky-looking flowers are 2½—3½ ins. across and each has
a beautiful bunch of purple stamens. They are borne in
July and August, at a time when few shrubs are in flower   — —

„   **monadelpha.**—S. Japan. An uncommon species, probably with us not more than a large shrub 15 ft. high. It
has 1½—2½ in. elliptical leaves slightly serrated and pubescent beneath. The 1—2 in. fragrant white flowers,
between two large bracts and with violet anthers, are
borne in the leaf axils during July **7/6 10/6**

„   **pentagyna.**—S.E. United States. One of America's
treasures, growing 6—12 ft. high and of bushy habit.
The flowers are creamy white, 3—4 ins. across, and with
a conspicuous cluster of yellow stamens, during July and
August **5/- 7/6 10/6**

„   „   **grandiflora.**—Georgia, U.S.A. The fringed
creamy-white flowers, 3—4 ins. wide, are probably the
most beautiful of the genus and are enhanced by a large
bunch of bright purple stamens. It is attractive again
in autumn when its leaves take on vivid tints. An
exceedingly rare shrub, beautifully illustrated in New
Flora and Silva, Vol. VIII, No. 1 page 58 ...   .   **21/-**

„   **pseudo-camellia.**—Japan. An invaluable, much-
branched shrub of pyramidal outline, 8—15 ft. high.
The many flowers during July and August are cup-
shaped, creamy-white, 2½ ins. across, with numerous
orange-yellow stamens. Its foliage during autumn
assumes brilliant red and yellow tints   ...   2/6 3/6   **5/6 7/6**

„   **serrata.**—Japan. This rarity makes a large shrub or
small tree of elegant habit and its foliage reminds one of
S. monadelpha. During June and July the 2—2½ in.
cup-shaped, creamy-white flowers, tinged with red on the
outside and with petals incised, are borne on short twigs.
The leaves turn a lovely colour before falling   ...   ...   — —

„   **sinensis.**—C. China. A fast-growing species, probably
15 ft. or more in height. The flattened boughs are freely
branched to carry the 1—3 in. oblong-elliptic, notched,
and hairy leaves. The beauty of its 1—1½ in. cup-
shaped fragrant flowers in June and July and its scarlet
foliage in autumn combine to place it among the most
beautiful of the Stewartias ...   .   **7/6 to 21/-**

The **Stewartias** flower freely during July and August
when flowering trees and shrubs are not too plentiful.
In lime-free soils they soon grow into large bushes but
like Cornus florida, C. Kousa, C. Nuttallii, Eucryphia
glutinosa, E. lucida, Oxydendrum arboreum, etc., they
like to have their roots shaded from the scorching sun.

E **Stranvaesia Davidiana.**—W. China. A splendid ornamental
where space is not limited as it quickly spreads to 25 ft.
or more across. Its corymbs of white flowers during
June are followed by quantities of scarlet hawthorn-like
fruits, which hang for a long time. It also makes a good
north or east wall shrub **2/6 3/6**

each.

E **Stranvaesia lucida (S. glaucescens of Trade).**—Himalayas. A large shrub or small tree with obovate leaves 5—7 ins. long and 2 ins. wide. These are bright green and shining, paler beneath. The corymbs of white flowers are succeeded by bright red pear-shaped fruits. From S. Nussia (glaucescens) it is quite distinct... ... 2/6   3/6   5/6

E   „   **Nussia (glaucescens).**—Himalayas. A strong grower, quickly reaching 15 ft. with tiers of spreading branches. The leaves are obovate, leathery, glossy green and slightly toothed. It bears flat corymbs of white flowers during June. Its fruits are pear-shaped and bright red 2/6   3/6   5/6

E   „   **salicifolia (Davidiana salicifolia).**—W. China. It is a beautiful pyramidal shrub of free growth, 8—12 ft. high. The dark green willow-like leaves are grey-green beneath and many of them become gorgeously coloured during winter. The corymbs of white hawthorn-like flowers in May and June are followed by brilliant red fruits, which hang until February. It grows freely in seaside gardens and, where space is limited, is a better ornamental than S. Davidiana 2/6   3/6   5/6

E   „   **undulata.**—W. & C. China. A form of very bushy habit, 3—5 ft. high, with brightly coloured growths and undulated leaves. The corymbs of white flowers are succeeded by orange-red fruits which are retained well into the new year 2/6   3/6   5/6

Styrax americanus. Virginia to Florida. American Storax. A rare shrub 6—12 ft. or more in height, for the warmer parts of these Islands. It is somewhat like S. japonica but it has larger leaves and narrower petalled flowers borne during June and July. It is then a very pretty plant   3/6   5/6

„   **dasyanthus.**—Hupeh, China. A rare species, of dense habit, 8—15 ft. high according to climate, and requiring a sheltered position. Its 3—4 in. terminal racemes of $\frac{1}{2}$—$\frac{3}{4}$ in. white flowers borne during July look very pretty among the obovate-oval lustrous metallic-green leaves ...   7/6

„   **Hemsleyanus.**—W. & C. China. This pyramidal shrub will easily reach 15 ft. in height and as much through. It has stiff brown branches decorated with striking obovate leaves, turning bright yellow in autumn. The ornamental semi-erect branching racemes of bell-shaped, snow-white, fragrant flowers are freely borne during June 3/6   5/6   7/6 10/6

„   **japonicus.**—The Japanese Snowdrop Tree is undoubtedly the best species for general planting in these islands and it requires similar conditions to those which suit Dogwoods, Stewartias, Eucryphia glutinosa, Enkianthus, etc. To obtain its full floral beauty, it should be encouraged to form a standard. The slender branches during June are laden with pendulous white flowers 2/6   3/6   5/6

„   **Obassia.**—Japan. In this district in semi-woodland gardens and on heavy soil, this forms a large plant 10—15 ft. high, with a wide spreading head. The large leaves are attractive and 6—9 in. racemes of drooping white flowers are borne in June and are delightfully scented 3/6   5/6   7/6

Styrax Wilsonii.—W. China. This very slender, twiggy shrub   each.
has attained 5—7 ft. in height. It begins flowering in
its infancy and its dainty white drooping flowers are
profusely borne during June. It requires shelter from
the north winds **2/6**   **3/6**   **5/6**

E **Sycopsis sinensis.**—C. & W. China. A beautiful shrub of
pyramidal habit, 5—8 ft. high, with dark green leaves.
The small red and yellow flowers are borne freely during
February and March. It also makes a splendid shrub
trained on a north or east wall, where its flowers are
seen to greater advantage **3/6**   **5/6**

Symplocos paniculata.—Himalayas to China and Japan. A
dense branched small-growing tree appreciating semi-
shade. Its short panicles of five-petalled, white, perfumed flowers during May are followed by oval fruits
of a charming blue, ripe in early autumn **2/6**   **3/6**   **5/6**

Syringa chinensis. (vulgaris × persica). This is also known
as the Rouen Lilac and S. rothomagensis and develops
into a twiggy bush 6 ft. or more high and as much
wide. It is beautiful during May when the ends of
the previous year's growths carry 3—6 in. loose panicles
of grey-blue flowers. It is pictured in Gardening
Illustrated, April 18th, 1936, page 225 ...   ...   **2/6**   **3/6**   **5/6**

    ,,   ,,   **rubra (Saugeana).** A pretty shrub with its mass
of 3—6 in. panicles of lilac suffused wine-red flowers
during May and early June **2/6**   **3/6**   **5/6**

    ,,   **emodi.**—The Himalayan Lilac is a vigorous shrub 8 ft.
or more high, with upright green-brown branches
dotted with light-coloured lenticels. It is easily recognised by its handsome 3—8 in. elliptic-oblong, smooth, green
leaves which are distinctly glaucous white beneath.
The 3—6 in. erect panicles of pale lilac flowers ageing to
white are borne in June **2/6**   **3/6**   **5/6**

    ,,   **japonica (amurensis japonica).**—Japan. Attains large
shrub size. It needs a warm position to bring out the
full floral beauty of its pyramidal panicles, up to 12 ins.
long, of white flowers in June and July **2/6**   **3/6**

    ,,   **Julianae.**—W. China. A graceful shrub 6 ft. or more
high, having hairy short twiggy growths and oval privet-
like leaves, grey on the underside and covered with downy
hairs. One of the most free-flowering of the genus, having
slender upright panicles of pale lilac-grey flowers during
May and early June **2/6**   **3/6**   **5/6**

    ,,   **Komarowii (Sargentiana).**—W. China. A stiff-branch-
ed shrub ultimately 8 ft. or more high. The scaly
growths carry large deep green oval or oblong-lanceolate
leaves and are gaily decorated during May and early
June with 4—6 in. curved racemes of rose-red flowers ...   **3/6**   **5/6**

    ,,   **oblata dilatata.**—Korea. This rarity attains 4—8 ft.
The brown-red shoots carry ovate-acuminate, undulated,
deep green, smooth leaves with vinous-red veins and
dark red stalks. The foliage is richly wine-coloured
when young and becomes brilliantly tinted during the
autumn. The violet-purple flowers are borne early
here and it is advisable to give the plant a position facing
S.W. **3/6**   **5/6**

each.

Syringa persica.—Kansu. The Persian Lilac is a delightful slender-branching shrub, about 4 ft. high, with narrow lance-shaped leaves and small panicles of lilac-coloured flowers during May **2/6   3/6**

,, **reflexa.** C. China. An upright, strong-growing and large-leaved species 6—16 ft. high. It is conspicuous during June with its 6—9 in. semi-drooping panicles of deep pink flowers and is worth a place in every garden **2/6   3/6   5/6**

,, **Sweginzowii.**—W. China. This slender-growing shrub, 6—10 ft. high, has dark brown shoots, with scattered light-coloured lenticels, and carries 2—4 in. ovate-lanceolate, rugose, wavy green leaves. Its 6—8 in. loose panicles of pink flowers, borne from mid-May till early June, are singularly beautiful **3/6   5/6**

,, **tomentella (Adamiana) (Wilsonii) (alborosea).**—W. China. This beautiful species soon grows into a large bush 8 ft. or more high. It is easily recognised by its charming 8 in. × 5 in. panicles of pretty pink flowers borne during May and June **3/6   5/6**

,, **vulgaris.**—E. Europe. The scented common Lilac ... **1/6   2/6**

,, ,, **alba grandiflora.**—The best white-flowering form of the scented common Lilac. Its wood and buds are yellow-green **2/6   3/6**

,, ,, **hybrids.**—A few kinds can be supplied on their own roots, from layers, which are undoubtedly better than grafted or budded plants **3/6   5/6**

,, **velutina (Koehneana).**—Korea. The Korean Lilac is a choice species, 8 ft. or more high, with its upright brown shoots covered with light-coloured lenticels. The reticulated leaves, velvety dark green above and paler beneath, are ovate-oval or lozenge-lanceolate in shape. The elegant panicles of flowers, pale lilac, tinged red, are produced in May and June. Previously distributed as S. Palibiniana **3/6   5/6**

,, **Wolfii.**—Korea & Manchuria. One of the handsomest and easiest of the genus, making a shapely bush, 8 ft. or more high, clothed with 3—7 in. oval-lanceolate rugose green leaves, grey beneath. The 6—12 in. attractive panicles of numerous lilac-coloured flowers, with yellow anthers, are exhibited during May and early June   **2/6   3/6   5/6**

,, **yunnanensis.**—Yunnan, China. Ultimately a shrub 8 ft. or more high and with upright stems and slender twigs. The puckered, elliptic-oblong-lanceolate, deep green and reticulated leaves are glaucous beneath and are held on red stalks. During June, it bears terminal showy 6—8 in. × 4—6 in. panicles of pink flowers which age to white before falling **3/6   5/6**

The **Lilac** species grow freely in almost any soil but especially those containing lime. They will thrive where highly bred hybrids are an absolute failure and bear masses of elegant fragrant flowers.

Taxodium distichum.—S. United States. The deciduous Cypress is one of the most elegant of trees. Once established, it will quickly develop a beautiful pyramidal head. It is very attractive during the autumn when its leaves turn brown-yellow and chestnut-colour   **3/6   5/6   7/6   10/6**

Tecoma grandiflora (See **Campsis**).

E **Telopea speciosissima.**—Australia. A beautiful evergreen but   each.
great patience is necessary as it is slow in producing its
Embothrium-like flowers. A 3 in. pot plant put out
three years ago is now 5 ft. high. The leaves are 7—10
ins. long, obovate or narrowly oblong, blue green and
glaucous beneath ; they are net-veined towards the
margins and unevenly notched. 10/6

E   „   **truncata.**—This is known as the Tasmanian Waratah and
differs by having 6—10 in. leathery oblanceolate leaves,
glaucous beneath and with several deep dents towards
the apex 10/6
The Telopeas love woodland conditions, in lime-free
soil, where their roots can be shaded. If happy, they
make 1—2½ ft. of growth yearly.

E **Ternstroemia gymnanthera (japonica).**—India, China, Japan.
An attractive evergreen for mild districts and perfectly
hardy in several Bournemouth gardens. Its chief merit
is its brilliantly glazed foliage, bright red in growth,
deepest green when mature. Its creamy-white flowers
are fragrant and produced during July and August   3/6   5/6   7/6

Tetracentron sinense.—C. & W. China. An extremely rare,
elegant, open-branched shrub or small tree related to
the Magnolias but not generally hardy 7/6 10/6

E **Teucrium fruticans (latifolium).**—S. Europe. A beautiful
and distinct open-growing grey shrub for seaside gardens
along the south and west coasts ; inland it requires a
south or west wall. Its flowers are pale lavender, produced from June to October 1/6   2/6

Thorns (See **Crataegus**).

EC **Trachelospermum asiaticum (crocostomum) (divaricatum).**
—Japan, Korea. A choice wall climber 8—15 ft. high,
quite hardy at Kew, of dense slender growth. The
young foliage is bronzy-red. Numerous sweetly-
scented Isabella-coloured flowers with orange throat
are borne from May to August 2/6   3/6   5/6

EC   „   **forma Wilsonii (W.776).**—China. A very pretty climber
with leaves veined and marbled above, bright green
beneath, and lanceolate to variable in outline 2/6   3/6

EC   „   **japonicum.**—Japan. A distinct semi-climbing shrub
with leaves broadly ovate, deep green, becoming brilliantly coloured towards autumn and remaining so all through
the winter. Flowers white, larger than in T. jasminoides   3/6   5/6

EC   „   **jasminoides (Rhyncospermum jasminoides).**—China,
Japan. This delightful climber is quite hardy on south
and west walls, along the south and west coast. It grows
to a height of 10 ft. In July and August the cymes of
fragrant pure-white flowers against the deep green leaves
are very effective. It is also a splendid cool house plant   3/6   5/6

E **Tricuspidaria dependens (Crinodendron dependens).**—
Chile. On a west wall or in mild localities it forms a
large bush. The snow-white, bell-shaped flowers
appear from August to October 2/6   3/6

		each.		

E **Tricuspidaria lanceolata (Crinodendron Hookerianum).**— Chile. This attractive shrub or small tree grows freely throughout the south and west, Ireland and the west of Scotland if planted in shade in lime-free soil, or on a sheltered north wall. The pendent urn-shaped flowers, a beautiful crimson, appear more striking by contrast with the deep green of the lance-shaped leaves. A beautiful sight from early May to mid-August ... **2/6   3/6   5/6**

Tripetaleia bracteata (Elliottia bracteata).—Japan. A treasure for the Ericaceae border, seldom more than 9 ins. high and producing stiff shoots from the collar. The tips of its current growths are delightfully decorated with 3 in. erect leafy racemes, each usually containing 6 pearl-white, pink-tinted flowers with 3 ligulate, almost angular, petals. Its $\frac{1}{2}$—$1\frac{1}{2}$ in. obovate green leaves are net-veined **7/6   10/6**

„ **paniculata (Elliottia paniculata).**—Japan. An exceedingly rare shrub for a semi-shady position or for the woodland garden, where it will quickly grow to 3 ft. in height. It has slender red-brown angled branches and 2—4 in. undulated green lanceolate-obovate leaves. The 3—6 in. spire-like panicles each contain 30-50 fascinating pale pink flowers with curved petals. Both species flower continuously from early July to the end of September ... **7/6   10/6**

Ulex europaeus plenus (Gorse or Whin). Native. The double form. This delightful shrub is best when planted in dry stony or sandy soils, and produces many fragrant rich yellow flowers from February to May. A famous American botanist once said that our double-flowering Gorse and common yellow Broom were two of the most beautiful ornamentals and two which any country should be proud to possess **1/6   2/6**

„ **nanus.**—Europe, including the south of England. It is surprising how little this shrub is appreciated although it is ideal for points on the rock garden, banks and the top of walls. It is crowded with flowers more or less from mid-August to May. In nature its branches are procumbent but under cultivation they will rise to 1—2 ft. **1/6   2/6**

E **Umbellularia californica (Oreodaphne californica) (Laurus regalis).**—N. America. The Californian Laurel is rare in these islands. It loves a semi-shady position, where it will make a noble shrub 10 ft. or more high, although in a few gardens in the south and west of Ireland it is 20—30 ft. Its handsome dark green, net-veined, willow-like leaves are 4—5 ins. long and pleasantly aromatic **3/6   5/6   7/6**

Vaccinium Arctostaphylos.—Caucasus. The true plant is a vigorous shrub up to 5 ft. high by as much wide and the annual growths have a rich red bark. It is perhaps the most notable of autumn plants, for its branches are conspicuously decorated from mid-August to October with beautiful bell-shaped crimson-tinted flowers, each $\frac{2}{3}$ ins. long and with five ridges. The $2\frac{1}{2}$—5 in. undulated, net-veined, green leaves have shallow teeth and become gorgeously coloured, remaining so until after Xmas. This splendid whortleberry, introduced in 1800, is surprisingly little known. V. padifolium is usually supplied in its place **7/6   10/6**

E **Vaccinium bracteatum (Andromeda chinensis).**—Japan,   each.
  China. This was known as long ago as 1830. It is a
  charming shrub 3—5 ft. in height and loves a semi-shady
  position. The dark red, slender stems carry elliptical or
  ovate leaves, a shining dark red ageing to deep green.
  It bears, even on baby plants, numerous 2—3 in. leafy
  racemes of cylindrical-ovoid white fragrant flowers,
  from mid-July to autumn frosts 2/6   3/6

„ **caespitosum.**—N. America. The true Dwarf Bilberry
  is exceedingly rare in British gardens although it is an
  ideal shrub for the Ericaceae border. It forms a tuft
  about 1 ft. high and has dense, pleasing bright green
  obovate-oblanceolate leaves, up to 1 in. long and ½ in.
  wide, which become richly coloured every autumn.
  The pretty, small, ellipsoid or pitcher-shaped, pale pink
  flowers are followed by small black fruits covered with
  blue bloom 5/-   7/6

„ **canadense.**—Canadian Whortleberry. This dense twiggy
  shrub of rather upright habit is much confused, though it
  can be easily distinguished by its 1—2 in. oblong-
  lanceolate leaves, which have a rusty appearance ; they
  become handsomely coloured during the autumn and
  are retained for weeks. The plant previously distributed
  as this species is the true V. pennsylvanicum angustifolium   —   —

„ **ciliatum.**—Japan, Korea. In its best form, it is a most
  attractive shrub, even in semi-shade, and will grow 3—5
  ft. high. Its 2—4 in. ovate-elliptical or obovate hairy
  leaves are richly coloured when unfolding, and they
  change to green towards mid-summer, becoming gorgeously tinted again in autumn. Its 2—4 in. leafy
  racemes of green-yellow, suffused red, lily-of-the-valley-
  like flowers are borne during June but are more or less
  hidden by the foliage 3/6   5/6

„ „ **glaucum.**—This distinct shrub is new to cultivation, having been introduced from N. China and Manchuria in 1934. It makes a dense bush, similar to the
  former, and has brightly coloured young leaves. These
  are conspicuously blue-grey beneath and become
  brilliantly coloured again during the autumn 3/6   5/6

„ **corymbosum.**—Blueberry. N. America. One of the
  most conspicuous for its autumn display of vividly
  coloured foliage, though one which is much confused in
  British gardens. The true plant quickly makes a dense
  twiggy shrub 4 ft. or more high in good soil. Its ovate or
  elliptic-lanceolate bright green, slightly puckered leaves
  are 2½—3½ ins. long and two-thirds as wide ; they are
  pale green and net-veined beneath and the margins often
  have minute bristly teeth. It bears clusters of pretty
  pale pink urn-shaped flowers in May and these are succeeded by attractive purple-black fruits covered with
  blue bloom. This shrub is clearly illustrated in Gardening Illustrated, Dec. 29th, 1934, page 760. The plant
  previously distributed is the true V. virgatum 3/6   5/6

„ „ **amoenum.**—This is a pleasing shrub, as its name
  implies, with spreading branches and growing to a
  height of 6 ft. or more. The reticulated bright green
  leaves, downy beneath and margined with shallow hairy
  teeth, become gorgeously coloured for many weeks
  during the autumn 5/-

each.

E **Vaccinium crassifolium.**—N. Carolina to Georgia. A charming procumbent shrub about 6 ins. high, liking a semi-shady position in the south. The red-tinted, slender stems carry small shining oval leaves of similar colour. The terminal racemes of ¼ in. bell-shaped rosy-red flowers are produced in May and June **2/6 3/6**

E „ **Delavayi.**—Yunnan, China. One of the prettiest evergreen dwarf shrubs we have and it is quite content in many positions. Densely clothed with tiny glistening box-like leaves, the tips of the previous year's growths produce groups of 3—7 tiny white, pink-tinted flowers which are followed by round purple-blue fruits with flat tops **2/6 3/6**

E „ **Dunalianum.**—Sikkim, W. China. This large shrub is only suitable for the warmer parts of these islands ; here it is cut to the ground every winter. It has attractive oval-lanceolate leaves 3—5 ins. long **5/-**

„ **erythrocarpum.**—Virginia to Georgia. An elegant species, 3—5 ft. high, of erect growth and with branching heads. During June the twigs are decorated with attractive pendulous tubular pale red flowers and these are succeeded by bright red, deepening to purple, fruits. Its ovate-pointed or oblong-lanceolate, reticulated green leaves are bronze tinted and become beautifully coloured in autumn **2/6 3/6**

E „ **fragile.**—W. China. This dainty shrub grows 9 ins. or more high and is thickly clothed with ovate-oval, green, bronze-tinted, hairy leaves. It is attractive from early May to August with leafy racemes of urn-shaped, flesh-coloured flowers. These are followed by black whortle-berry-like fruits. It is not hardy in midland gardens... **3/6**

E „ **glauco-album.**—Himalayas. This attractive species seldom exceeds 6 ft. in height. The dense oval grey-green leaves are blue-white beneath, making a beautiful setting for the 2—3 in. racemes of cylindrical pink flowers and globose black fruits covered with blue bloom. Not hardy in midland gardens **2/6 3/6 5/6**

„ **hirsutum.**—Mts. of N. Carolina. The Hairy Huckle-berry is easily distinguished by its twiggy growths, un-dulated, ovate-oval leaves, pretty cylindrical white, tinged pink, flowers and small globular blue-black fruits. It loves a semi-shady position in the south, where it will grow to 2—3 ft. The leaves are richly coloured and held for many weeks during the autumn **7/6**

E „ **intermedium (Myrtillus × Vitis-idaea).**—England. This interesting natural hybrid from Staffordshire makes a dense shrub 9 ins. or so high. The green wiry growths carry many ½—¾ in. obovate and oblong-oval glossy green serrated leaves. It is evergreen here and produces pretty pale pink, red-tinged, bell-shaped flowers from May to August. These are succeeded by dark violet coloured fruits **2/6 3/6**

„ **japonicum.**—Japan, Korea. An uncommon and attractive species with angular branches attaining 4 ft. in height. It is a pretty shrub with tubular lobed pale red flowers in June and July and drooping globose bright red fruits in August and September. The net-veined ovate-oblong sharply acuminated, green bronze-tinted leaves take on brilliant red tints in October and November **5/- 7/6**

E **Vaccinium Mortinia.**—Ecuador. An elegant branched shrub   each.
2—5 ft. high, with numerous small ovate leaves. The
extending growths are red and beautiful in contrast. It
bears in June, dense racemes of cylindrical rosy-pink
flowers and is perfectly hardy in the south and west   ...   2/6   3/6

E „ **moupinense.**—W. Szechuan, China. A pleasing compact
shrub 18—24 ins. high with downy brown twigs crowded
with small oval glossy leaves with shallow teeth. Its
numerous short racemes of 13—20 or more pretty
chocolate-red flowers are borne during May and June and
are followed by fruits very similar to those of V. Delavayi   3/6   5/6

„ **Myrtillus.**—N. & C. Europe. Grown as a single specimen, it is an attractive shrub of dense habit, 2—3 ft. high.
The branches are crowded during May with showy
¼ in. globe-shaped, pale pink flowers. It is the well-
known Wortleberry or Bilberry 1/6   2/6

E „ **nummularia.**—N. India. One of the gems of the genus
but not hardy in the midlands. It develops into a compact shrub 6—9 ins. high, with bristly short growths
densely clothed with small, leathery, glossy green, ovate-
orbicular leaves. It bears clusters of small cylindrical
rose-red flowers in May and June and well-flowered
specimens are much admired at the Alpine Society's
Show every spring. There is a beautiful illustration of a
magnificent plant in flower in 'Ericaceous Plants',
(page 155) by Dr. F. Stoker 3/6   5/6   7/6

„ **ovalifolium.**—B. Columbia. The stiff erect angled
growths and side branches carry mucronulate oval-
oblong, glaucous green leaves which assume dark red,
gold and crimson tints during late summer and early
autumn. It forms a dense bush 3—5 ft. high   ...   2/6   3/6   5/6

E „ **ovatum.**—Vancouver Island. This forms a handsome
compact shrub 7—10 ft. high and is beautiful for many
weeks during spring with its brightly-coloured young
growths. It is wreathed during June and July with pink
lily-of-the-valley-like flowers. The many small fruits
ripen to dark red during September and October   ...   2/6   3/6

„ **padifolium (maderense).**—Madeira. This beautiful, upright, red-branched shrub grows 5—8 ft. in height.
It is semi-evergreen ; the ovate leaves, closely set, are
1¼—2½ ins. in length, reticulated and finely toothed.
These become dark red on both sides during autumn.
The many short racemes of bell-shaped pale yellow
flowers, tinted with purple, borne from June to August are
succeeded by showy purple-black fruits covered with
blue bloom 2/6   3/6   5/6

„ **pallidum (corymbosum pallidum of Gray).**—Virginia.
This distinct rarity has semi-arching growths and
attains 2—3 ft. in height. Its 1½—2½ in. wavy oval
tapering leaves are grey-green and glaucous beneath. It
produces numerous showy cylindrical pale pink flowers in
June and these are followed by round fruits, dark red
ageing to purple-black and covered with blue bloom. It
should be given a position in every garden on lime-
free soil on account of its never failing autumn colours   3/6   5/6

each.

Vaccinium parvifolium.—Western N. America. A slender-branched and more or less upright shrub, 5—8 ft. high, densely furnished with variable ¼—1 in. entire green leaves. The twigs bear small nodding, pink-white, globe-shaped flowers but they are more beautiful when carrying the conspicuous ¼—½ in. orange-red fruits, ripe during July and August 2/6 3/6

„ **pennsylvanicum.**—East U.S.A., Canada. A compact and pleasing shrub which has not attained a height of 18 ins. in the 10 years it has been in a woodland border. Its downy wiry stems are clothed with ¾—1½ in. partly net-veined, elliptic or oblong-lanceolate, serrated leaves. From early April to October, the ends of the twigs are seldom without a show of pale pink flowers, the first crop producing many attractive purple-black fruits covered with blue bloom. It is worth a place for its lovely autumn tints 2/6 3/6

„ „ **angustifolium.**—Mountains of New Hampshire and New York. Previously distributed as V. canadense. An excellent compact shrub seldom more than 12 ins. high in a woodland border. The thin wiry twigs are thickly clothed with hairy lance-shaped leaves, partly net-veined, and shallowly serrated, ½—1¼ in. long by one-third as wide. The green-white, pink-tinted bells are produced as freely as those of the former. From July to September it shows both flower and fruit, and its foliage becomes gaily coloured during October and November 2/6 3/6

„ „ **myrtilloides.**—Labrador to Hudson's Bay and Massachussetts. This grows into a shrub 2—3 ft. high, of rather open habit and clothed with reticulated myrtle-like green leaves. It is attractive during May and early June with its numerous clusters of pale pink, ridged flowers and in August and September with its heavy crop of conspicuous purple-black fruits covered with bloom. It is also a good ornamental for the autumn garden 2/6 3/6 5/6

E „ **retusum.**—Sikkim. This uncommon shrub is of stylish appearance and may grow to 12 ins. or more in height. Its thin, stiff, downy and wiry growths are thickly clothed with leathery, toothless, broad-elliptical, grey-green leaves ; these are ½—1 in. long, glaucous beneath and distinctly showing veins on the upper side. The terminal racemes of urn-shaped pink flowers have crimson tinted lobes 3/6 5/6

E „ **species. Forrest 29078.**—W. China. This elegant and rare member has slender, arching, brown, hairy branches and may attain 3 ft. or more in height. It is evenly furnished with elliptical-oblong-acuminated leaves, 1½—3 ins. long by one-third as much wide ; they are pale green beneath and are neatly serrated. It has not yet flowered 7/6

„ **stamineum.**—East N. America. It should find a place in every garden on lime-free soil and it grows into a dense twiggy shrub 3 ft. or more high. The elliptic or ovate-oblong green leaves, pale and glaucous beneath, become brilliantly coloured towards the autumn. The 2 in. leafy racemes of white flowers, each with 5 petals, are perhaps the prettiest of the genus and are very similar to those of Solanum jasminoides album ... 5/- 7/6

E **Vaccinium urceolatum.**—Mt. Omi, W. China. One of the most   each.
distinct of the genus, with stiff growths and carrying
attractive leathery ovate-oblong acuminate, dark green
toothless leaves. It is proving quite hardy on the north
side of a woodland border and it may not grow more
than 3 ft. high. It has not yet flowered 10/6

„ **vacillans.**—New England to N. Carolina and Missouri.
It is a pity that the Huckleberry is so little known in
British gardens for it is one of the treasures of the family.
It grows 2—3ft. high and its 1—2½ in. almost toothless,
oval to obovate-acuminate green leaves, held on thin
yellow-green glaucous shoots are a delightful blue beneath
and become as vividly coloured as those of Berberis
Sieboldii. During May the end of almost every shoot is
daintily decorated with pretty ¼ in. cylindrical pink,
red-tinged flowers which are succeeded by small black
fruits covered with blue bloom 3/6   5/6

„ **virgatum.**—East U.S.A. Previously distributed as V.
corymbosum and known under this name in many
gardens. It grows 3—5 ft. high and is a charming sight
in May and June when its erect stems, with branching
heads, carry clusters of conspicuous, ½ in. tom-tom-like
pale pink flowers. The leathery, glossy green, ovate-
oblong to cuneate-lanceolate leaves are partly reticulated
shallowly serrated and ¾—3½ ins. long by one third as
much wide. They colour even in semi-shade and the
tints are as good as those of Pieris Mariana, remaining so
from late September until the new year. At Sheffield
Park, where it grows 5 ft. × 5 ft., it is one of the star
ornamentals, as well as at the R.H.S. Gardens, Wisley 2/6   3/6   5/6

E   „ **Vitis-idaea.**—N. Hemisphere. This charming creeping evergreen, a native shrub, grows 6—9 ins. with
shining box-like leaves. Throughout May and June it is
crowded with nodding bell-shaped rosy flowers, followed
by globular dark red fruits, ripe in September and
October 1/6   2/6

    The genus **Vaccinium** contains many beautiful and
interesting plants easily grown in gardens on lime-free
soils. Many of them are invaluable for their glorious
display of coloured leaves from mid-September until
the new year.

  Viburnum acerifolium. " Dockmackie."—U.S.A. Belongs
to the V. Opulus section, and grows into a large shrub.
The flowers are poor but the fruits are bright red, ageing
to purplish-black. The handsome three-lobed leaves
turn dark crimson in autumn 3/6   5/-

„ **affine hypomalacum.**—Quebec to Manitoba. This
guelder rose grows into a twiggy headed bush 5—8 ft.
high and it bears 1½—3 in. cymes of white flowers succeeded by showy blue-black fruits. Its chief attraction
is disclosed in autumn when the 1½—3 in. ovate-acuminate
leaves become brilliant scarlet 3/6   5/6

Viburnum alnifolium.—N. America. " Hobble-bush."—This   each.
rare and little known species has perhaps the noblest
foliage of all the cultivated Viburnums. Given woodland conditions, it will attain 5—8 ft. in height and it is
clothed with handsome 4—6 in. × 4 — 6in. orbicular or
cordate downy green leaves ; these are deeply veined
and serrated and their dark crimson tints are a glorious
sight during the autumn. The picturesque heads of
flowers, as large as those of Hydrangea serrata rosalba,
are edged with ¾—1 in. white bracts and are borne during
May and June **5/- 7/6**

„ **betulifolium.**—C. & W. China. Of rather upright habit,
6—10 ft. high, and with birch-like leaves. A beautiful
shrub in autumn with swaying branches carrying large
cymes of round bright-red fruits. It should be included
in every collection and is much prized in western
gardens 2/6 **3/6 5/6**

„ **bitchiuense (Carlesii var syringiflorum).**—Japan. An
upright slender-branching shrub 5 ft. high, sparingly
clothed with ovate-oval, metallic-green leaves. Its
branches are gay from May to August with clusters of
pretty tubular flesh-pink, fragrant flowers. In southern
gardens it is more free-growing than V. Carlesii. A
beautiful plate of this ornamental appears in W. J. Bean's
Trees and Shrubs, Vol. III, page 497 ... ... **3/6 5/6**

E „ **buddleifolium.**—W. Hupeh, China. Semi-evergreen
in the south and west, 6—8 ft. high and clothed with
long velvety pale green leaves, grey beneath. It bears
corymbs of white flowers in May and the fruits are red,
ageing to black **3/6 5/6**

E „ **Burkwoodii.**—A hybrid between V. utile and V. Carlesii,
growing into a shapely bush 4—6 ft. high. The leaves
are characteristic of both species and are evergreen or
semi-evergreen according to locality. During April
and May, the twiggy growths are a pleasing sight carrying
many terminal cymes of fragrant tubular white flowers,
tinted pink. In the south it hates a position in full
sun 2/6 **3/6 5/6**

„ **Carlesii.**—Korea. In the south experience proves that
this delightful shrub does best when planted in semi-
shade, where it grows freely up to 3—4 ft. producing every
April clusters of ¾ in. sweetly-scented white flowers
suffused pink. A good seaside shrub. Grafted plants
seem to produce the finest specimens. Worked plants 2/6 **3/6 5/6**
On own roots ... **3/6 5/6**

„ **cassinoides.**—North U.S.A. This upright bushy ornamental attains 5 ft. or more in almost any kind of soil.
The unfolding ovate-oval leaves are brilliantly coloured,
ageing to dark green during the summer and changing
during autumn to crimson and scarlet. It is also
attractive from August to November when laden with
4 in. cymes of ovoid fruits, bright red, ageing to blue-
black 2/6 **3/6 5/6**

E „ **cinnamomifolium.**—Mt. Omi, W. China. This noble
evergreen is related to V. Davidii and grows 5 ft. high by
as much wide. It has thinner and larger acuminated
leaves with branching veins, also looser corymbs of
smaller fruits. It loves a semi-shady position in the south **3/6 5/6**

each.

Viburnum cotinifolium.—The Himalayan form of our native Wayfaring Tree grows into an upright large bush or small tree. Its ovate-orbicular leaves, up to 5 ins. long, are covered on the underside with a silvery pubescence. The white, pink-tinged, ¼ in. flowers are succeeded by long fruits, red ageing to black. It is worth a good position for its brilliant crimson foliage which hangs for many weeks during autumn 3/6 5/6

E „ **cylindricum (coriaceum).**—Himalayas, W. China. This species seems much happier near the sea than inland, growing there to a large shrub of rounded form. The large leaves are grey-green whilst the flowers are white with protruding lilac-coloured stamens, borne from July to September 2/6 3/6 5/6

„ **dasyanthum.**—W. China. An upright-branched species allied to V. betulifolium, with showy corymbs of bright red fruits in early autumn 3/6 5/6

E „ **Davidii.**—W. China. This forms a low, spreading compact shrub, 2 ft. high and many feet wide. The branches are hidden by handsome three-veined leathery bright green leaves. It is pretty during autumn and early winter with heads of deep blue fruits 2/6 3/6 5/6

E „ „ **foemina.**—W. China. The female form is necessary to the above in order to obtain the beautiful blue fruits 3/6 5/6

„ **dilatatum.**—Japan. This rare species grows 4—8 ft. high and its many clusters of white flowers are followed by a heavy crop of vivid red fruits which hang long after the distinct, broadly ovate or orbicular, coarsely-toothed leaves fall 2/6 3/6

„ **foetens (Decaisne 1844).**—Recently re-introduced by the late Captain Simpson-Hayward and not to be confused with V. foetidum, the odorous Viburnum. This worthy shrub, a relative of V.fragrans and V.grandiflorum is a valuable addition to late winter and early spring-flowering ornamentals. It is of good habit, growing to 5 ft. or more in height and as much in width, and it loves woodland conditions. The stiff spreading branches are almost hidden by the handsome 2½—6 in. ovate pointed bright green leaves, which have wedge-shaped bases, sunken veins and are edged with neat teeth. The leafless twigs produce 2—4 in. corymbs of ½—¾ in. tubular white flowers which often become pink tinted in some soils ... 10/6

„ **fragrans.**—N. China. This splendid addition to our hardy shrubs is of pyramidal habit, possibly reaching 10 ft. It takes several years before it settles down to make short flowering growths. The tubular fragrant flesh-pink flowers are borne plentifully during autumn and early winter, at the same time as Prunus subhirtella autumnalis 2/6 3/6 5/6

„ **furcatum.**—Japan. The plant previously distributed is the rare V. alnifolium. This rarity is a relative of V. alnifolium and it is a handsome species 5 ft. or more in height. Its upright nut-brown branches are attractively furnished with 3—5 in. × 3—5 in. broad, cordate acuminate leaves ; these are rugose, crenulated and metallic-green, pale beneath and become as richly coloured as those of V. alnifolium 3/6 5/6

			each.
Viburnum grandiflorum (nervosum).—Bhotan. In a recent article on Viburnums, this was quoted as "The cream of flowering shrubs." It is of thin upright habit 5—10 ft. high and loves a semi-shady position. The red-brown branches bear deeply ribbed 3—4 in. ovate-lanceolate, red-tinted leaves, on crimson stalks, fading to bronze-green. The leafless twigs carrying dense heads of rich rose, ageing to pink, ½—¾ in. flowers are a welcome sight from January to the end of April. The leading shoots should be pinched to encourage a bushier habit ...			**10/6**

E „ **Harryanum.**—W. China. This distinct compact shrub slowly grows to 2—4 ft. in height. It is densely clothed with tiny, leathery, orbicular and broadly ovate leaves, carried in twos and threes, and bears small clusters of white flowers during late spring ...   **3/6   5/6**

E „ **Henryi.**—C. China. A splendid ornamental with erect stems, carrying many side branches, freely growing to 10 ft. or more high and wide, with oblong leathery dark green leaves and panicles of white flowers. The branches are weighted during autumn with showy bright red fruits, finally black ...   **2/6   3/6   5/6**

„ **hupehense.**—C. China. A stiff-branched, very bushy shrub, 6—10 ft. high, the foliage covered with thick down, giving the plant a grey appearance. The branches are wreathed during autumn with glistening bright red fruits ...   **2/6   3/6   5/6**

„ **ichangense.**—C. & W. China. This attains 4—6 ft., with open growths and many clusters of bright red fruits in early autumn ...   **3/6   5/6**

E „ **japonicum (macrophyllum).**—Japan. A handsome shrub, according to locality 6—8 ft. high, with large, glossy, deep green leaves. The scented white flowers are borne in June... ...   **2/6   3/6   5/6**

„ **Lantana (Wayfaring Tree).**—Native. Specimens growing in the hedgerows and woods 6—15 ft. high are a splendid sight during autumn with the clusters of red fruits and dark crimson leaves ...   **1/6   2/6**

„ **Lentago.**—N. America. One of the very best shrubs, for its large green leaves, tawny beneath, never fail to brighten up our gardens with their brilliant tints in autumn. It is a good grower, of upright habit, 6—10 ft. high, according to soil and position ...   **2/6   3/6   5/6**

„ „ **var. nanum (bullatum).**—This distinct and uncommon shrub of fastigiate habit slowly attains 2 ft. in height. It is ideal for points on the rock garden, borders, etc., where its puckered metallic-green leaves will give a splash of rich autumn colour ...   **2/6   3/6**

„ **lobophyllum.**—C. & W. China. One of the most distinct of the family, having stout red-brown glaucous shoots clothed with pretty 3—6 in. net-veined, ovate or orbicular-ovate, long-pointed, bronze-green leaves; these have crimson tinted veins, wide spiny teeth and are pale beneath. It is one of the best for its numerous 4 in. clusters of round or sub-globose glistening red fruits. It will attain 6—10 ft. ...   **3/6   5/6**

		each.	
Viburnum macrocephalum.—China. A slow-growing, bushy shrub, ultimately 5 ft. high, requiring a sheltered position. It is seldom seen in good condition in this country as its early tender growths are often injured by spring frosts. Its 6—9 in. glomerate drooping heads of pure white sterile flowers are borne during May and early June		3/6	5/6
„ **nudum.**—East & South U.S.A. An upright-growing shrub 5—6 ft. in height. The 2—4 in. oval or ovate dark glossy green leaves become attractively coloured from October to late December 2/6		3/6	5/6
E „ **odoratissimum (Awafuki).**—China. This noble-looking shrub with its large leathery and dark green glossy leaves is usually seen growing on walls or in sheltered gardens around the south and west coasts. Many of its lower leaves become magnificently coloured throughout the winter and spring months		3/6	5/6
„ **Opulus.**—The native Guelder Rose. For weeks every autumn many hedges and woods, especially on chalk soil, are brilliant with the mass of showy red fruits nestling among the beautiful, crimson-tinted foliage		1/6	2/6
„ „ **sterile (Snowball Tree).**—This shrub was much valued in the past when flowering shrubs were not so plentiful as they are to-day. Few plants, including the best of the new ones from China, give a greater show of bloom. It is laden with its round balls of snow-white flowers in May and June 1/6	2/6	3/6	
„ „ **xanthocarpum (fructu luteo).**—This makes a handsome bush 5—10 ft. high. It is particularly attractive from July to December when its branches are heavily laden with ½ in. apricot-yellow fruits. To obtain the best effect, it should be planted in front of one of the red-fruiting forms		2/6	3/6
„ **orientale.**—Orient. This shrub is closely related to V. acerifolium and is exceedingly rare in gardens. Its red fruits turn black and they remain so long after the leaves fall. The plant previously distributed is a form of V. Opulus		—	—
„ **ovatifolium.**—W. China. Strong-growing, of open habit, 6—10 ft. high. The coarse broadly ovate leaves are bronze-tinted and have recurved teeth. It bears small clusters of crimson-red fruits		3/6	5/6
„ **phlebotrichum.**—Japan. This uncommon species is one of the most distinct of the Japanese Viburnums and grows 6—10 ft. high. It sends up strong shoots, these being thinly clothed with narrow ovate-oblong, long-pointed, bronze-green, 3—6 in. leaves ; in the adult stage these have spiny teeth and are prettily net-veined like those of V. lobophyllum. From August to late autumn the branches carry numerous drooping clusters of crimson-red fruits ; these are flat, finally becoming oval-elliptical in shape. The foliage is beautifully crimson-tinted before falling 2/6		3/6	5/6
E „ **propinquum.**—C. & W. China. Distinct and compact, with short growths, forming a bush 3—5 ft. high. Its leaves are ovate-lanceolate, glossy, and pale green beneath. It is pretty during autumn with its blue-black fruits		3/6	5/6

			each.	

Viburnum prunifolium (pyrifolium).—N. America. A stiff-branched, spreading, large shrub or small tree. It bears many cymes of white flowers in June succeeded by ½ in. edible dark fruits. The leathery, red-tinted, plum-like leaves are brightly coloured for many weeks during the autumn 2/6   3/6

    „   **pubescens.**—N. America.—An interesting uncommon species of erect and compact habit, a few feet high. Its short stiff growths are clothed with hairy ovate leaves, the upper half coarsely toothed. These change in autumn to a rich purple. It bears 2 in. cymes of white flowers in June 2/6   3/6

E   „   **rhytidophyllum.**—C. China. A noble and very hardy evergreen, but for sheltered positions, otherwise its oblong and shining deep green wrinkled leaves, up to 10 ins. long and 3 ins. wide, become damaged by winds. The clusters of pinkish flowers in May and June are followed by bright red fruits, ageing to black. It is of free growth, up to 15 ft. high and as much through ...   2/6   3/6   5/6

E   „   **rigidum (rugosum).**—Canary Isles. In the south and west, Ireland and the west of Scotland, it forms a large bush, 5—8 ft. high. Its large, bright green, oval-ovate, reticulated, hairy leaves, pale beneath, are its chief attraction 3/6   5/6

    „   **rufidulum (rufotomentosum).**—South U.S.A. It is upright in youth but becomes spreading with age and grows 5—10 ft. high. It can easily be distinguished by its annual growths which are covered with a rusty tomentum. The 3—5 in. corymbs of ¾ in. pure white flowers are followed by blue berries. In some soils the leathery, oval-obovate, shiny leaves become richly coloured for many weeks during the autumn 5/-

    „   **Sargentii.**—N. China. This belongs to the V. Opulus section. It has large deeply-lobed leaves and many 4—6 in. cymes with marginal sterile flowers of a creamy white, during June. Its numerous clusters of bold rectangular or globose, brilliant crimson fruits are the largest of this section ; they are a beautiful sight from mid-August to the end of October, nestling among the yellow and crimson leaves. It is one of the best of ornamentals in southern and western gardens 2/6   3/6

E   „   **Schneiderianum.**—This new hardy evergreen was collected by the late Mr. Geo. Forrest on one of his many expeditions to Western China. It develops into a twiggy shrub 3—6 ft. high and as much wide. The opposite, reticulated, wavy, dark green leaves are 1—3 ins. long, ovate or elliptical-acuminate and they are edged with a few spine-tipped teeth. It produces many terminal clusters of small white flowers during June and July 3/6   5/6

    „   **setigerum (theiferum).**—C. & W. China. A beautiful species of upright habit 6—10 ft. high. The 3—6 in. ovate-lanceolate, long-pointed leaves are dark red when unfolding, ageing to bronzy-green, and have wide spiny teeth. It is particularly attractive during the autumn when heavily laden with large ovoid fruits ...   2/6   3/6   5/6

Viburnum Sieboldii (reticulatum).—Japan. In sheltered   each.
gardens this grows to 6 ft. or more high and as much
through. The flowers are creamy-white, followed by
pink fruits ageing to blue-black. The obovate glossy
dark green leaves turn bronzy-red in autumn but their
odour is not pleasant 3/6

E   „   **suspensum (Sandankwa).**—S. Japan. In the south
and west of Ireland this is a compact bushy shrub, 4 ft.
high and as much wide. The 2—3½ in. ovate-oblong
furrowed leaves are dark green above, paler beneath.
The corymbs of small tubular flesh-coloured and perfumed flowers with red stamens are freely borne in June
and July 3/6   5/6

E   „   **Tinus (Laurustinus).**—Mediterranean region. An old
but always beautiful shrub, producing yearly its 3—4 in.
flat clusters of rosy flowers, ageing to white, according
to the weather, from November to April   ...   1/6   2/6   3/6

„   **tomentosum.**—Japan. This grows into a dense bush
5—8 ft. high, striking during June with many umbels of
marginal sterile white flowers. It is also valued during
the autumn for its dark red and crimson leaves...   ...   2/6   3/6

„   „   **Lanarth Variety.**—This grand robust form from
Cornwall loves a semi-shady position in the south. It is
well clothed with long pointed leaves and the flowers are
much larger than those of the type. It deserves a place
among the choicest of flowering shrubs 3/6   5/6

„   „   **Mariesii.**—One of the many good ornamentals
from Japan. It attains 4—8 ft., with tiers of spreading
branches wreathed from end to end with umbels of white
flowers in May and June. Where possible it should be
given a dark background and it should be in every collection 2/6   3/6   5/6

„   „   **plicatum.**—The Japanese Snowball Tree. A
bushy free-growing shrub 5—8 ft. high, very attractive
during June with its branches wreathed from end to end
with globose balls of ivory white flowers 2/6   3/6   5/6

„   „   „   **grandiflorum (Hort.)**—A beautiful form
with larger heads of pure white flowers, but not such a
strong grower 2/6   3/6   5/6

E   „   **utile.**—C. China. A slender, branching shrub 5—10 ft.
high, of open graceful habit, decorated with oblong dark
glossy green leaves. It bears terminal clusters of white
flowers during May...   ...   .   2/6   3/6

„   **Veitchii.**—The Chinese form of our native Wayfaring
Tree. The greyish leaves turn dark crimson and yellow
in autumn 2/6   3/6

„   **Wilsonii.**—W. China. An elegant, slender, wiry-branched
shrub 5—8 ft. high. The leaves are ovate-oval, and its
young foliage bronzy, ageing to dark green. Numerous
small clusters of pinkish flowers, followed by globose,
dark crimson, downy and blistered fruits, are borne   2/6   3/6   5/6

„   **Wrightii.**—Japan. This is quite distinct from any of the
other cultivated species and it develops into a spreading
bush 4—6 ft. high and as much wide. The handsome
ovate-acuminate or obovate, metallic-green leaves have
sunken veins and coarse teeth and are 3—5 ins. long by
two-thirds as much wide. It is attractive from August to
October with cymes of glistening red globose-ovoid fruits   3/6   5/6

			each.	

Viburnum Wrightii Hessei.—Japan. It is similar in habit to the former and has ovate-obovate, metallic-green leaves 3—5 ins. long ; these have sunken veins and wide, incurved, spiny teeth. Its foliage, like that of the former, turns a beautiful crimson during October and November   **3/6 5/6**

The genus **Viburnum** contains some of the loveliest of ornamental shrubs, and provides cut sprays for indoor decoration during the autumn months. The fruits of V. betulifolium, Sargentii, hepehense, Opulus, O. xanthocarpum, etc. retain their colour for six weeks or more.

C **Vitis Coignetiae.**—Japan. A noble ornamental of vigorous growth. The cordate leaves are 9 ins. long and as much wide, covered on the underside with brown felt, and changing in autumn through many shades of crimson. These are retained for many weeks **2/6** **3/6 5/6**

C   „   **Davidii (armata).**—C. China. Very rampant, with spiny shoots. The large shiny green cordate leaves assume dark crimson and scarlet tints **3/6 5/6**

C   „   „   **Veitchii (cyanocarpa).**—C. China. Strong growing. The cordate leaves are lustrous green, becoming magnificently coloured in autumn **3/6 5/6**

„   **Henryana.**—C. China. Self-clinging, quickly climbing two or three storeys high. The leaves, composed of three to five leaflets, are deep velvety green with midrib and veins white and pink, prominent as the leaves turn brilliant red during autumn. In the south it should be grown on a north or east wall **2/6 3/6**

C   „   **heterophylla.**—E. Asia. This robust climber is at its best when draping a low bank or trained to a low wall, in full sun. It has variable cut leaves and is a lovely sight during late summer and early autumn with its numerous porcelain- or bright blue fruits **2/6 3/6**

C   „   **inconstans (Ampelopsis Veitchii).**—China, Japan. One of the most conspicuous of all plants during autumn and early winter with its vividly coloured leaves. A self-clinging climber for walls and old trees **1/6 2/6**

C   „   **micans (flexuosa Wilsonii).**—C. China. Of slender, elegant growth, clothed with small leaves which are lustrous and bronzy. It needs a semi-shady wall   ...   **3/6 5/6**

C   „   **pulchra (flexuosa major).**—Japan. It is a strong grower and will soon cover a wide area. The handsome lobed leaves, green suffused dark red, are 8 ins. across and as much wide. During the autumn they become as brilliantly coloured as those of V. Coignetiae **3/6 5/6**

C   „   **quinquefolia (Ampelopsis hederacea) (muralis).**— N. America. The Virginian Creeper is one of the most useful of all climbing plants, either for old buildings, fences or trees. Its leaves, composed of three or five leaflets, are a gorgeous sight every autumn **1/6 2/6**

EC   „   **striata (Ampelopsis sempervirens).**—Chile, Brazil. It is free-growing in the south and west counties, on a south or west wall. It is self-climbing, quickly covering space two storeys high **2/6 3/6**

C **Vitis Thomsonii.**—Himalayas, C. China. A slender, vigorous   each.
grower. The leaves, composed of five leaflets, are vinous
red during spring, ageing to purplish-green and changing during autumn to dark crimson and scarlet   ...   3/6   5/6

C   „   **vinifera Brandt.**—A free-growing, hardy, fruiting vine.
The large green lobed foliage changes in autumn through
brilliant tints of yellow and orange to rosy-crimson and
scarlet 2/6   3/6   5/6

C   „   „   **purpurea.**—The Claret Vine, so called for its
continuously vinous purple foliage, becoming much
deeper coloured before the fall of the leaf 3/6   5/6

Weigela (See **Diervilla**).

E **Weinmannia racemosa.**—New Zealand. A rare shrub, suited
to the milder districts and the coast. Its trifoliate
leaves are borne in pairs and are of a glossy bronzy-green,
with serrated edges. The numerous small flowers are
white and are borne in racemes like a Veronica, in June ...   3/6   5/6

E   „   **trichosperma.**—Chilean Andes. This distinct and
beautiful evergreen is hardy in gardens around the
south and west coasts, Ireland and the west of Scotland,
within reach of the salt air. The opposite dark green
pinnate leaves, with 9—13 toothed leaflets, have leaf stalks
flanked with wedge-shaped wings. The many short
racemes of small creamy white flowers are produced
in May and June 5/-   7/6

C **Wistaria floribunda (multijuga).**—Japan. A selected form with
drooping racemes of pale lilac-coloured flowers, 3 ft.
long, and 4 ins. wide, during May and early June   3/6   5/6   7/6

C   „   „   **alba.**—Japan. This distinct form produces much
smaller racemes of white flowers, tinted with pale violet
according to soil 3/6   5/6   7/6

C   „   „   **rosea.**—Japan. It is as strong growing as the
type and its long racemes of pale pink or rose-coloured
flowers have purple wings 3/6   5/6   7/6

C   „   **sinensis (chinensis).**—China. One of the most beautiful
of all climbing shrubs during May and early June.
Well known for its quantities of 1 ft. drooping racemes of
large, pale mauve, scented flowers 2/6   3/6   5/6

C   „   **venusta.**—China, Japan. A rare and beautiful climber,
producing in quantity, short stocky racemes of large,
white, deliciously scented flowers. These are borne in
May and June 5/6   7/6

Xanthoceras sorbifolia.—N. China. A most beautiful large
shrub or small tree. In a moist position or in woodland
it is free-growing, attaining 8—15 ft. It should be encouraged to form a single leader. It bears elegant
pinnate leaves and 8 in. spikes of white horse-chestnut-
like flowers during May and early June 3/6   5/6

E **Xylosma racemosa (Myroxylon racemosum).**—C. & W. China.
A rarity belonging to the Azara order, with ovate-round-
ish, glossy, dark green leaves. The branches are armed
with stout spines. It is of bushy habit 5/-   7/6

each.

E **Yucca filamentosa.**—S.E. United States. This has a rosette of many 1—2½ ft. reed-like leaves rising from the ground and these, either erect or arching, are margined with curly threads. It is a beautiful plant, producing in July and August 2—5 ft. broad panicles of drooping creamy flowers 1/6   2/6   3/6

E   „   **flaccida.**—S.E. United States. The flowers of this plant are very similar to those of Y. filamentosa. It differs in having much shorter and stiffer incurved leaves margined with longer curly threads 2/6   3/6

E   „   **glauca (angustifolia).**—S.E. United States. An uncommon plant with 1—2 ft. erect or spreading narrow linear glaucous-green leaves with white margins. It requires a sloping sunny position to encourage its 3—4 ft. erect racemes of green-yellow flowers in July and August 3/6   5/6   7/6

E   „   **gloriosa.**—S.E. United States. (Adam's Needle). A handsome species attaining with age 6—8 ft. in height, with dense rosettes of 1½—3 ft. green leaves, broad and rigid. From July to September it bears 3—4 ft. conical panicles of campanulate creamy-white flowers, tinged with red 3/6   5/6   7/6

E   „   **recurvifolia.**—S.E. United States. This beautiful Yucca ultimately develops a naked trunk 3—6 ft. in height. It has a handsome rosette of 2—3 ft. glaucous leaves, broad and arching. The 2—3 ft. massive panicles of creamy-white flowers are similar to those of Y. gloriosa, but it is a freer flowering plant 3/6   5/6   7/6

E   „   **Whipplei.**—California, Arizona. An uncommon stoloniferous plant requiring a sloping sunny position to bring out its striking elegant inflorescences of green-white flowers. It forms a dense rosette of leaves, rigid and linear, from the ground, and is the bluest species possible for open culture in this country 3/6   5/6

Zanthorhiza apiifolia.—East U.S.A. In the south it requires a semi-shady position. The 1—2 ft. erect stems carry pinnate or bipinnate leaves and they become attractively dark purple or bright yellow tinted. The drooping panicles of small flowers have little beauty 2/6   3/6

Zanthoxylum piperitum.—N. China, Korea, Japan.—An interesting and distinct shrub 5—10 ft. high, with branches armed with short flat spines. The graceful pinnate leaves are composed of eleven to twenty-three small dark green leaflets and are pleasantly fragrant 3/6   5/6

Zelkova serrata (acuminata).—Japan. An elegant spreading tree, rarely growing more than 20 ft. in height with us and requiring a sheltered open position. Its twiggy branches are decorated with 2—4½ in. ovate-lanceolate green leaves, these becoming bright yellow tinted in autumn ...   3/6   5/6

Zenobia pulverulenta (speciosa).—N. Carolina to Florida. This charming compact shrub has stiff stems and seldom grows 3 ft. high. It is furnished with handsome broad, oval, glaucous-blue leaves. The numerous pure white bells, ½ in. or more wide, are a beautiful sight during June and July. This plant and its variety are worthy of wider cultivation 2/6   3/6   5/6

Zenobia pulverulenta nuda (speciosa viridis. Hort.) each.
(**Andromeda cassinifolia**).—In nature, it is found with
the type. Its branches are more slender and it will grow
to 3—5 ft. high. The oblong-ovate leaves are green on
both sides and half as large as those of the type. The
best form produces many pure white flowers, ½ in. or
more wide, quite as beautiful as those of Z. pulverulenta.
After blooming, both plants should have their flowering
branches cut away ... ... 2/6　3/6　5/6
　　In the south, the **Zenobias** love semi-shade and will
grow in almost any soil that is free from lime.

HALF STANDARD AND STANDARD ORNAMENTAL TREES.

Acer	cappadocicum	...	...	...	...	...	5/6	7/6
,,	dasycarpum	...	...	...	...	...	3/6	5/6
,,	,, rubrum	...	...	...	...	...	5/6	7/6
,,	Dieckii ...	...	...	...	...	...		10/6
,,	macrophyllum	...	...	...	...	...	5/6	7/6
,,	palmatum	...	...	...	...	...	7/6	10/6
,,	platanoides	...	...	...	...	3/6	5/6	7/6
,,	,, Schwedleri	...	...	...	5/6	7/6	10/6
,,	pseudoplatanus	...	...	...	...	...	3/6	5/6
,,	rubrum	...	...	...	...	3/6	5/6	7/6
,,	rufinerve	...	...	...	...	3/6	5/6	7/6
,,	spicatum	...	...	...	...	3/6	5/6	7/6
Aesculus	carnea (rubicunda)	...	...	...	...		7/6	10/6
,,	,, Briotii	...	...	...	...	7/6	10/6	12/6
,,	turbinata ...	...	...	...	...	10/6	15/6	21/-
Almonds (See **Prunus Amygdalus**)								
Amelanchier	alnifolia	...	...	...	...	...	5/6	7/6
,,	asiatica	...	...	...	...	5/6	7/6	10/6
,,	canadensis	...	...	...	...	...	5/6	7/6
,,	levis ...	...	...	...	...	5/6	7/6	10/6
,,	rotundifolia	...	...	...	...	3/6	5/6	7/6
Cornus Kousa	...	...	...	...	...	...	7/6	10/6
Crabs (See **Malus**).								
Crataegomespilus grandiflora	...	...	...	...	...	5/6	7/6
Crataegus	arnoldiana	...	...	...	...	...	5/6	7/6
,,	coccinea	...	...	...	...	...	5/6	7/6
,,	Crus-galli	...	...	...	...	...	5/6	7/6
,,	Ellwangeriana	...	...	...	...	...	5/6	7/6
,,	orientalis	...	...	...	...	5/6	7/6	10/6
,,	oxyacanthoides plena alba ...	...	...	...	...	5/6	7/6
,,	,, ,, coccinea	...	...	...	5/6	7/6
,,	,, ,, rosea	...	...	...		5/6
,,	,, punicea	...	...	...	...	5/6	7/6
,,	,, rosea	...	...	...	...	5/6	7/6
Halesia carolina	...	...	...	...	...	...	5/6	7/6
Hamamelis japonica	...	...	...	...	...	...	5/6	7/6
Laburnum	Adamii	...	...	...	...	3/6	5/6	7/6
,,	alpinum	...	...	...	...	3/6	5/6	7/6
,,	anagyroides	...	...	...	...	2/6	3/6	5/6
,,	Vossii ...	...	...	...	...	3/6	5/6	7/6
,,	Watereri	...	...	...	...	3/6	5/6	7/6

							each.		
Liquidambar styraciflua	...	...	...	...	...	5/6	7/6	10/6
Malus aldenhamensis	...	...	...	...	...		5/6	7/6
„ atrosanguinea	...	...	...	...	...		5/6	7/6
„ coronaria	...	...	...	...	...		5/6	7/6
„ „ Charlottae	...	...	...	...	...		7/6	10/6
„ earlhamensis	...	...	...	...	...		5/6	7/6
„ Eleyi ...	...	...	...	...	...		5/6	7/6
„ florentina	...	...	...	...	...		5/6	7/6
„ floribunda	...	...	...	...	...		5/6	7/6
„ Hartwigii	...	...	...	...	...		5/6	7/6
„ hupehensis	...	...	...	...	...		5/6	7/6
„ kansuensis	...	...	...	...	...		5/6	7/6
„ magdeburgensis	...	...	...	...	...		5/6	7/6
„ micromalus ...	...	...	...	...	...		5/6	7/6
„ orthocarpa	...	...	...	...	...		5/6	7/6
„ Prattii ...	...	...	...	...	...		5/6	7/6
„ prunifolia	...	...	...	...	...		5/6	7/6
„ „ fructu coccineo	...	...	...	...		5/6	7/6
„ „ rinki (Ringo)	...	...	...	...		5/6	7/6
„ „ xanthocarpa	...	...	...	...		5/6	7/6
„ pumila Dartmouth	...	...	...	...		5/6	7/6
„ „ John Downie	...	...	...	...		5/6	7/6
„ „ Lady Northcliffe	...	...	...	...		5/6	7/6
„ „ Veitch's Scarlet	...	...	...	...		5/6	7/6
„ „ Wisley Crab	...	...	...	...		5/6	7/6
„ purpurea	...	...	...	...	...	5/6	7/6	10/6
„ Scheideckeri	...	...	...	...	...		5/6	7/6
„ Sieboldii	...	...	...	...	...		5/6	7/6
„ Tschonoskii	...	...	...	...	...		5/6	7/6
„ yunnanensis ...	...	...	...	...	...		5/6	7/6
„ „ Veitchii	...	...	...	...	...		5/6	7/6
„ Zumi ...	...	...	...	...	...		5/6	7/6
„ „ calocarpa	...	...	...	...	...		5/6	7/6
Parrotia persica	...	...	...	...	...	10/6	15/6	21/-
Photinia villosa	...	...	...	...	...	3/6	5/6	7/6
Prunus cerasifera Pissartii	...	...	...	...		3/6	5/6
„ „ „ Woodii	...	...	...	3/6	5/6	7/6
„ (Cherry) avium	...	...	...	...	...		3/6	5/6
„ „ „ plena	...	...	...	...			7/6
„ „ Cerasus Rhexii	...	...	...	...		5/6	7/6
„ „ Conradinae	...	...	...	...		7/6	10/6
„ „ „ semi-plena	...	...	...			7/6
„ „ incisa ... ... on own roots			...	5/6	7/6
„ „ „ serrata ... on own roots		5/6	7/6	10/6
„ „ Lannesiana	...	...	...	...			7/6
„ „ Maximowiczii	...	...	...	...		5/6	7/6
„ „ Sargentii on own roots or grafted	5/6	7/6	10/6
„ „ serrula tibetica	...	...	...	5/6	7/6	10/6
„ „ serrulata pubescens ...	...	...		7/6	10/6
„ „ Sieboldii ...	...	...	...	...		7/6	10/6
„ „ subhirtella ... on own roots	3/6	5/6	7/6
„ „ „ ascendens on own roots	...	5/6	7/6
„ „ „ autumnalis on own roots	5/6	7/6	10/6
„ „ „ pendula ... 5/6	7/6	10/6	12/6
„ „ „ „ rubra ...	...		7/6	10/6
„ „ Vilmorinii	...	...	...	...		7/6	10/6
„ „ yedoensis ... on own roots or grafted	7/6	10/6
„ „ „ perpendens	...	...	...		7/6	10/6

Prunus (Cherry)	Amanogawa	...	...			each.		
„	„	Ariake	...	...	...			
„	„	Daikoku	...	...	...			
„	„	Fugenzo	...	...	...			
„	„	Hokusai	...	...	...			
„	„	Ichiyo	...	...	...			
„	„	Jo-nioi	...	...	...			
„	„	Kiku-Shidare	...	...			
„	„	Kirin	...	...	...			
„	„	Kwanzan	5/6	7/6	10/6			
„	„	Ojochin	...	...	Japanese Cherries		
„	„	serrulata albo-plena	...	all at	7/6	10/6
„	„	„ semperflorens				
„	„	Shiro-fugen	...	...			
„	„	Shirotae	...	...			
„	„	Shogetsu	...	...			
„	„	Shujaku	...	...			
„	„	Sumizome	...	...			
„	„	Tai-haku	...	...			
„	„	Taizan-Fukun	...	...			
„	„	Temari	...	...	...		
„	„	Ukon	...	...	...		
„	communis (Amygdalus communis) (Almond)	...	5/6	7/6		
„	„	Pollardii	...	...	...	...	...	— —
„	„	roseo plena	...	...	...	...	7/6	10/6
„	Padus	...	...	...	...	...	3/6	5/6
„	„	Watereri (grandiflora)	...	...	5/6	7/6	10/6

AUCUPARIA (MOUNTAIN ASH) SECTION.

Sorbus	Aucuparia	...	...	...	...	...	2/6	3/6	5/6
„	„	xanthocarpa	...	...	...	5/6	7/6
„	decurrens	...	...	...	...	...	5/6	7/6
„	discolor	...	...	...	...	...	5/6	7/6	10/6
„	gracilis	...	...	...	...	...	5/6	7/6
„	hupehensis	...	...	...	...	5/6	7/6	10/6
„	hybrida	...	...	...	...	...	5/6	7/6
„	„	Gibbsii	...	...	...	...	5/6	7/6	10/6
„	intermedia	...	...	...	...	...	5/6	7/6
„	Koehneana	...	...	...	...	...	7/6	10/6
„	Matsumurana	...	...	...	...	5/6	7/6
„	pohuashanensis	...	...	...	...	5/6	7/6
„	rufo-ferruginea	...	...	...	5/6	7/6	10/6
„	scalaris	...	...	...	...	...	5/6	7/6
„	Vilmorinii	...	...	...	...	...	5/6	7/6
„	Wilsoniana	...	...	...	...	...	5/6	7/6

ARIA SECTION.

Sorbus	alnifolia	...	...	...	...	...	...	5/6	7/6
„	Aria	...	...	...	...	...	...	3/6	5/6
„	„	majestica	...	...	...	...	5/6	7/6	10/6
„	Folgneri	...	...	...	...	...	5/6	7/6
„	magnifica	...	...	...	...	...	5/6	7/6	10/6
„	umbellata	...	...	...	...	...	5/6	7/6
Stewartia pseudo-camellia	...	...	...	7/6	10/6	12/6
Styrax japonicus	...	...	...	...	...	10/6	15/6	21/—
Wistaria sinensis	...	...	...	...	...	...	15/6	21/—
„	„	alba	...	...	...	...	...	15/6	21/—

DWARF-GROWING CHINESE AND HIMALAYAN RHODODENDRONS.

Rhododendron aperantum.—In many forms. These have been on trial here for six years and have now been discarded as they proved to be very poor growers and were shy-flowering ... ...

each.

„ **Blue Tit (impeditum × Augustinii).**—A lovely shrub for the back of the Ericaceae border and with a little pruning it can be kept to about 3 ft. From April onwards it is bright with groups of 1½ in. wavy-petalled, pale violet flowers ... ... | 5/6 | 7/6

„ **calciphilum.**—A spreading shrub 9—18 ins. high with small grey leaves, bronze tinted during the winter. The pretty rose-pink flowers are carried in May and June 2/6 | 3/6 | 5/6

„ **calostrotum.**—One of the most contented and the easiest to grow of all dwarf Rhododendrons. It is 9—18 ins. high and has dense shoots thickly clothed with small, aromatic, grey leaves, buff or brown-red beneath. The 2 in. flat, deep rose-crimson, pansy-like flowers are borne during April and May and often again in the autumn ... ... | 5/- | 7/6

„ „ **(form).**—Quite as beautiful as the former, but with slightly smaller and paler flowers ... ... 2/6 | 3/6 | 5/6

„ **campylogynum.**—This slowly attains 9—15 ins. and has stiff branches carrying small, leathery, bronze-tinted leaves. The nodding ¾—1 in. bell-shaped flowers are mahogany-red, with 5 deep recurved lobes, and are held on 2—3 in. stalks from May to July ... ... 7/6 | 10/6 | 12/6

„ **camtschaticum (Therorhodion camtschaticum).**—It forms a dense tuft, 4—6 ins. high and 1—2 ft. wide and it requires a semi-shady position in the south. The many 1 in. rose-crimson flowers are seen in May and June. There is an illustration of a magnificent specimen in the Alpine Society's Bulletin, Vol. IV, No. 1 (March, 1936), page 70 ... ... 5/6 | 7/6 | 10/6

„ **cephalanthum.**—This species slowly attains 12 ins. and has short, rigid growths. Heads of pretty white or pale yellow Daphne-like flowers are produced in April and May ... ... | 7/6

„ **chamaetortum.**—It grows 6—12 ins. high and carries heads of rose-coloured, Daphne-like flowers in May and June. It is related to the former species ... ... | 7/6

„ **chameunum.**—A true little alpine shrub which slowly grows to 6 ins. or so high. The deep rose-red flowers are marked with crimson and they are large for the size of the plant ... ... | 5/6 | 7/6

„ **charidotes.**—Of semi-prostrate habit and only a few inches high. Its growths are lit up from early April to June by the mass of glowing magenta-crimson flowers 5/6 | 7/6 | 10/6

„ **charitopes.**—It is related to R. glaucum and grows 1—2 ft. high by 2—3 ft. wide. During May it bears crimson-spotted, apple blossom-pink, bell-shaped flowers. The leaves are wavy, grey-green above and glaucous beneath 5/6 | 7/6 | 10/6

each.

Rhododendron chryseum.—An erect shrub 1—2 ft. high with very showy deep-yellow flowers during May and June and again in the autumn... ... ...   5/6   7/6

„ **ciliatum.**—It is often seen in gardens and is of rather open habit 18—24 ins. high, though it will grow much taller in Cornwall, etc. During March and April it produces many rose-red ageing to pale pink flowers. It is one of the very best of flowering shrubs for a cool house ...   3/6   5/6

„ **cosmetum (pamprotum).**—Of semi-prostrate habit, 6 ins. high and 2 ft. wide. The ¾—1 in. wine-coloured flowers begin to open in April and continue to the end of June 7/6   10/6

„ **crebreflorum.**—An uncommon and attractive compact shrub, 12—18 ins. high, which produces pale pink, honey-scented flowers from mid-April to the middle of June and often again during the autumn 7/6   10/6

„ **dauricum.**—A deciduous, twiggy shrub, 3—5 ft. high. It should be planted on the north side of an evergreen so as to shelter the many pleasing bright rose-purple flowers which open during February. Quite tiny plants bloom 5/6   7/6   10/6

„ **deleiense.**—A compact grower, 1½—2½ ft. high and requiring a sheltered position to protect it from the cold spring winds and late frosts. It is related to R. tephropeplum but has rounder leaves and deeper rose-coloured tubular flowers borne during May and June. It is beautifully illustrated in A. T. Johnson's "Woodland Garden" 5/6   7/6

„ **diacritum (pycnocladum).**—A compact shrub slowly growing 1—2 ft. high and composed of many upright short twigs. It has dense small grey-green leaves and the deep rose-purple flowers are produced from April to June 7/6

„ **didymum.**—One of the most attractive whether in or out of bloom. It is compact growing, 1—2 ft. in height but much more in width, and it freely produces clusters of bell-shaped, deep crimson flowers from early June to August 7/6   10/6

„ **Edgarianum (oresbium).**—A bush, 15—30 ins. high, clothed with small grey-green leaves. It is decorated with 1 in. flat, indigo-blue ageing to violet-purple flowers from April to mid-June and again during the autumn   ...   5/6   7/6

„ **fastigiatum.**—One of the forms of R. impeditum is often seen under this name. The true plant is compact and fastigiate in habit and about 2 ft. high by half as much wide. The slender twigs are crowded with tiny, shiny green leaves and the numerous violet-purple flowers are produced from March to autumn 3/6   5/6   7/6

„ **ferrugineum.**—Better known as the Alpine Rose of the Alps of Europe. A compact shrub slowly growing to 18—24 ins. high and one of the best of the dwarf growers during June when carrying many deep rose flowers   2/6   3/6   5/6

„   „ **album.**—In the south, the white-flowering form is not often happy and free-growing   ...   2/6   3/6   5/6

„ **flavidum (primulinum).**—Of neat upright growth, 18—24 ins. high. Its 1—1½ in. primrose-yellow flowers appear from early March to June and often again during the autumn 5/6   7/6

each.

Rhododendron Forrestii (repens).—This is usually considered a difficult plant to establish but it will do well if planted in semi-shade in an old oak stump or if sandstone is placed around its roots. It is one of the most treasured of dwarf Rhododendrons and has lovely bell-shaped, rich crimson flowers, carried on creeping growths, during April and May ... ... 7/6 to 21/-

„   „   **chamaethauma.**—A rare form, 6—12 ins. in height but much more in width. It has stiffer semi-prostrate growths and larger leaves. It also differs from the type in that its bell-shaped, rose or carmine flowers are in trusses of four or five 10/6

„   **fragariflorum.**—A rare small-growing shrub with tiny grey-green leaves. Its flowers are unique, with short trumpets, ½ in. wide, and are white suffused pink, the colour deepening towards the base 5/6   7/6

„   **glaucum.**—One of the oldest and choicest of Rhododendrons, 2 ft. high and 4 ft. or more wide according to climate. From mid-April to June, the end of almost every shoot carries ¾—1¼ in. bell-shaped, rose-coloured flowers 2/6   3/6   5/6

„   **glomerulatum.**—Of upright growth, 12—24 ins. high and composed of many short twigs neatly furnished with small grey leaves. During April and May and again in autumn, it displays clusters of small purple-mauve flowers 7/6

„   **Hampreston (glaucum × russatum).**—A unique natural hybrid making a compact shrub 18 ins. high. The leaves are similar to those of its male parent while the flowers are the shape as those of R. glaucum, but very much larger. They are crimson-purple in bud, ageing to rose-purple and are borne during May and early June. 1938 delivery 10/6

„   **hemitrichotum.**—A very hardy free-growing twiggy species, 2—3 ft. high. Even on tiny plants, the branches are lit up during March and April and again in early autumn with numerous funnel-shaped, pale rose flowers with rose-red margins 5/6   7/6

„   **hippophaeoides.**—In the open it makes a well-shaped specimen 2—3 ft. high and has dense 1 in. oblong-ovate, grey-green, aromatic leaves. The numerous ¾—1 in. mauve flowers are borne during April and May and again in late summer and autumn 3/6   5/6

„   **hirsutum.**—This is best described as the hairy form of the Alpine Rose Rhododendron and it is very pretty during June when the tips of the twigs carry clusters of Daphne-like rose-pink flowers 2/6   3/6

„   **hypolepidotum.**—A round dense shrub, 1½—3 ft. high, which should be planted in the open, where it will bloom freely during June and July. The many ¾—1 in., 5-petalled, flat, lemon-yellow flowers are held above the 1—2 in. aromatic green leaves, scaly and blue-white beneath 3/6   5/6   7/6

„   **impeditum (semanteum).**—A dense twiggy shrub of rather flat habit, 9—15 ins. high though often 2 ft. wide. It is thickly clothed with blue-tinted leaves and has numerous small violet-purple flowers from mid-March to autumn 2/6   3/6   5/6   7/6

Rhododendron impeditum green-leaved form.—The flowers of this form are produced from mid-March to autumn and are of a lighter colour ... ... 3/6   5/6   7/6   each.

„   „   **Indigo.**—This choice form makes 1—3 ins. of growth yearly, developing into a bushy shrub 9—12 ins. high but 18—24 ins. wide. It has dense grey-blue leaves and is crowded with clusters of indigo-blue flowers from early April to mid-May and again during late summer   10/6

„   „   **pygmaeum.**—One of the daintiest of the family and of pin-cushion-like habit, never exceeding 6 ins. in height. The tiny leaves touch each other but they are almost hidden by the small violet-blue flowers in spring and again in early autumn. It is often called R. Bunch of Violets 5/6   7/6   10/6

„   **imperator.**—In the shade of tall Rhododendrons and Oaks, it quickly grows into a dense plant a few inches high and 9—15 ins. wide. It is a pretty sight every April and May when carrying its numerous 1—1½ in. funnel-shaped, unspotted, rose-red flowers ... 2/6   3/6   5/6   7/6

„   **intricatum.**—A bushy plant, 1—2 ft. high and as much wide. The wiry shoots are thickly clothed with small grey-green leaves and from mid-March to June and again during the autumn, they bear mauve or lavender-blue flowers 3/6   5/6   7/6

„   **Keiskei.**—This twiggy species grows 1½—2½ ft. high, according to position and it loves a little shade during the summer months. The 1½—2½ in. oval-ovate leaves are pale green and pointed and have numerous dark scales on the underside. Many clusters, each containing 4 or 5 pretty 1½—2 in. lemon-yellow flowers, are produced during April and May 3/6   5/6

„   **keleticum.**—A charming semi-prostrate shrub 6—9 ins. high and 1—2 ft. wide, densely clothed with deep green oval-ovate leaves with hairy margins. Almost every twig bears flat purple-crimson flowers, with deeper markings, during May and June 2/6   3/6   5/6

„   **lapponicum.**—In semi-shade, it will attain 1½—2 ft. It is furnished with tiny green leaves and is quite pretty from early May to late July with its violet-purple flowers. 5/6   7/6

„   **ledoides.**—This shrub grows 18—30 ins. high and is of rather loose habit. The leading shoots should be pinched out to make it more bushy. The clusters of pretty Daphne-like pale pink or flesh-coloured flowers are borne, even on small plants, during April and May ... 7/6   10/6

„   **lepidostylum (Evergreen form).**—This slowly grows into a compact bush, 1½—2 ft. high, and should be given an open position. The short growths are covered with long hairs and the dense 1—2 in. oval-elliptic, blue-grey leaves are attractive at any time of the year. The 1—1½ in. flat primrose-yellow flowers are borne during June and July 5/6   7/6   10/6

„   **lepidotum.**—An upright-growing semi-evergreen, 12—24 ins. high, with brown-green leaves covered with a woolly tomentum. In May and June it produces its 1 in. star-like plum-red or dark crimson flowers 3/6   5/6   7/6

each.

Rhododendron leucaspis.—A choice shrub, 1—2 ft. high, loving a semi-shady position in the south. During March and April its beautiful 2 in. milk-white, flat flowers are a lovely sight resting upon the elliptic-obovate, hairy leaves, these blue-grey beneath 3/6   5/6   7/6

„   **luridum K.W. 7048.**—An upright grower, 2—3 ft. high, with stems and leaves covered with rusty tomentum. The end of almost every shoot produces groups of 5—7 deep purple flowers during April and May and again in early autumn 5/6   7/6

„   **lysolepis.**—Of fastigiate habit, 18—30 ins. high. The thin growths are densely clothed with small green leaves. Small rose-violet flowers are profusely borne from mid-February to May and again from mid-August to October 3/6   5/6   7/6

„   **megeratum.**—A desirable shrub, 1—2 ft. high, which should be grown in semi-shade. The short, stiff, hairy shoots carry small green leaves, blue-grey beneath. The rich yellow bell-shaped flowers are freely borne during April and May 3/6   5/6   7/6

„   **microleucum.**—An exceedingly rare plant which was first noticed growing among coloured forms of R. lapponicum in a Gloucestershire garden. It grows 1 ft. high and has dense, ½—1 in. pale green, linear-oblanceolate leaves with buff-coloured reverse. The heads of dainty white flowers are borne in April and May and again in early autumn 10/6

„   **moupinense.**—In a bleak Bristol garden in early February, a small group of spreading bushes was very conspicuous. Each was laden with short tubular scented 2 in. white flowers with purple or red spots ... 5/6   7/6 10/6

„   **muliense.**—This very hardy shrub is of good habit, 1½—2½ ft. high and has small oblong-oval dull green leaves, grey beneath. Attractive clusters, each of five or six 1 in. bright yellow flowers, are freely produced during May and June 7/6 10/6

„   **myrtifolium (ovatum).**—A very hardy and useful bushy shrub, 1½—2½ ins. high. It is of garden origin, before 1824, and one of the best for general planting. It is densely furnished with 1—2½ in. bronze-tinted leaves, pointed at both ends, and is decorated from mid-May to the end of June with numerous funnel-shaped, rose-pink flowers 2/6   3/6   5/6

„   **myrtilloides.**—This valuable dense, twiggy plant grows 3—6 ins. high but 12 ins. or more wide and does well in semi-shade. The small, glistening, bronze-tinted leaves form a fine background for the numerous ½ in. plum-red or claret, bell-shaped flowers ; these are held on 1—3 in. erect stems and appear in May and June. There is an illustration of a fine specimen in flower in W. J. Bean's "Trees and Shrubs," Vol. III, page 399   3/6   5/6   7/6 10/6

„   „   **form.**—A stronger grower, 6—12 ins. high, with larger leaves and flowers of a lighter colour 10/6

each.

Rhododendron nivale.—This extremely scarce plant grows
6—12 ins. high and has slender twigs thickly clothed with
tiny ovate, brown-green, aromatic leaves, spotted on both
sides with brown. From mid-February to June, it is
bright with ¾ in., 5-lobed, crinkly flowers. These are
not white as the name implies, but dog-violet-coloured ... 10/6

„ **orthocladum.**—A fascinating, round, compact shrub for
collectors of the uncommon. It makes 1—3 in. growths
annually and ultimately reaches a height of 18 ins. It is
thickly clothed with minute, linear, brown-green leaves
and during April small mauve flowers are produced from
the tip of almost every shoot 5/6   7/6

„ **patulum.**—This rarity seldom exceeds 6 ins. in height
and from mid-March to May it is almost covered with
1—1½ in., funnel-shaped, rose-red, ageing to rose-pink
flowers 10/6

„ **pemaköense.**—Of dense, semi-prostrate habit, this
beautiful shrub grows to about 1 ft. high and 2 ft. or more
wide. It is handsomely clothed with 1 in. glistening,
elliptical-oblanceolate, green leaves, glaucous beneath.
The attractive 1½—2 in. funnel-shaped, pale mauve
flowers are borne in profusion during early April 2/6   3/6   5/6   7/6

„ **praecox (ciliatum × dauricum).**—A compact grower,
2—4 ft. high. The many lovely 1½—2 in. rose-purple
flowers are produced from early February to April,
according to weather conditions 2/6   3/6   5/6

„ **prostigiatum (prostratum × fastigiatum).**—In habit
of growth it much resembles R. impeditum and one
wonders now that the true R. fastigiatum is known if
this is really its second parent. It is undoubtedly one
of the best of the small growers and has small blue-
tinted leaves. It is almost covered with church-purple
or violet-purple flowers during spring and again in the
autumn 5/6   7/6 10/6

„ **prostratum.**—A stiff-branching prostrate shrub slowly
growing to a height of 4—6 ins. The small shining green
leaves are blue-grey or buff-coloured beneath, with
scattered brown hairs, and have reflexed edges. Pleasing
flat, rich rose-purple flowers, 1—1½ ins. wide, are borne
during April and early May 5/6   7/6 10/6

„ **proteoides.**—This is a choice and most distinct alpine
shrub. A specimen 10 years old may not exceed a height
of 6 ins. and a width of 10 ins. Its 1—2 in., oblong-
obovate, thick, green leaves have reflexed edges, are
tinted with dark crimson and covered with dense tomentum beneath. Unfortunately its crimson-spotted, primrose-yellow flowers are not produced freely on young
plants 10/6

„ **pumilum.**—Captain Kingdon Ward sent this home as
R. Pink Baby. It is one of the most charming of the
dwarf growers and has tiny leaves, glaucous beneath.
Its dainty ½—¾ in. bells are of a soft pink and deeply
lobed, held on 1—3 in. stalks, from early April to late
June. It is related to the beautiful R. myrtilloides ... 10/6

each.

Rhododendron racemosum (of Wilson).—A selected form, 1½—2½ ft. high, of twiggy compact habit and one of the first of the smaller growers to plant. At least one-third of each growth is crowded with 1—1¼ in. bell-shaped flowers, apple-blossom-pink with edges of a deeper colour, during April and early May 2/6   3/6   5/6

„   „   **Forrest 19,404.**—This excellent form is of similar habit though perhaps not quite so tall. It has clear rose-pink upright flowers and is indeed a beautiful shrub   3/6   5/6

„   „   **oleifolium.**—This fine form is of looser habit and quickly grows to a height of 3 ft. It has larger leaves and is a beautiful sight during March and April carrying numerous rose-pink flowers, the colour deepening towards the margins. Immediately after flowering, long shoots should be pruned back to one third of their length   3/6   5/6

„   **radicans.**—Of cushion-like habit, 4 ins. or more high and 1—2 ft. wide with annual, imbricated growths 2—3 ins. long. A delightful plant, decorated in May and June with ¾ in. flat, violet-purple blooms. A choice companion for R. impeditum pygmaeum and R. Sargentianum 3/6   5/6   7/6   10/6

„   **radinum.**—Related to R. ledoides but smaller-growing and bearing clusters of dainty, daphne-like flowers, pink ageing to blush in colour 7/6

„   **ravum (cheilanthum).**—A very hardy species about 2 ft. high, with twigs clothed with variable, ¾—2 in. deep green leaves, yellow-brown beneath. Clusters of 4—6 funnel-shaped, ¾—1 in. deep rose flowers are borne in May and June 5/6   7/6

„   **riparium.**—An upright bushy shrub, 12—18 ins. high with 1 in. oval-elliptical, grey-green, glutinous leaves, covered beneath with light brown tomentum. Bright red-pink flowers are borne in profusion from mid-April to June 3/6   5/6   7/6

„   **rupicola.**—It grows 18—24 ins. high and has many thin twigs clothed with small green oval-oblong, rounded leaves. During April and May its ¾—1 in. rich plum-red, short-tubed flowers are very attractive 7/6

„   **russatum (cantabile) (osmerum).**—In its best form, it is a beautiful ornamental and soon makes a bushy shrub 2—3 ft. high. It has dense, ¾—2 in. oval-oblong, dark green, scaly leaves and blooms freely during March and April and again in early autumn, each truss containing 5—10 vivid purple-blue flowers, 1 in. wide   5/6   7/6   10/6

„   **saluenense.**—Of upright habit, 1—2 ft. high and with leaves very similar to those of R. calostrotum. The handsome deep purple-crimson, 1¼ in. flowers are produced from May to August 5/6   7/6

„   **Sargentianum.**—This little gem is of dense habit, about 9 ins. high and 12 ins. or more wide and makes ⅓—1 in. of growth annually. From mid-April to June, the plant is almost hidden by the dainty daphne-like, ½ in. lemon-yellow flowers, these held on short stalks 7/6   10/6

„   **scintillans.**—The erect twiggy shoots form a dense bush 18—30 ins. high by as much wide, thickly clothed with small oblong-lanceolate leaves. Numerous conspicuous ¾—1 in. lavender-blue flowers are produced from mid-March to June and again in early autumn 3/6   5/6

Rhododendron semibarbatum.—A deciduous shrub, 3—5 ft. | | each.
high and with slender growths, suitable for the autumn
garden as its leaves assume brilliant tints. The tiny
white flowers are borne during May and early June ... | 5/6 | 7/6

„ **telmateium.**—This dense, branching shrub attains 1—2
ft. and is clothed with tiny green leaves. It exhibits its
many small dog-violet-coloured flowers in April and
early May ... ... | 3/6 | 5/6

„ **tephropeplum.**—Of bushy, spreading habit, 1½—3 ft.
high and with pretty 1—1¼ in. funnel-shaped flowers,
even on quite small plants, during May. Here, in the
open, it is often damaged by early and late frosts, while
plants in semi-shade are not touched ... ... 3/6 | 5/6 | 7/6

„ **trichocladum.**—A semi-evergreen, 2 ft. or more high,
with stiff upright growths and oblong, hairy, dark green
leaves in groups. During May, it carries clusters of
dainty 1—1¼ in. flat, yellow-green or primrose-yellow
flowers. It should be pruned immediately after flower-
ing to encourage a bushier habit ... ... | 5/6 | 7/6

„ **uniflorum.**—This choice shrub seldom grows more than
9 ins. high, but is 1—2 ft. wide. It is related to R. imperator and R. patulum and has slender twigs bright with
rose-red flowers during April and May ... ... | | 10/6

„ **Valentinianum.**—A distinct spreading shrub slowly
attaining a height of 2 ft. or more. In foliage it reminds
one of R. leucaspis. Here, the clusters of magnificent
1½ in. flowers are buttercup yellow but as in many of the
dwarf growers, the depth of colour varies according to
the soil. It is not hardy in many gardens but is a lovely
shrub for the alpine house ... ... | 7/6 | 10/6

„ **Williamsianum.**—Most of the specimens seen in gardens
are 1—1½ ft. high and 2—3 ft. wide. The leaves are of
various sizes, orbicular-ovate, with a heart-shaped base.
The beautiful 2¼ in. flowers are rose-red, ageing to rose-
pink, and are unfortunately often damaged by late
frosts ... ... 3/6 5/6 | 7/6 | 10/6

Specimen plants of some of the above **Rhododendrons**
can be supplied.

ADDENDA.

RECENT ADDITIONS TO THIS LIST.

Berberis quelpaertensis.—Quelpart Island, Korean Archipelago.
One of the loveliest of the genus for its numerous racemes
of 9—13, large, cylindrical, carmine-red fruits held from
September to December. It grows 3—4 ft. high and
is armed with yellow spines. The ¾—2 in. ovate
to oblanceolate net-veined leaves, glaucous-beneath,
become beautifully coloured in autumn ... ... | 7/6

E **Leptospermum Rodwayanum.**—E. Tasmania. A valuable
shrub for gardens in the south and west and in similar
climates. It is similar in habit and height to L. s.
Nichollsii, its white 1—1¼ in. flowers nestling among the
grey oblanceolate leaves from August to the winter.
A good form is offered ... ... | 5/6

Notospartium glabrescens.—South Island, New Zealand. This species is new to cultivation and will attain 5—10 ft. From mid-May to July, the elegant, semi-pendulous, ribbon-like growths produce many 1—2 in. racemes of flowers, their petals delicately veined with violet   ...   each.   7/6

Prunus Padus commutata.—Manchuria. A large bush or small tree 12—20 ft. high, usually in full leaf by the end of March, in the south and west. The racemes of $\frac{1}{2}$ in. flowers are borne during April. It has proved to be one of our best autumn colouring plants and the foliage is of the same tint as that of Amelanchier levis 3/6   5/6

E **Vaccinium pubicalyx.**—Yunnan, China. A rare semi-evergreen or evergreen species about 5 ft. high. The majority of its leathery, pale green, lanceolate acuminate leaves are 1—1$\frac{1}{2}$ ins. long, with the undersides of the nerves pubescent. The flowers are white tinged with rose and $\frac{3}{16}$—$\frac{1}{4}$ in. long, on axillary inflorescences. Delivery 1938.   5/6

Viburnum koreanum.—Korea, 1933. This plant belongs to the Opulus section and will grow to a height of 5—8 ft. The red annual growths carry 3—5 in. × 4—6in., deeply 3-lobed, puckered, green leaves, cordate in outline and widely serrated. During autumn, the foliage is quite as bright as that of Acer japonicum. It has not yet flowered 5/6

BUSINESS TERMS.

TERMS AND CONDITIONS.—I believe that all Trees and Plants sold by me are of the description and kind specified at the time of sale, but owing to the impossibility in many cases of being certain of this, I give no undertaking that such Trees and Plants correspond with the description under which they are sold, and all such sales are subject to this condition. I further give no warranty, expressed or implied, as to their growth, description or quality.

If the purchaser does not accept the goods on these terms they are at once to be returned.

PACKING AND CARRIAGE.—All goods are delivered free on rail at West Moors Station, Southern Railway, and consigned per Passenger Train, Purchaser's Risk, Carriage Paid, unless otherwise notified. The carriage will be added to invoice whether dispatched in one or two consignments.

Packing material is charged at cost price.

One half allowed on Baskets, Crates and Boxes only, if returned Carriage Paid, in good condition within 14 days, duly advised and labelled with name of sender. Credit cannot be given for empties until they are received by me.

COMPLAINTS.—No complaints can be entertained unless made immediately on receipt of goods.

CLAIMS.—No claims will be allowed, beyond the Invoice Price of any item at fault.

REMITTANCES.—Accounts rendered monthly.

$2\frac{1}{2}$ per cent. discount allowed on all accounts of 20/- and upwards, less carriage, if paid within 30 days from date of invoice, afterwards net.

Cash or Banker's Reference must accompany orders from unknown correspondents.

All goods offered, subject to being unsold on receipt of order.

TELEGRAMS.—Marchant, Stapehill, Wimborne.

STATION.—West Moors (Southern).

J. LOOKER, LTD.,
THE WESSEX PRESS,
POOLE, DORSET, ENGLAND.